Agricultural
Production Economics

The Author

Dr. K. Nirmal Ravi Kumar is presently working as Professor and Head (Agricultural Economics) in Agricultural College, Mahanandi in Acharya N.G. Ranga Agricultural University. He had a brilliant academic career and he specialized in 'Agricultural Marketing' both in his post-graduate and doctoral programmes. He is actively involved both in agricultural research and teaching activities during the past thirteen years in the University. He published 44 articles in popular agricultural journals. He also contributed two technical bulletins on economic aspects of irrigation water management highlighting the research priorities in major irrigation commands of Andhra Pradesh and need based technological interventions to address the same during his active stint in "Andhra Pradesh Water Management Project", an international project funded by The Royal Netherlands Embassy. His interested areas include International trade of Indian agriculture, Farming systems approach, Irrigation water management etc. The following are the other major contributions (books) by the same author:

☆ Indian Agriculture in the 21st Century: Challenges and Opportunities

☆ World Trade Agreement and Indian Agriculture: Implementation Experience

☆ Microeconomic Analysis in Agriculture in 2 Vols (Set)

☆ Objective Agricultural Economics (Two Editions)

☆ Farmers Indebtedness in India – An Economic Analysis

☆ Research Methodology for Agricultural Economics

☆ Methodology for Social Sciences Research in Agriculture

☆ Agricultural Marketing in 2 Vols (Set)

☆ Farm Managerial Economics

☆ Practical Knowledge in Agricultural Economics

Agricultural Production Economics

Volume 2

K. Nirmal Ravi Kumar

Professor and Head (Agricultural Economics)
Acharya N.G. Ranga Agricultural University
Agricultural College,
Mahanandi

2015
Daya Publishing House®
A Division of
Astral International Pvt. Ltd.
New Delhi – 110 002

Agricultural Production Economics
(2 Volume Set)

Volume 1: Page 001-464
Volume 2: Page 465-812

© 2015 AUTHOR

Cataloging in Publication Data—DK
  Courtesy: D.K. Agencies (P) Ltd. <docinfo@dkagencies.com>
Ravi Kumar, K. N. (Kotamraju Nirmal), 1969- **author.**
  Agricultural production economics / K. Nirmal Ravi Kumar.
  2 volumes   cm
  Includes bibliographical references (pages   ).
  ISBN 9789351308560 (Vol.2)
  ISBN 9789351306948 (Set)

  1. Agriculture—Economic aspects—India. 2. Agricultural productivity—India. 3. Factors of production—India.   I. Title.
DDC 338.10954   23

Published by   : **Daya Publishing House®**
                         A Division of
                         Astral International Pvt. Ltd.
                         – ISO 9001:2008 Certified Company –
                         4760-61/23, Ansari Road, Darya Ganj
                         New Delhi-110 002
                         Ph. 011-43549197, 23278134
                         E-mail: info@astralint.com
                         Website: www.astralint.com

Laser Typesetting   : **Classic Computer Services**, Delhi - 110 035

Printed at   : **Thomson Press India Limited**

PRINTED IN INDIA

– Dedicated to –
Late K. RAMA CHANDRA RAO

K. PURNA CHANDRA RAO
Formerly Principal Scientist
(Village Level Studies)
ICRISAT

Phone : 9848081608
E-mail: kpcr_48@rediffmail.com

Foreword

Agricultural sector plays an important role in the economy of every country. In a developing country like India, it provides employment to about one half of the labor force in the country and supplies raw material to many industries, although its share in the Gross Domestic Product has been steadily declining to reach only about 13 per cent in the recent years. The relatively low labor productivity of agriculture all over the world has been a sign of structural retrogression and is perplexing to the policy makers. While there are many explanations to this phenomenon, none consider it a desirable state of affairs. Till the twentieth century, there were many famines in India due to which many people lost their lives due to shortage of food. In the present century, famines are avoided due to increased production and better food distribution system, but many farmers are taking their lives by suicides due to financial hardship and business failure. Agriculture is failing to attract youth due to its low remunerative nature and many policy makers and analysts are concerned about its future and the food security of the countries.

In this context, a book that unravels the intricacies of agricultural production at the farm firm level is welcome. There were many books on the subject over the last century which blazed the path of knowledge and filled the curiosity of the students and researchers. One more book on the subject is welcome. The author made no claim of originality but tried to explain the concepts in popular style so that the beginners can easily grasp them. I congratulate Dr. K. Nirmal Ravi Kumar for his initiative, enterprise and hard work to bring out this book so early in his career. I hope that the professionals and students find it useful.

K. Purna Chandra Rao

ACHARYA N.G. RANGA AGRICULTURAL UNIVERSITY
AGRICULTURAL COLLEGE, MAHANANDI

M.C. FARM – 518 502, MAHANANDI, KURNOOL DISTRICT

Dr. K. NIRMAL RAVI KUMAF
Ph.L
Professor & Hea
Dept. of Agricultural Economic

ιone : +91-9295350511
nail: drknrk@gmail.com

Author's Note

I consider this as a bold attempt to present a comprehensive text material on the fundamental aspects of Agricultural Production Economics. With a limited experience in the field of teaching (7 years) in the Acharya N.G. Ranga Agricultural University, I will not dare enough to make a tall claim regarding the originality of the material incorporated in this text book entitled, 'Agricultural Production Economics', but I certainly admit that, the concepts are dealt in-detail in a lucid form, so as to enable the students and Academicians to learn, understand and conceptualize the same. The present volume can serve as a standardized text book for the graduates, post-graduates and doctoral students, who wish to pursue their career in the field of Agricultural Economics in different State Agricultural Universities.

This task of writing and publishing the textbook on the advanced versions of '*Agricultural Production Economics*' has been one of the most challenging and satisfying experiences of my life. I am especially thankful to my student Ms. V. Usha Shree for the help rendered during the pursuit of this work. Finally, last but by no means least, a grateful kiss goes to my wife, Meena, my sons, Sri Ram and Kasyap, my brother Vijay and cheerful thanks to my mother Janaki for their love and support. Their devotion, patience and understanding were indispensable. I gratefully dedicate this piece of work to my late father, K. Rama Chandra Rao, who instilled in me at an early age the importance of education and the value of hard work. I only wish you could have been here to see me finish the journey I started with your efforts and initiatives. I know you would have been so proud.

K. Nirmal Ravi Kumar

Contents

Volume 1

*Factors of Production – Goals and Objectives of Agricultural Production
Economics – Subject Matter of Agricultural Production Economics – Basic
Production Problems in Agriculture – Causes of basic production problems –
Tools of Agricultural Production Economics – Consumption theory vis-à-vis
Theory of Agricultural Production Economics – Features of Modern Agricultural
Production – Agricultural Production vis-à-vis Industrial Production – Basic
terms and concepts in Agricultural Production Economics*

path – Ridgeline – Deriving production function from isoquant map and ridge lines – Effect of changes in factor price on factor usage – Substitution relationship between the factors – Complementarity relationship between the factors – Factors are perfect substitutes – Factors are perfect complements – Difference between expansion path and price-factor curve – Elasticity of factor substitution – Examples – Exercises.

MRP – VMP – AFC – MFCx – Factor pricing under perfect competition – Remuneration paid to the factor is equal to its marginal productivity – Firm's equilibrium in the short run – Long run industry equilibrium – Payment for the factor across different firms – Factor pricing under imperfect competition – Examples – Exercises.

Volume 2

firms under varying cost conditions – Concept of equality of MR=MC in imperfect (monopoly) competition – Equilibrium of monopoly firm or industry in the short run – Equilibrium of monopoly firm or industry in the long run – Profits function – Properties of the Profit Function – Exercises.

Acronyms

AC: Average Cost
AFC: Average Fixed Cost
AE: Allocative Efficiency
AFC_x: Average Factor Cost
APP: Average Physical Product
AR: Average Revenue
ARC: Average Revenue Curve
ARP: Average Revenue Product
ATC: Average Total Cost
AVP: Average Value Product
BCR: Benefit Cost Ratio
BEP: Break Even Point
BFS: Basic Feasible Solution
CES: Constant Elasticity of Substitution

CMR: Contribution Margin Ratio
CPM: Critical Path Method
CVP: Cost-Volume-Profit
EE: Economic Efficiency
EFT: Earliest Finishing Time
E_{OC}: Output elasticity of LRTC
E_P: Elasticity of Production
E_S: Elasticity of Substitution
EST: Earliest Start Time
FAO: Food and Agriculture Organization
GC: Gini Coefficient
GM: Genetically Modified
IDC: Indifference Curve
IRR: Internal Rate of Return
LCC: Least Cost Combination
LCM: Least Cost Method
LDR: Law of Diminishing Returns
LFT: Latest Finishing Time
LP: Linear Programming
LRAC: Long Run Average Cost
LRATC: Long Run Average Total Cost
LRMC: Long Run Marginal Cost
LRS: Long Run Supply
LRTC: Long Run Total Cost
LST: Latest Start Time
LVP: Law of Variable Proportions
MC: Marginal Cost
MES: Minimum Efficient Size
MFC_X: Marginal Factor Cost
MIRR: Modified Internal Rate of Return
MODI: Modified Distribution
MPP: Marginal Physical Product
MR: Marginal Returns or Marginal Revenue
MRC: Marginal Revenue Curve
MRP: Marginal Revenue Product
MRPS: Marginal Rate of Product Substitution
MRS: Marginal Rate of Substitution

MRTS: Marginal Rate of Technical Substitution
MSPs: Minimum Support Prices
MU: Marginal Utility
MVP_x: Marginal Value Product of a factor
NB: Net Incremental Benefits
NBIR: Net Benefit Investment Ratio
NPV: Net Present Value
NPW: Net Present Worth
NWC: North West Corner Rule
OCC: Opportunity Cost of Capital
OPC: Optimum Product Combination
PBP: Pay Back Period
PERT: Programme Evaluation and Review Technique
PI : Profitability Index
PPC: Production Possibility Curve
PPF: Production Possibility Frontier
PWB: Present Worth of Benefits
PWC: Present Worth of Costs
P_x: Price of the variable input 'X'
P_Y: Price of the output or product 'Y'
R&D: Research and Development
RTS: Returns to Scale
SDR: Social Discount Rate
SRATC: Short Run Average Total Cost
SRAVC: Short Run Average Variable Cost
SRMC: Short Run Marginal Cost
SRS: Short Run Supply
SS: Social Surplus
SRD: Social Rate of Discount
SRTC: Short Run Total Cost
SRTVC: Short Run Total Variable Cost
TAI: Technology Adoption Index
TC: Total Cost
TE: Technical Efficiency
TFC: Total Fixed Cost
TFC_x: Total Factor Cost
TPP: Total Physical Product

TR: Total Returns
TRC: Total Revenue Curve
TU: Total Utility
TVC: Total Variable Cost
TVP: Total Value Product
VAM: Vogel's Approximation Method
VAP: Value of the Average Product
VMP: Value of Marginal Product
WTO: World Trade Organization

6

Economies and Diseconomies of Scale

In the earlier discussion (Chapter 5), we studied that, increasing and diminishing RTS in a long run production programme are influenced by economies of scale and diseconomies of scale respectively. Further, we also discussed that, the behaviour of cost curves in the long run are influenced by both economies of scale and diseconomies of scale. So, it is high time now, to discuss these aspects of economies of scale and diseconomies of scale, as they give the true picture regarding the production behaviour of the firm or an industry as a whole.

6.1. Economies of Scale

We know, a farm-firm is an independently administered business unit (say, cattle farm) by the farmer, while an industry is made up of a number of firms producing broadly similar items or items that are connected to each other (dairy industry). Depending upon the level of output, firms and industries may be of small-scale or large-scale. As every firm or industry aims to maximize the output, they expand the business, thereby, reap profits and during this process, they are able to secure certain benefits that are not available to small firms or industries. These benefits or advantages are referred to as economies of large scale and they result in reduction of LRATC of production due to expanding the output in the production programme. So, an economies of scale refers to, when a larger output is associated with lower per unit cost of production (*i.e.*, low average cost of production) in a production process. Thus, economies of scale are the cost advantages exploited by expanding the scale of production by the firm in the long run. It is, otherwise, defined as the efficiency gained in a production process due to increase in the rate of production. It can also be defined as a state, when the number of goods or services produced goes up by a sizeable margin, but that hardly affects the cost of production and input costs remain the same. These definitions infer that, the growth of an individual firm or industry is possible only when economies of scale is attained, as it ensures two benefits *viz.,* increase in output and decline in average cost of production. In any production programme, where large scale private investments are flowing into the sectors, economies of scale are the goal and this will enable the firm to gain a competitive advantage in the market. This is exemplified through the Table 6.1 and Figure 6.1.

Table 6.1: Economies of Large Scale in a Sugar Factory

Scale	LRTC (Rs.)	Output of sugar (Units)	LRATC (Rs/unit)
1 Capital + 1 Labour	250000	12500	20.00
2 Capital + 2 Labour	280000	16000	17.50
3 Capital + 3 Labour	368000	23000	16.00
4 Capital + 4 Labour	486400	32000	15.20
5 Capital + 5 Labour	518000	35000	14.80
6 Capital + 6 Labour	528000	44000	12.00
7 Capital + 7 Labour	533600	46000	11.60
8 Capital + 8 Labour	573750	51000	11.25
9 Capital + 9 Labour	590000	59000	10.00

The Table 6.1 shows a simple example for a firm (sugar factory) enjoying economies of large scale. The rate of increase in output of sugar is more compared to the rise in LRTC and this contributes to decline in LRATC of sugar production in the factory. As long as the LRATC is falling with increase in output of sugar, it implies, economies of scale are being exploited by the firm. This also infers that, if the firm shows increasing RTS, it enjoys economies of large scale production. So, as the firm increases the factor scale, LRTC rises, but LRATC falls, as the percentage change in output is more than the percentage change in costs. The same is explained through Figure 6.1. If the sugar factory operates and expands from one scale of production to another, the output increases in the factory, as we move from $SRATC_1$ to $SRATC_2$ to $SRATC_3$. Each SRATC curve represents a given quantity of scale of factors. So, the movement from $SRATC_1$ to $SRATC_2$ to $SRATC_3$ reflect that, as the scale of factors increases, output increases and this is accompanied by the decline in SRATC. The LRATC curve is drawn enveloping the SRATC curves of different plants and it shows that, upto OQ_3 level of output, the LRATC falls with increase in scale of factors and at

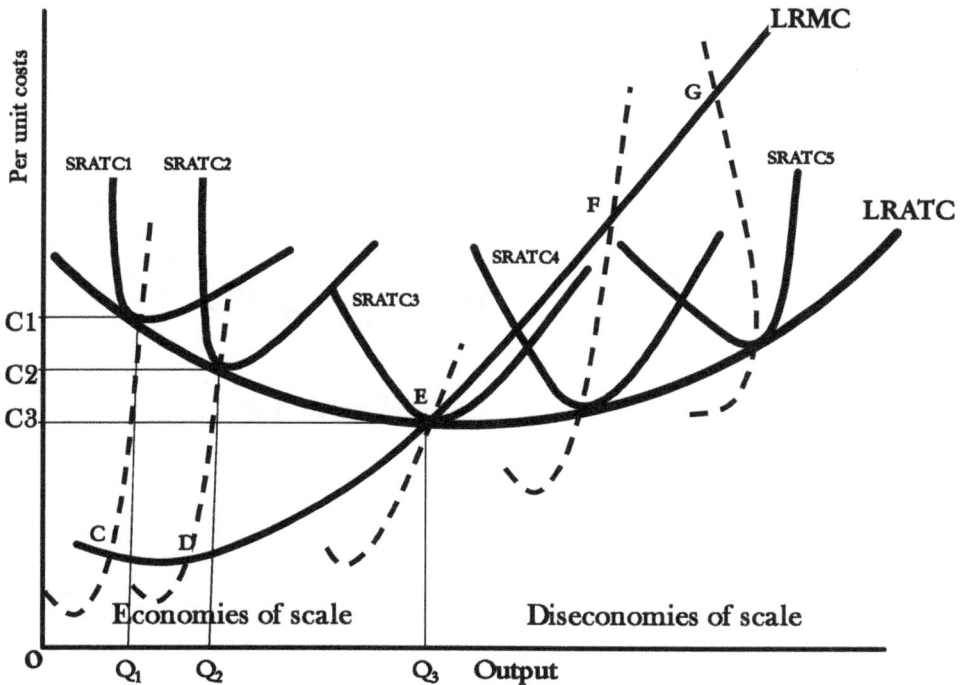

Figure 6.1: Economies of Large Scale – Decline in SRATC and LRATC with Increase in Scale.

OQ_3 level of output, LRATC is the lowest and up to OQ_3 level of output, the firm enjoys economies of large scale.

The above example indicates that, if the firm experiences increasing RTS, it enjoys economies of large scale. This is especially true in case of large firms like Coromandel Fertilizers Limited, Nagarjuna Fertilizers Limited, Bayer India limited etc., which produce larger output at huge fixed costs. For these large scale firms, the striking aspect is, the MC involved in the production of an additional unit output is nearly zero. The lower MC will further reduce the LRATC and the firm gains more reputation from the farming community, as it can offer the product at lower price. Lower costs normally mean higher profits and increasing financial returns to the firm. From the above discussion, we can infer that, the economies of scale can be studied from the LRATC curve (Figure 6.2). If the LRATC curve is falling, it implies that, with increase in output, the LRATC of commodity is decreasing, thereby, the firm is experiencing economies of large scale. At OQ_1 level of output, the LRATC of sugar is OC_1. With increase in output to OQ_3, the LRATC of a sugar is OC_3, indicating that, at OQ_3 level of output, the LRATC is minimum for sugar, thereby, the factory is experiencing economies of scale between points A and B on LRATC curve. But, beyond OQ_3 level of output, LRATC curve rises, indicating, diseconomies of scale sets in into the sugar factory. At this juncture, it is essential to differentiate between economies of scale and economies of experience. Economies of scale refer to the cost advantage the firm

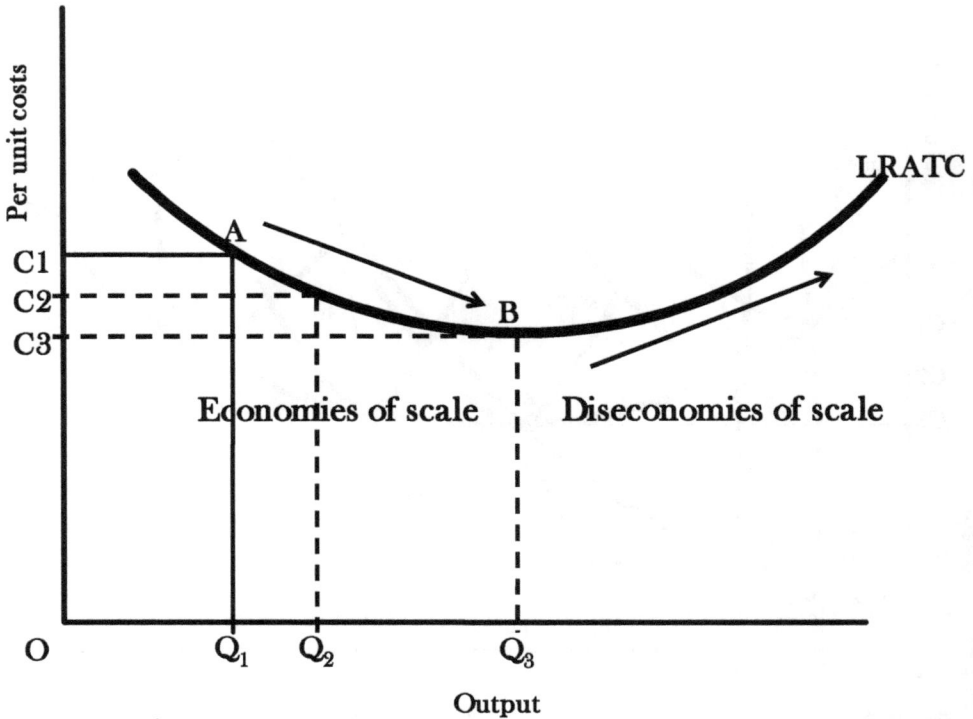

Figure 6.2: Economies and Diseconomies of Scale in a Sugar Factory.

enjoys in producing a larger output at a given point of time. Economies of experience (also called Learning by doing) refer to cost advantage the firm enjoys in producing the output from accumulated experience over an extended period of time and the same is already discussed in the earlier Chapter 5.

6.2. Importance of Economies of Large Scale

The following are the advantages for the business firm, if it enjoys economies of large scale:

☆ Large-scale business is possible at lower LRATC, thereby, market share of the business firm increases significantly.

☆ With the decline in LRATC due to economies of large scale, the firm need not cut the market price, rather, it can charge same price for the product and accept higher profit margins. For example, a sugar factory produces 1000 units of sugar at a cost of production of Rs. 500/unit. At a market price of Rs. 600/unit, the entrepreneur sells the product, thereby, he derives the profit margin of Rs. 100000. If the firm experiences increasing RTS, the factory produces 2000 units of sugar at a cost of production of Rs. 400. At the same market price of Rs. 600/unit, the entrepreneur sells the product, thereby he derives the profit margin of Rs. 400000. So, by charging same market price, the factory can maximize the profits through enjoying economies of large scale.

☆ In cases of cut-throat competition, the business firm enjoying economies of large scale can go for destroyer pricing, such that, the price quoted by the firm for the product will be lower than LRATC of other firms.

☆ The lower LRATC attained by the business firm is a measure of an improvement in productive efficiency and it can be passed on to the consumers in the form of lower market prices. This also gives the firm a competitive advantage both in the domestic and international markets. These advantages are recently seen in the software sector. Just a few years back, high-performance personal computers are sold at very high prices, but with the experience of economies of large scale, the same are sold now at affordable prices.

☆ Economies of large scale serve as an incentive for the business firm to grow.

☆ Because of reduced costs, business firms can price their products to be more profitable.

6.3. Types of Economies of Large Scale

According to Alfred Marshall, there are two kinds of economies of scale. These include Internal economies of scale and External economies of scale (Figure 6.3). Internal economies of scale refers to the benefits or advantages to one particular firm, as it goes into large-scale production. External economies of scale refers to the benefits accrued to entire industry that has been localized or concentrated in a particular area. They are discussed in-detail in the following pages:

I. Internal Economies of Large Scale

Internal economies of scale relate to the lower LRATC a single firm can obtain by growing in size itself. So, it is related to the economies of production, which accrue to the business firm through enjoying increasing RTS. This makes the business firm to expand the output, so that, the cost of production will fall considerably and hence, the firm will be in a better position to compete in the market effectively. So, internal economies of scale show a greater potential impact on the cost-reduction, thereby, on the profitability of a firm. Thus, economies of scale of a firm refer to Internal economies. To put it in other way, internal economies of scale are the savings, which occur within a firm and it is independent of other firms. So, the factors responsible for this are purely within the establishment or endogenous or internal of the business firm. Thus, internal economies of scale are solely enjoyed by the individual firm when its scale of production changes, independent of the actions of other firms. Hence, the factors will benefit the firm only and not the entire industry in minimizing the LRATC of the product through enjoying economies of large scale. They are not the result of inventions of any kind, but are due to the uses of known methods of production, but more scientifically. These economies of scale in the firm include,

a. Labour Economies

This is Adam Smith's idea of the division of labour. It can be achieved by specialization. In large firms, the complex production process is splitted into separate

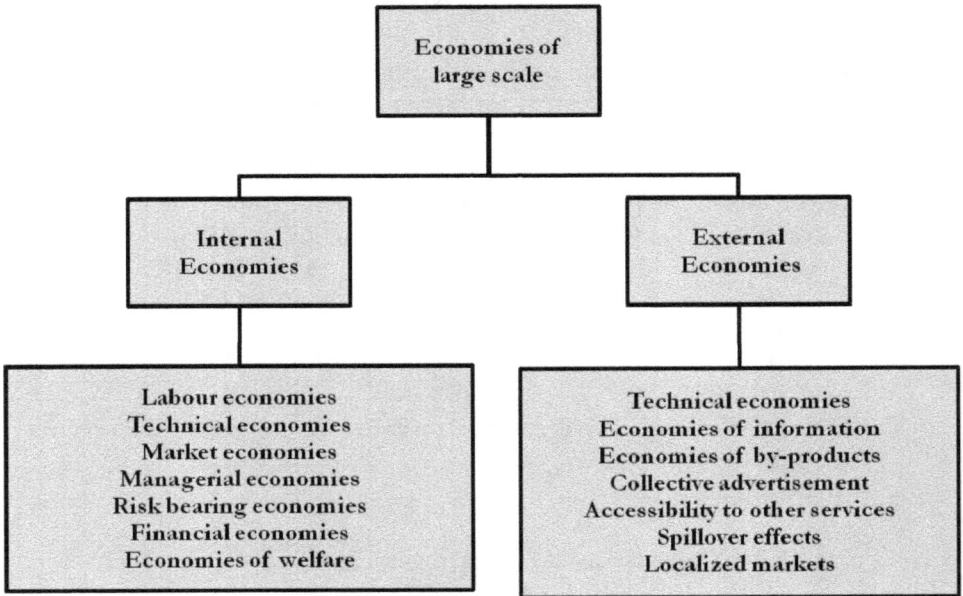

Figure 6.3: Different Types of Economies of Scale.

tasks or activities and for accomplishing each activity, specialized skilled workers will be employed. Division of labour in mass production of motor vehicles, manufacturing of electronic products, fruit processing etc., are good examples. Thus, with specialization, the labour or workers in a firm become more efficient at a particular job, when specialization occurs. It also means, no time is lost due to labour changing jobs in the middle of a shift. With people specializing in certain activities of the business, their levels of experience and expertise will also increase, thereby, resulting in more output through cost-effectiveness. This is because, with increased specialization, a less number of labour will be required and hence, the cost for hiring labour will subsequently decline. The quality of output also increase, if the firm employs specialists in every aspect of production.

b. Technical Economies

These are often called as economies in the use of factors of production *i.e.,* they are related to the production process itself. Prof. Cairncross has given the following kinds of technical economies:

☆ Large-scale business firms employ expensive, specific and modern machinery that contributes to higher output through cost-effectiveness. For example, if a firm manufacturing dairy products installs expensive machinery that ensures higher output through cost-effectiveness, it enjoys low LRATC and thus, it easily competes out other firms in the dairy industry.

☆ The 'Law of Increased Dimensions' or the 'Container Principle' also contributes to technical economies of scale. When a godown's length, breadth and height are doubled, eight times the quantity can be stored inside. This is an important economies of scale in areas, where bulky material are handled. The same law can be employed in increasing the size of processing firms, fertilizer, pesticide and other such firms to increase the output through cost-effectiveness. This is because, the size of machinery can be doubled in these firms, without doubling the labour and material costs. Similarly, by using bigger size plant and equipment, large-scale production can be attained even at lower average cost. For example, the cost of a 1,00,000 units capacity plant will not be double than that of 50,000-units capacity plant. Engineers go by what is called Two by Three (2/3) Rule, wherein when the volume is increased by 100 per cent, the material increases only by two-thirds. Thus, technical economies are available only from large size equipment, improved methods of production process and when the products are standardized.

☆ A large firm can also afford to invest more in R&D. This is because, as the firm expands, it can afford to install highly technical and expensive equipment needed for in-depth experiments. This leads to employment of highly skilled and technically qualified persons, who can experiment and develop modern techniques of production that ensures cost-effectiveness in large scale production. Further, the modern production techniques employed by the firm are suitable for using cheaper raw materials. The products developed from such modern technologies enjoy low LRATC and thereby, the firm can easily compete out the competing firms. Further, the firm can enjoy higher margin of safety (discussed in Chapter 7). The expenditure on R&D will not pose any burden on the part of the firm, as the firm produces larger output that too through cost-effectiveness. So, the returns will flow significantly into the business, as large quantities of output are sold and such higher returns makes the R&D expenditure affordable on the part of the firm. If the Government feels the product produced by the firm will benefit the society, it might, offer funding for encouraging R&D and will promote the firm. Likewise, private sector might also be willing to offer support to the firm by providing beneficial services such as transportation and communication to the growing industry.

☆ Effective utilization of by-products is possible in case of large scale production, unlike small scale production. For example, in a sugar factory (large size firm), the by-product, molasses can be used in the production of alcohol. This valuable by-product enable the entrepreneur to start a subsidiary industry or he can sell the by-product as raw material to other firms engaged in the production of alcohol. This will result in the saving in cost of production of sugar by the firm (compensate the cost of production in the sugar factory and thereby, cost of production of sugar is minimized indirectly).

☆ Linking the activities of production will save expenses incurred on intermediaries, thereby, reduces the cost per unit of output. For example, a large sugar factory may have its own sugar cane production farms, manufacture sugar, packing, transportation and distribution network etc., and these contribute to economies of large scale.

☆ There is a growing interest in the concept of a network economy of scale. Some networks and services have huge potential for economies of scale. That is, as they are more widely used or adopted, they become more valuable to the business. The basic idea behind the net work economies of scale is that, the MC of adding one more user to the network is close to zero, but the MRs derived from each new user is very high and this contributes large economies of scale. The rapid expansion of e-commerce is a good example of the exploitation of network economies of scale. This type of economies of scale is linked more to the growth of demand for a product.

☆ The business firm enjoys internal economies of scale through the concept of 'learning-by-doing'. So, the entrepreneur uses all his experience in the production process and aims to minimize the costs, so that, LRATC of production will fall through increasing the output. The earlier studies conducted on different industries revealed that, 70 to 90 per cent of manufacturing costs are declined due to learning experiences of the entrepreneur. The same is explained through the Figure 6.4. By implementing the production strategies through the experiences gained in the past production processes, the entrepreneur could minimize the cost of production of sugar by C_1C_2 in producing OY output.

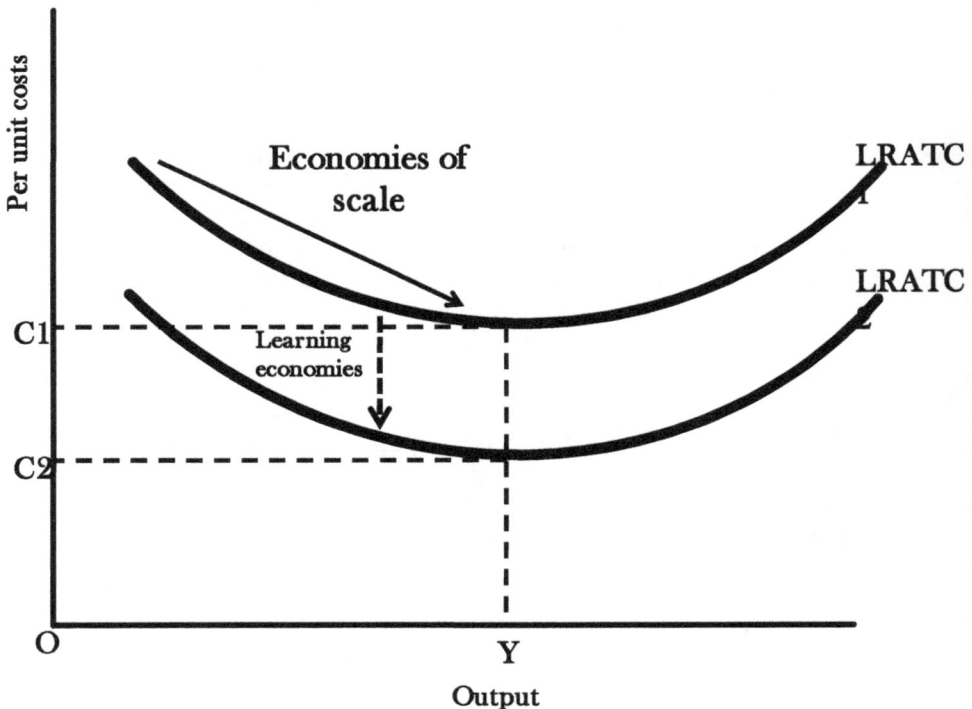

Figure 6.4: Learning Economies in a Sugar Factory Contributing to Fall in LRATC Curve.

★ Because of indivisibility of capital equipment, only a single largest firm in the industry can afford to buy the heavy machinery at a high price. For example, blast furnace by a steel plant, thereby, it can easily compete out other small firms engaged in manufacturing steel.

c. Market Economies

This gives the highest benefit to the firm engaged in large scale production. It includes buying economies and selling economies.

i. Buying Economies

It includes,

★ Larger firm will have the ability to purchase the raw materials in bulk at discounted prices, if it enjoys monopsony (buying) power in the market. For example, a fruit processing firm enters a contract with the fruit growers in a particular area regarding the supply of fruits to the firm after the harvest.

★ As the firm expands the business, the demand for raw material increases. This further increases the firm's order value and eventually it obtains more bargaining power with the suppliers. It may be able to purchase the raw materials in bulk quantities and obtain discounts and lower prices for the raw materials and this is referred to as Bulk-buying economies. For example, a processing firm purchases potatoes from farmers in bulk to make French fries, thereby, it enjoys volume discounts.

★ In terms of localization, proximity to its suppliers will enable the firm to reduce transportation costs for inputs. Also, a convenient location, where there is plenty of access to public transport, will minimize the distance for the customers to have the product in large quantities in right time.

ii. Selling Economies

It includes,

★ Every part of marketing has cost, particularly promotional costs, such as advertising and employing and running a sales force. Many of these marketing costs are fixed costs and so as the business gets larger, it is able to spread the cost of marketing over a wider range of output and sales, thereby, cutting the average marketing cost per unit. The successful results of such promotional methods will be increased demand and brand loyalty towards the product and both will benefit the firm.

★ For selling the output, the firm can plan for exporting the product to distant markets, where it enjoys more comparative advantage.

★ The firm enjoys economies of freight, as it can maintain full cargo, thereby, the transportation cost per unit of product will be low.

d. Managerial Economies

This is a form of division of labour. As the firm expands its operations, it need not expand its administrative staff to the same degree or percentage, as the expansion in terms of operations. So, the large-scale firm employ managers, who specialize in various fields like marketing management, human resource management, finance management, pricing management, materials management etc., and they supervise the production systems more efficiently, as they possess higher qualifications and expertise compared to one person in a small firm trying to perform all these roles. This 'functional specialization' contribute much to economies of large scale through better ways of organization, production, communication etc. These managerial economies reduce per unit cost of management because, with the expansion of firm, various department managers will manage large output as efficiently as they were managing small output in the same salary.

e. Risk Bearing Economies

Compared to small scale firms, a large scale firm can handle risk in a better way. This is because, a large scale firm produces variety of products and sale them in different areas or markets. So, by the diversification of its production process, the large firm is able to reduce risk, as loss in one product can be counter balanced by returns from another product. Similar is the case of procurement of raw material, as large scale firm enjoys assured supply of raw material from several sources rather than a single source, as in case of a small size firm.

f. Financial Economies of Scale

Large firms raise capital more easily (credit worthy) when compared to small firms, as they have more capital assets and high risk bearing ability. This is because, if one market goes down, the firm can still make money in the others. In this context, small firms find it hard to obtain finance and when they do, the cost of the finance is often quite high. Large firms, therefore, find it easier to locate potential lenders and to raise money at lower interest rates. They are seen as less likely to become bankrupt and able to repay their loans in right time and thus, banks may actually compete for their accounts.

g. Economies of Welfare

Large scale firm with its huge resources can provide better working facilities both inside and outside the factory. The firm can run subsidized canteens, resting rooms for the workers etc., within the factory premises and provide staff quarters, educational and medical facilities, provisional stores, recreation clubs etc., outside the factory. Though providing such facilities involves huge cost, yet the factory aims to increase the productive efficiency of the workers, through which it raises the production and cover these costs. The business expansion might even allow the firm to afford the sponsorship of sporting events and become popular among the customers. Such activities of a large firm also promote good customer relations and create a good impression in the eyes of the public. In due course, the firm benefits from increased sales.

II. External Economies of Large Scale

External economies of scale occur outside of a firm but within an industry. So, external economies of scale occur, when a firm benefits from lower unit costs as a result of the whole industry growing in size. That means, a firm may enjoy certain cost savings, not through its own expansion, but by being a part of a well-organized and large industry. So, external economies are shared by a number of firms, when the entire industry prospers. That means, the external economies are not monopolized by any single firm in the industry. So, the factors responsible for economies of large scale are external to firm and they not only influence the firm, but the whole industry. So, economies of scale of an industry refers to External economies. They accrue to a firm due to technological influences on the total output produced in the industry, which reduces per unit cost of production. So, all the firms in industry will develop due to technological interdependence of firms. The external economies include:

☆ *Technical economies:* This is related to division of labour and specialization. The supply of skilled labour may locate in the vicinity of the industry and this will cause firms in the industry to have an easy access to the type of labour they need at low costs. This ensures specialization of labour among the firms in the industry, which contributes higher output to the industry. For example, in cotton textile industry, some firms may specialize in manufacturing threads, some in dyeing, some in long cloth, some in dhotis, some in shirting etc. This enhances the production efficiency of the firms thereby, cost of production falls. Further, a network of suppliers or support industries may grow in size and locate close to the main industry and they specialize in various activities like preparing tools, implements, repairs and maintenance etc., thereby, lowering unit cost of production of all the firms. So, an individual firm has a greater chance of finding a high quality, yet affordable supplier close to its site. Agglomeration economies may also result due to clustering of similar businesses in a distinct geographical location.

☆ *Economies of information:* The firms exchange ideas and publish articles and magazines (Trade journals) that promote the spread of technical information throughout the industry. The industry will be in a better position capable enough to establish research laboratories, as it can pool large amount of resources. All these will help the firms in raising the production efficiency and reduction in per unit costs.

☆ *Economies of by-products:* When industry is localized, it turns out large quantities of waste materials, such as molasses in sugar industry, iron scrap in steel industry etc. New firms enter the industry to purchase these waste materials (for example, an alcohol firm will purchase molasses from sugar industry to prepare a spirit or alcohol) at reasonable prices and use them in manufacturing by-products. So, the firms in industry enjoy economies of scale in two ways *viz.,* no expenses are incurred in disposing off the waste material and revenue is earned through selling by-product to other manufacturers.

☆ *Transport and communication links will improve:* If an industry establishes itself and grows in a particular region, the Government will provide better transport and communication links to improve accessibility to the region. This will lower transportation costs for firms in that area and it attract more potential customers.

☆ *Training and education becomes more focused on the industry:* Universities and colleges will offer more courses suitable for a career in the industry, which has become dominant in a region or at national level. For example, considering the potentiality of processed food products in the export basket of the country, many State Agricultural Universities in India have started Food Science and Technology colleges. Similarly, new courses on Information Technology (IT) are started in the Engineering colleges, as the whole IT industry expanded in India. This will benefit the firms in the industry in getting a larger pool of skilled workers in accomplishing the technical duties. Besides educational facilities, research and training facilities also improves, thereby, all firms in the industry can benefit from such facilities.

☆ *Collective advertisement:* Industry can also benefit from collective advertisement, which is cheaper than each firm undertaking its own advertising. This is more commonly seen in case of tourism industry.

☆ *Accessibility to other services:* When the entire industry prospers, banks, insurance, catering, cleaning and other businesses will be located in the vicinity to the major industry, allowing them to save on costs. Normally, firms will have to pay more for such things, if they are not located near to them.

☆ *Centralized maintenance services:* Firms in the industry can benefit from centralized maintenance services, thereby, the cost of maintenance to each firm will be much less than, if each undertook its own maintenance.

☆ *Spill over effects:* The entire industry prospers due to spill over effects. That means, if one firm enjoys economies of large scale due to modern technology, the same will be spread across different firms in the industry, thereby, the entire industry prospers and it will also lead to the creation of standards within an industry.

☆ *Localized markets:* The expansion of an industry in a particular locality will lead to the development of well-organized markets and this ensures fair returns to all the firms in the industry.

To summarize, external economies of scale occur, when cost per unit of output depends on the size of the industry whereas, internal economies of scale occur when the cost per unit of output depends on the size of a firm. So, external economies of scale are the advantages the firms can gain as a result of the growth of the industry (normally associated with a particular area) and internal economies arise as a result of the growth of the individual firm. Thus, internal economies are those, which arise from the expansion of the plant size of the firm and is internalized. This means internal economies are exclusively available to the expanding firm. Exploitation of internal economies of scale is a move towards productive efficiency in the long run. On the contrary, external economies accrue to the expanding firms from the advantages arising outside the firm. Both external and internal economies of scale have different implications for the structure of industries:

☆ An industry, where economies of scale are purely external, will typically consist of many small firms and be perfectly competitive.

☆ Internal economies of scale result when large firms have a cost advantage over small firms, causing the industry to become imperfectly competitive.

6.4. Diseconomies of Large Scale

As mentioned earlier, in any production programme, when large corporations rule the business landscape, economies of scale are the goal. Not all expansions, however, produces positive results. Diseconomies or disadvantages could result (Figure 6.5). The diseconomies of scale are the forces that cause large firms to produce goods and services at increased per-unit costs. But, they are less well-known than what Economists have long understood about economies of scale. So, when the firm experiences diseconomies of scale, LRATC do not continue to decline as business expands its output (Figure 6.1), but rises and this is the result of diminishing RTS. This implies that, there are inefficiencies within the firm or industry, thereby, resulting in rising LRATC. The causes of diseconomies of scale are numerous and may not be obvious without comprehensive analysis of individual cases. Basic causes, however, can still be defined. The diseconomies will be looked at under two headings *viz.*, internal diseconomies of scale (disadvantages to the firm of large-scale production) and external diseconomies of scale (disadvantages or drawbacks of the industry affecting individual firm).

I. Internal Diseconomies of Large Scale

This arises due to the following reasons:

☆ *Managerial diseconomies:* Managerial problems are often specific to diseconomies of scale. When the firm greatly expands, managers have a

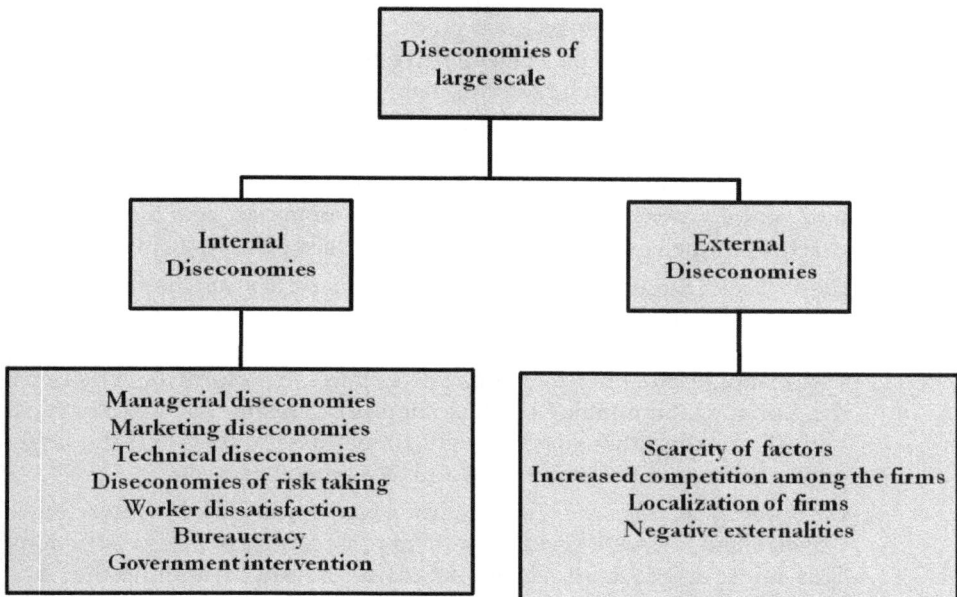

Diseconomies of
large scale

Internal
Diseconomies

External
Diseconomies

Managerial diseconomies
Marketing diseconomies
Technical diseconomies
Diseconomies of risk taking
Worker dissatisfaction
Bureaucracy
Government intervention

Scarcity of factors
Increased competition among the firms
Localization of firms
Negative externalities

harder time for coordinating tasks and processes. That means, it becomes difficult on the part of the business managers to co-ordinate the complicated production processes across several plants in different locations. This results in a loss of competitive advantage due to inefficiencies or mismanagement or inexperience with scale. All these leads to slackness, waste, confusion, low morale of the workers etc., contributing to rise in costs more than proportionately compared to the rise in output. This inability to monitor the large scale production programme by the top administrator has been called *'Control loss'* by Oliver Williamson.

☆ *Marketing diseconomies:* When the firm expands greatly, raw material availability in right time and in right quantity may become a problem (may be due to scarcity). The demand for a product may fall, as a result of changes in tastes of the people. The organization may fail to foresee the changes in market conditions and hence, the sales of products might fall.

☆ *Technical diseconomies:* Specialization and massive investment in machinery and equipment though contributes to higher output, but may also lead to loss of flexibility necessary to respond quickly to changes in demand. The expansion of business firm beyond the optimum size, may lead to repeated breakdown in plants and hence, the firm may not function up to its installed capacity.

☆ *Diseconomies of risk taking:* As the scale of firm expands, risks also increase with it. An error of judgement, say regarding the price fixation of product, adversely affects the trade and it leads to greater loss.

☆ *Worker dissatisfaction:* Workers in large firms may feel a sense of alienation and subsequent loss of morale. If they do not consider themselves to be an integral part of the business, their productivity may fall leading to wastage of factors of production. The collective feeling and morale towards the organization are less in large firms than in small firms. Both the managers and workers of large firms feel more secured in the organization and have no fear of getting sacked. This makes them lethargic and devoid of entrepreneurship. The workers find it easier to form into groups such as, trade unions, workers associations, labour unions etc., and the restrictive practices of such groups may result in increased costs for firms.

☆ *Bureaucracy:* Diseconomies of scale are particularly likely in the public sector, as Government bureaucrats may be ill-equipped to manage large organizations. Nepotism and Red tapism are rampant and these coupled with elaborate and time-consuming procedures to perform the activities in these organizations makes the customers not to realize the benefits on par with their expectations and in right time, thereby, they find the larger organizations are too impersonal and lack personal touch.

☆ *Government intervention:* As the firm expands, it may be subjected to Government intervention in the form of price control or other restrictions. This is especially true, if the expansion results in monopolies and oligopolies.

II. External Diseconomies of Large Scale

These arise due to the following reasons:

☆ *Scarcity of factors:* When an industry expands, the demand for factors like labour, capital equipments, raw materials etc., will increase. Thus, there may be shortage of these factors in the economy and they will be available at higher prices. Hence, cost per unit of output increases.

☆ *Increased competition among the firms:* As the number of firms in the industry increases, competition becomes stiffer, thereby, the firms have to invest more on advertising and propaganda about their products and this raises the cost per unit of the output.

☆ *Localization of firms:* Localization of firms in an industry leads to more social costs, which impacts negatively on the firms or the industry and on society at large.

☆ *Negative externalities:* If one or two firms in the industry suffer decline, all other firms in the industry might feel the same adverse effects.

All the above diseconomies are external to each firm in the industry because, these diseconomies are not caused by the expansion of any single firm, but are the consequences of the expansion of the whole industry.

To summarize, economies of scale are the cost advantages that a firm obtains due to expansion. Diseconomies of scale are the disadvantages of being too large. Economies of scale lead to cost saving (fall in LRATC) and the diseconomies of scale lead to the rise in cost (rise in LRATC). Economies and Diseconomies of Scale also determines the RTS. When the economies are more that the diseconomies, the RTS increase. When the diseconomies are more than the economies, the RTS decrease. When the economies balance the diseconomies, the RTS are constant.

6.5. Avoiding Diseconomies of Large Scale

The Economists believe that, effective management techniques and the appropriate incentives can do much to reduce the risk of rising LRATC. The following are the suggestive measures to overcome the diseconomies of scale in large-scale business:

☆ Developments in human resource management should be focussed on priority basis. By this, the productive efficiency of the workers can be greatly improved through streamlining the areas like worker recruitment, training, promotion, retention and support of faculty and staff. These counts much, especially, when the firm experiences shortage of skilled workers.

☆ Offering incentives to workers based on their work performance in the firm counts much in promoting the work culture thereby, leading to higher productivity. This also motivates the other staff in the firm to function towards the directed goals and objectives.

☆ Recently, large scale businesses are engaged in out-sourcing of production and distribution activities, as they aim to expand the sales even to ever-distant markets. By doing so, the costs can be greatly reduced, but at the same time, the firm can retain control over the production and distribution activities.

The above discussion infers that, the two concepts *i.e.,* economies of scale and diseconomies of scale influences the shape of LRATC curve. The economies of scale make the firm to enjoy lower LRATC by increasing the output and reverse is the case for diseconomies of scale. If some firms in an industry enjoy economies of scale, it will influence the structure of the industry, as it encourages towards forming mergers in the industry.

6.6. Measurement of Economies of Scale

It implies, measurement of, how sensitive the LRTC is to the changes in the output in the production programme. This can be said as 'Output elasticity of LRTC (E_{OC})'. This concept is parallel to Price elasticity of demand and Income elasticity of demand, where the sensitiveness of quantity demanded of a commodity is studied in relation to price of the commodity and income of the consumer respectively. So, E_{OC} can be studied as the ratio between percentage change in LRTC to the percentage change in output in the production programme. This is given by:

E_{OC} = (per cent change in LRTC/per cent change in output)

= per cent ΔLRTC/per cent ΔY

So, to calculate the E_{OC}, we need to know, what the percentage change in LRTC is and what the percentage change in output in the production programme is. It is best to calculate these one at a time.

Percentage Change in LRTC

The formula used to calculate the percentage change in LRTC is:

[LRTC (New) – LRTC (Old)]/LRTC (Old)

= Change in LRTC/LRTC (Old)

Percentage Change in Output

The formula used to calculate the percentage change in output in the production programme is:

[Output(New) - Output(Old)]/Output(Old)

= Change in output/Output (old)

So, $E_{OC} = (\Delta LRTC/LRTC) \div (\Delta Y/Y) = (\Delta LRTC/\Delta Y) \times (Y/LRTC)$

where, LRTC = Original (Old) LRTC, Y = Original (Old) output, ΔLRTC = Change in LRTC, ΔY = Change in output.

Interpretation of E_{OC}

The computation of E_{OC} is helpful to see, how sensitive the LRTC is to the change in firm's output. The higher the E_{OC}, the more sensitive is the LRTC to output changes. A very high E_{OC} suggests that, when the output of a commodity increases, the LRTC will increase by a great deal and *vice versa*. The following are the rules of thumb to interpret the E_{OC}:

☆ If $E_{OC} > 1$ then, LRTC of the firm is output elastic (*i.e.*, LRTC is more sensitive to output changes)

☆ If $E_{OC} = 1$ then, LRTC of the firm is unitary elastic

☆ If $E_{OC} < 1$ then, LRTC of the firm is output inelastic (*i.e.*, LRTC is less sensitive to output changes).

In computing the E_{OC}, we use percentages rather than absolute amounts with reference to both LRTC and output changes. By using percentages, we can correctly compare the LRTC responsiveness to changes in the output of the firms. E_{OC} being a ratio in terms of percentages, it will have no units for measurement. Also note that, the E_{OC} is equal to the ratio of LRMC to LRATC of a firm *i.e.*, (LRMC/LRATC) and their relation is already studied through Figure 5.24. So, the relation between LRATC and LRMC indicates the economies of scale and this guides the relationship between E_{OC} and economies of scale in the long run production programme (Table 6.2). It is clear that, E_{OC} varies inversely with output elasticity *i.e.*, when the firm experiences economies of scale, the E_{OC} is less than and *vice versa*. When the firm is with $E_{OC} = 1$, the LRATC is at minimum *i.e.*, there is constant RTS.

Table 6.2: Relation between E_{OC} and Output Elasticity

LRATC vs LRMC	E_{OC} (LRMC/ LRATC)	Behaviour of LRATC as Output Increases	Economies of Scale or Diseconomies of Scale	RTS
LRATC > LRMC	< 1	Decreases	Economies of Scale	Increasing RTS
LRATC = LRMC	= 1	Constant (LRATC is minimum)	Neither economies of scale nor diseconomies of scale	Constant RTS
LRATC < LRMC	> 1	Increases	Diseconomies of Scale	Diminishing RTS

6.7. Economies of Scope

The concept of economies of scope is similar to economies of scale discussed earlier. The concept of economies of scale of a firm refers to the fall in average total cost associated with increasing the scale of production of a single product, whereas the concept of economies of scope also refers to lowering the average total cost of a firm, but producing two or more products. Thus, economies of scope is an extension of the concept of economies of scale to the multi product case. This concept of economies of scope ensures product diversification in an efficient way. That is, it is economical for the firm to produce two products together in its production programme rather than producing these two products separately. So, when a firm enjoys economies of scope, it is cost-effective (economical) to produce two or more products together than the cost of producing each product separately. This can be represented as given below:

$C(A, B) < C(A,0) + C(0,B)$

where, C = Total Cost, A = Product A, B = Product B.

The above expression infers that, joint production is less costly than production of single product (Table 6.3). Thus, economies of scope can result, if two or more products share the same production facilities. This concept of economies of scope can be attributed to Panzar and Willig. Economies of scope are determined with the following formula:

Table 6.3: Economies of Scope in Producing Two Products

Units of Product A	Units of Product B	Cost (A, B)
Case I		
100	0	(250, 0)
0	500	(0, 550)
100	500	700 Cost (A + B)
Case II		
200	0	(1000, 0)
0	1500	(0, 4000)
200	1500	4600 Cost (A + B)

$$S = \frac{C(Q_A) + C(Q_B) - C(Q_A + Q_B)}{C(Q_A + Q_B)}$$

In the above equation,

$S =$ Economies of scope. It measures the percentage cost saving that occurs, when the products A and B are produced together. Thus, 'S' is greater than zero, when economies of scope exist, and the larger the positive value for S, the greater the economies of scope and *vice versa*.

$C(Q_A) =$ The total cost of producing the product A with quantity Q_A separately

$C(Q_B) =$ The total cost of producing the product B with quantity Q_B separately

$C(Q_A + Q_B) =$ The total cost of producing the quantities of two products A and B together with the same production facilities.

The above concept can be easily understood from the following example: Assume a firm produces two products A and B. The cost of producing 1000 units of product A is Rs. 100000 and the cost of producing 2000 units of product B is Rs. 1,20000. If both product A (1000 units) and product B (2000 units) are produced together, the total cost is Rs. 200000. Then the economics of scope 'S' is given by:

$$S = \frac{C(Q_A) + C(Q_B) - C(Q_A + Q_B)}{C(Q_A + Q_B)}$$

$$S = \frac{100000 + 120000 - 175000}{175000} = 0.26 = 26 \text{ per cent}$$

Thus, the cost of producing both the products A and B together is 26 per cent less than the cost of producing them separately. Note that, when a firm has economies of scope, the costs of producing the products together is less than the cost to produce them separately, but it can be difficult to determine the true costs of each individual product even when they are being produced together.

Sources of Economies of Scope

We know, economies of scope arises, when there are cost savings associated with the broadening of a firm's scope of activities. The economies of scope arises for a firm in one or many of the following ways:

☆ Economies of scope can arise through marketing. For example, if a firm deals with several products, it can market them in similar ways. Thus, marketing strategies, product branding, and product design costs are spread over a large number of products. Finally, economies of scope arise from reduced distribution cost.

☆ Economies of scope can arise, if the sales force of a firm sells several products rather than selling a single product. In selling several products by the same sales force, the cost of travel and selling time are distributed over a greater revenue base and thereby, efficiency improves. Further, by selling different products at a time, it enables the firm to offer a right combination of product mix to the customers than would offering a single product.

☆ Economies of scope also arise through improving distribution efficiencies. That is, by transporting several products to a single location increases efficiency than by transporting a single type of product to that location.

☆ When cost-saving to the firm arises by employing by-products in the production process, economies of scope will occur. For example, production of alcohol from the molasses by a sugar factory leads to economies of scope.

☆ If the firm sells several product lines to different customers across different countries, it will enjoy economies of scope. This is because, if one of its product lines falls out of fashion or if one country's economy has slowed down, the firm will likely be able to continue trading on other products.

Examples of Economies of Scope

They include:

☆ *Production of timber and particle board.*

☆ *Corn and ethanol production.*

☆ *Production of beef and hides.*

☆ *Power generation and distribution*

☆ *Global wholesale distribution of cheese, salad dressing, and cigarettes (example: Phillip-Morris-Kraft).*

☆ McDonalds can produce both hamburgers and French fries at a lower average cost than what it would cost two separate firms to produce the same goods. This is because McDonalds hamburgers and French fries share the use of food storage, preparation facilities and so forth during production.

☆ Proctor and Gamble, produces hundreds of products from razors to toothpaste. They can afford to hire expensive graphic designers and marketing experts, who will use their skills across the product lines. Since the costs are spread out, this lowers the average total cost of production for each product.

Examples

1. A firm's cost function, which relates its LRATC to its cumulative output in thousands of units of output 'Y' and its plant size in terms of thousands of units of output produced per year 'y', within the production range of 10,000 to 50,000 units of output is given by: LRATC = 10 - 0.1Y + 0.3y. Is there a learning curve effect? Are there economies or diseconomies of scale?

Solution

In the above LRATC function, LRATC decreases as cumulative output 'Y' increases, and hence, there is learning curve effect. When there is learning effect, there is economies of scale, as the LRATC declines with increase in output (y) in each year.

2. Considering the above LRATC function, the firm has produced a total of 40 units of output and is producing 10 units this year. Next year, it plans to increase its production to 12 units. Will its LRATC increase or decrease? Explain.

Solution

First, let us workout LRATC for this year:

$LRATC_1 = 10 - 0.1Y + 0.3y = 10 - (0.1)(40) + (0.3)(10) = 9.$

Now, calculate the LRATC for next year:

$LRATC_2 = 10 - (0.1)(50) + (0.3)(12) = 8.6.$

Note that, by the next year, cumulative output has increased from 40 to 50 units. So, the LRATC decreases for the next year, and this is due to learning effect.

Exercises

1. For the given data below, compute LRATC and plot the graph.

Long Run Output	Total Cost (Rs.)
1,000	8,500
2,000	15,000
5,000	36,000
10,000	65,000
20,000	120,000
50,000	280,000
100,000	490,000
500,000	2,300,000

2. Assume that a firm produces two products X and Y. The cost of producing 1000 units of product X is Rs. 200000 and the cost of producing 2000 units of product Y is Rs. 2,50000. If both product X (1000 units) and product Y (2000 units) are produced together, the total cost is Rs. 400000. Then, compute economics of scope in producing both the products.

6.8. Economies and Diseconomies of Scale vis-à-vis Economies and Diseconomies of Size

As discussed above, in the concept of economies of scale or diseconomies of scale for a firm, the farmer must vary all the factors (*i.e.*, no factor is fixed) and that too in the same proportion. Say, if all the factors are doubled, and if the output is tripled, it implies, there is economies of scale. If all the factors are tripled, and if the output is doubled, it implies there is diseconomies of scale. if all the factors are doubled, and if the output is also doubled, it implies there is no economies or diseconomies of scale. However, in economies or diseconomies of size, there is a change in the level of output, but all the factors need not change in the same proportion. Thus, in economies or diseconomies of scale, not only must output change, but each factor must change in the same proportion. To understand clearly, economies of scale implies, what happens to per unit cost of production (ie., decrease in LRATC), when all the factors are changed in the same proportion say, doubled or tripled or quadrupled or halved. The diseconomies of scale implies, what happens to per unit cost of production (ie., rise in LRATC), when all the factors are changed in the same proportion say, doubled or tripled or quadrupled or halved. In this context, the term economies of size implies, what happens to per unit cost of production (say, decrease in SRATC), when all the factors need not change proportionately. The diseconomies of size implies, what happens to per unit cost of production (say, increase in SRATC), when all factors need not change proportionately. Thus, the terms economies or diseconomies of size are used in the context of both time and variability of factors. In the short run production programme, where some inputs are fixed and some are variable, the economies or diseconomies of size is studied to analyze, how SRATC changes with reference to increase or decrease of one or more (but not all) variable factors, but not of fixed factors.

As discussed through Figure 5.21 (in Chapter 5), the LRATC curve represents a planning curve for the firm, as the farmer can plan his economies of scale of production (downward slope of LRATC) and try to operate where LRATC his minimum. This fall in LRATC implies there is economies of scale in the long run production programme. On the rising portion of LRATC, there is diseconomies of scale in the long run production programme. Each of the SRATC curves represent possible changes in output that could occur within a much shorter period of time. This possible changes in output in the short run is due to varying of one or more (but not all) variable factors, but not of fixed factors. Thus, each SRATC curve represent possible levels of output during a long period that is sufficient enough to vary some factors, but short enough so that, all factors cannot be varied.

7

Concepts of Revenue and Firm's Equilibrium

In modern days of business, every firm, either small or large tend to produce and market the commodities with the aim of maximization of profits. The amount of money which the firm earns by selling the output is called Revenue. So, every firm aims to earn more of the revenue, so as to cover the TC incurred in the production programme. So, in the business, the firms play dual role *viz.,* as a producer and as a seller. As a producer, it aims at minimization of costs and as a seller, it aims at maximization of profits. In this process of selling the output in the market, the firm earns revenue to sustain in the business. There are different concepts of revenue *viz.,* Total Revenue (TR), Average Revenue (AR) and MR and these concepts are widely useful for analyzing the firm's equilibrium with reference to optimization of output or maximization of profits. So, before discussing different approaches to arrive at the firm's equilibrium, it is essential to study different concepts of revenue under different forms of market competition.

I. Different Concepts of Revenue

A. TR

TR is the amount of money or income that the firm gets from the sale of its product in the market. This is derived by multiplying the quantity of product or output sold by the firm in the market with the price at which it is transacted to the buyer. The concept of TR helps to derive both AR and MR of the firm. The curve, which depicts the TR of the firm refers to Total Revenue Curve (TRC).

B. AR

In simpler terms, the term AR was quoted as 'Price' received by the firm in selling the product in the market. Using the term AR often provides a connection to other related terms, especially TR and MR. We know, TR refers to the total income or returns earned by the farmer or firm in selling the product in the market. So, AR refers to the ratio between TR to the quantity of output sold in the market. It is given by AR = TR/Y. This infers that, TR relates to total income earned by the firm from the total output transacted in the market, whereas, AR refers to the revenue (price) earned per unit of the product. In the concepts of SRATC and LRATC, we studied the cost per unit of output in the short run and long run production programmes respectively and in the concept of revenue, AR refers to the revenue or price earned by the seller per unit of output transacted in the market. The concept of AR is of vital importance for the firm, as it indicates the firm's profits and its future prospects of expanding the business in the long run production programme. The concept of AR is represented by Average Revenue Curve (ARC). The ARC is also called as Demand curve because, the demand curve indicates the various quantities of a commodity purchased by the buyer at different prices, from which, we can compute the price or AR at which each unit of the commodity is transacted by the seller. The price paid by the buyer constitutes the revenue to the seller.

AR vs Price

In Economic sense, we generally use the terms AR and price interchangeably. But, in all cases, they both are not the same. This is because, if the farmer sells various quantities of a commodity at the same price, AR is equal to price, but if the seller offers different quantities of a commodity at different prices, then AR is not the same as price. Say, for example, if the farmer sells 100 quintals of paddy to rice miller at Rs. 1000/quintal and 50 quintals of paddy to wholesaler at Rs. 1000/quintal, the TR obtained by the farmer is Rs. 1.50 lakhs. The AR obtained by the farmer is Rs. 1000/qtl, which is same as price/quintal of paddy. Let us consider another case, where the farmer sells 100 quintals of paddy to rice miller at Rs. 1000/quintal in Andhra Pradesh and 100 quintals of paddy to another rice miller in Tamil Nadu at Rs. 1200/quintal. Then, the TR obtained by the farmer is Rs. 2.20 lakhs and the AR obtained by the farmer is Rs. 1100/qtl, which is not equal to the price/quintal of paddy. This infers that, when the farmer or firm discriminates the price across the markets, the AR he receives is not equal to price of the commodity. This is the case normally we see, when a monopoly firm discriminates the markets. But, in general, the farmer transacts the large quantities of commodities at the same price, thereby, AR equals to price and hence, we use these two terms interchangeably.

C. MR

The concept of AR only indicates the average price per unit of output sold by the seller to the buyer. But, it won't indicate the change in TR due to additional unit of output transacted by the seller to the buyer and the same is indicated by MR. That means, MR indicates, how much extra revenue the firm receives by selling an extra unit of output. We can derive this MR as the slope of the TR curve. So, MR is the net revenue added to the seller's revenue, when an extra unit of output was transacted in the market. This word 'net' clearly infers that, the MR is not equal to the price (AR) of the commodity, unless the firm operates under perfect competition. This is because, in perfect competition, the firms are simply price takers and a single firm cannot influence the price of the commodity. Further, the commodity being homogeneous, the firm gets same additional revenue for an additional unit of output transacted in the market. Hence, MR equals to AR under perfect market competition. However, in other (imperfect) markets, different quantities of output are sold at different prices in accordance with the law of demand, thereby, MR is not equal to the price (AR) of the commodity. The concept of MR is represented by Marginal Revenue Curve (MRC).

i. Measurement of MR

There are three methods of computation of MR. For example, a farmer transacted 10 quintals of paddy at Rs. 1000/qunital. Due to decrease in price to Rs. 950, the farmer could transact 11 quintals of paddy.

Method 1

MR is computed as the difference between TR of quantity of output sold at new price and TR of quantity of output sold at old price. This is given by the formula : MR = TR_{n+1} - TR_n So, MR = (11 × 950) – (10 × 1000) = 450. This infers that, by selling additional unit (quintal) of paddy, the farmer gets additional revenue or net revenue or MR of Rs. 450.

Method 2

MR is, otherwise, explained as the ratio between change in TR to the change in quantity of output sold by the farmer in the market. So, the MR is given by, $\Delta TR/\Delta Y$. This implies that, the slope of TR indicates MR. In the above example, the change in TR is Rs. 10450 – Rs. 10000 = Rs. 450 and change in quantity of output sold by the farmer is one quintal, thereby, MR = Rs. 450.

Method 3

Computation of MR can be studied in a different way. When the price of paddy is decreased in the market from Rs. 1000 to Rs. 950, it implies, the farmer is losing Rs. 50 on each quintal he transacted earlier, thereby, the total loss on the previous 10 units will be Rs. 500. But, for the 11th unit (quintal) of paddy, the farmer is getting the price Rs. 950. So, the net gain (MR) to the farmer by selling 11th unit of paddy is 950 minus total loss incurred by the farmer on the previous 10 units due to fall in price of paddy *i.e.,* MR = Rs.950-Rs.500 = Rs. 450. So, we can derive the formula for computation of MR and it is given by,

MR = Price of additional unit of output – Loss in revenue on previous units sold due to price fall

The above discussion infers that,

☆ When different quantities of commodities are offered at different prices by the farmer or firm, the MR is not equal to the price.

☆ MR of transacting additional unit of paddy (Rs. 450/quintal) is not equal to price of paddy (Rs. 950) at which the 11th quintal of paddy is sold. That means, when additional unit of output is sold at less new price (Rs. 950) than the old price (Rs. 1000), then MR (Rs. 450) is less than the new price. But, when additional unit of output is sold even when there is no change in price, then MR is equal to the price.

☆ From Method 2, we can also infer that, the slope of TR indicates MR. So, given a TR curve, we can easily compute the MR of each and every additional unit of output transacted by the firm in the market.

As discussed under the relationship between SRMC and SRAVC curves, there exists the same marginal-average relation between MRC and ARC. This can commonly be seen in imperfect market competition. That means, when AR falls, MR also falls and lies below AR. When AR is constant, MR is also constant and is equal to the AR. This is common in perfect market competition. Among these three concepts of TR, AR and MR, the concepts of AR and MR are important to draw comparative picture across different market structures.

II. ARC and MRC in different Forms of Market Competition

The concepts of AR and MR are represented in the form of ARC and MRC respectively. The relation between these two curves in relation to output depends upon the market structure (Table 7.1 and Figure 7.1). For a perfectly competitive firm, AR is not only equal to price, but also equal to MR. So, for a perfectly competitive firm, the ARC is a horizontal line parallel to X-axis or perfectly elastic (as the firm is only a price taker) and MRC coincides with ARC. But, in case of imperfect market competitions *viz.,* monopoly, oligopoly and monopolistic competitions, for a firm, the AR is greater than MR and they both fall when larger quantities of output are transacted. So, for monopoly, oligopoly and monopolistic competitive firms, both

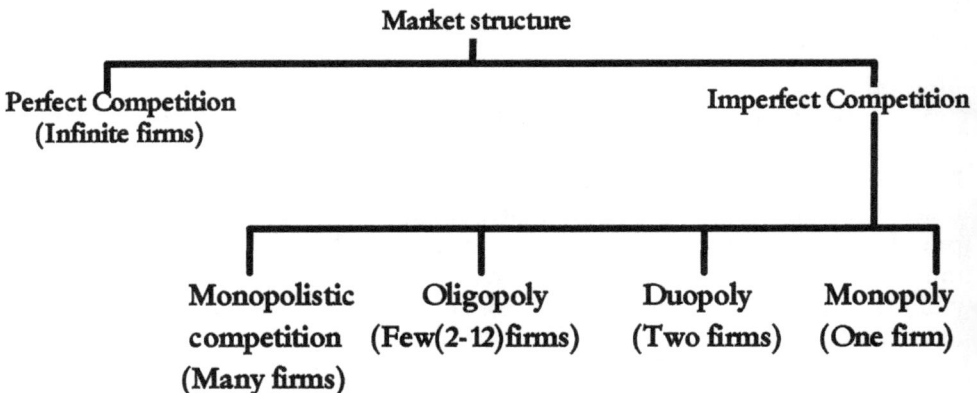

Figure 7.1: Different Types of Market Structures Based on Competition.

Table 7.1: Basic Features of different Types of Market Structures

Market Structure	Number of Firms	Degree of Product Differentiation	Firms Degree of Control Over Price	Examples
I. Perfect competition	Infinite number of firms	Homogeneous	No control over price	Agricultural commodities, Internet service
II. Imperfect competition				
a. Monopoly	One firm	Product with no close substitutes (Homogeneous)	Considerable control over price	Microsoft is held to have monopolized market for computer operating systems, Public utilities like railways, electricity, irrigation etc.
b. Duopoly (A pure duopoly occurs very rarely in practical world and the more common is two dominant firms hold majority of the market share)				
☆ Perfect Duopoly	Two firms	Homogeneous	Some control over price	Visa and MasterCard control a large proportion of the electronic payment processing market, Hindustan Petroleum vs Bharat Petroleum
☆ Imperfect Duopoly	Two firms	Heterogeneous	Some control over price	Pepsi vs Coca-Cola in soft drink market, Gillette vs Wilkinson Sword in razor blade market, Kodak vs Fujifilm in the color 135 film market
c. Oligopoly				
☆ Perfect Oligopoly	Few firms	Homogeneous	Some control over price	Organization of Petroleum Exporting Countries (OPEC), Steel industry in USA, Cement
☆ Imperfect Oligopoly	Few firms	Heterogeneous	Some control over price	Automobile industry in USA, Computers, Electrical appliances, Television etc.
d. Monopolistic competition	Many firms (but less than perfect competition)	Heterogeneous	Some control over price	Retail outlets of fertilizers, pesticides, restaurants, clothing, shoes etc.

|

ARC and MRC are negatively sloped. In each case, the ARC is above the MRC, but with different elasticities. As explained earlier, the ARC is also the demand curve facing the firm under both perfect and imperfect market competitions. The point of optimality in the production programme is indicated by the equality between MC=MR. If MR>MC, the firm can still increase the output till the equality MR=MC is ensured. On the other hand, if MR<MC, the firm has to reduce the output till the equality MR=MC is ensured. The ARC indicates the price at which the optimal output has to be transacted to maximize the profits. Hence, ARC is otherwise termed as Demand curve of the firm. Let us discuss the pattern of ARC and MRC across different market competitions.

A. ARC and MRC under Perfect Market Competition

We know, perfect competition is a market structure with an infinite number of small firms, each selling a homogenous good. All the perfect competitive firms have perfect knowledge about the market and perfect mobility into and out of the market. The firms under perfect competition are simply price takers, thereby, they have no market control and receive the same or going market price for all the output sold. So, at the same price, the firms have to transact all the output and this implies, the demand curve or ARC are perfectly elastic. Since, the firm has no control over the price, it has to sell the additional units of output at the same price, thereby, MRC is also constant and it is equal to ARC. So, for a perfect competitive firm, both ARC and MRC are equal and when ARC is constant, MRC must be constant. The same concept is explained through Table 7.2 and Figures 7.2 and 7.3.

Table 7.2: TR, AR and MR of a Perfect Competitive Firm Transacting Paddy

Output (Quintals)	Price (Rs/quintal)	TR (Rs.)	AR (Rs/quintal)	MR (Rs/quintal)
0	1000	0	—	—
1	1000	1000	1000	1000
2	1000	2000	1000	1000
3	1000	3000	1000	1000
4	1000	4000	1000	1000
5	1000	5000	1000	1000
6	1000	6000	1000	1000
7	1000	7000	1000	1000
8	1000	8000	1000	1000
9	1000	9000	1000	1000
10	1000	10000	1000	1000

In the Table 7.2, it was shown that, the farmer transacted various quantities of paddy at the same price, as under perfect market competition, same price will prevail for the same commodity at the same time. From the quantity-price data, the TR, AR and MR are computed. TR is computed in the third column as the product between quantity of paddy transacted and price received. AR is computed in the fourth column

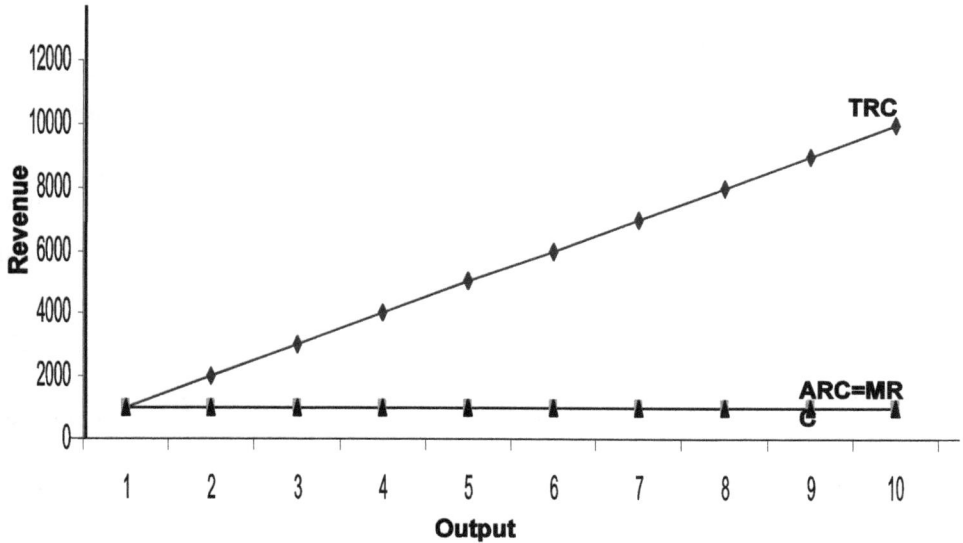

Figure 7.2: TR, AR and MR Curves of a Firm Under Perfect Market Competition.

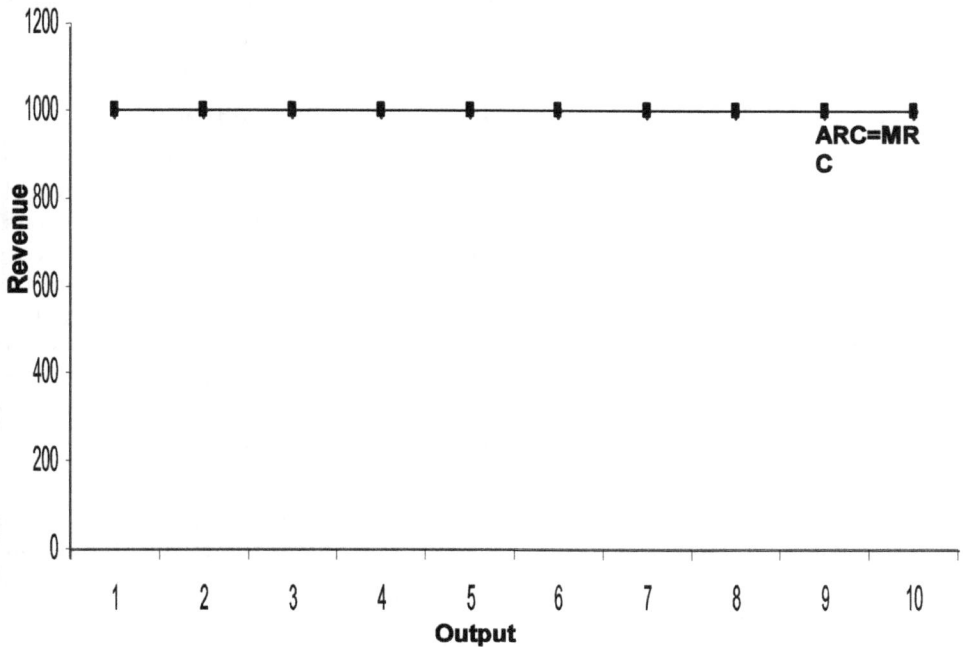

Figure 7.3: ARC and MRC of a Firm Under Perfect Market Competition.

by dividing the TR with quantity of paddy transacted. The obvious point here is that, AR is equal to Rs. 1000 for each and every unit (quintal) of paddy sold. The reason is that, price is constant at Rs. 1000 for each and every unit (quintal) of paddy sold. So, AR is price or price is AR and these two are one and the same. MR is calculated by dividing the change in TR by the change in quantity of paddy sold. For example, when the farmer sells ninth (*i.e.,* one) quintal of paddy, he receives Rs. 1000 MR and if he sells 10th quintal of paddy, still he receives Rs. 1000 MR. So, the MR is equal to Rs. 1000 for every extra quintal of paddy sold. This results because, price is constant at Rs. 1000 for every quintal of paddy sold. So, for every extra quintal of paddy sold by the farmer, he receives an extra Rs. 1000, which is the going market price. So, MR is equal to price and AR for a perfectly competitive firm. The same results are shown through Figures 7.2 and 7.3, where the vertical axis measures the revenue and the horizontal axis measures the quantity of output (paddy) sold by the farmer. The ARC and MRC curves are perfectly elastic and hence, they lie parallel to X-axis. That means, if the farmer sells one quintal of paddy, he receives Rs. 1000 AR and Rs. 1000 MR. If the farmer sells 10 quintals of paddy, still he receives Rs. 1000 AR and Rs. 1000 MR (for 10th quintal), but the TR increases from Rs. 1000 to Rs. 10000. This implies that, TR continuously slopes upwards with increase in quantity of paddy sold by the farmer, but the AR and MR received by the farmer remains same irrespective of the quantity of paddy transacted by the farmer. So, MRC coincides with ARC. Another interesting aspect here is, under perfect competition, the AR and MR coincides with price of the output. So, AR is just another term for price and this ARC is actually the demand curve. Under the perfect market competition, the MRC of the farmer is also his demand curve, as MRC coincides with ARC. But in imperfect competition, ARC alone indicates the demand curve for the farmer, as MRC is negatively sloped and lies below the ARC (demand curve) and the same is discussed here under.

B. ARC and MRC Under Imperfect Market Competition

As mentioned earlier, monopoly, oligopoly and monopolistic competitions are the important forms of imperfect market competition. While conceptually AR and MR are the same for these market structures, as the firms under these competitions are price makers rather than price takers, there are a few key differences. All these market structures face negatively-sloped demand curve (ARC), thereby, the price received by the firm is not fixed, but depends on the quantity of output sold in the market. When ARC slopes downward from left to right, MRC also slopes downward from left to right and lies below ARC. This is because, if ARC falls, MRC must fall and lies below ARC, (*i.e.,* MRC falls more rapidly than ARC), as MRC is related to one additional unit of output, but ARC is related to all the units of output.

i. Monopoly Competition

Let us assume, a monopoly firm enjoys patent for marketing Bt cotton seed in the market and it offers various quantities of seed for sale at different prices and the same are shown through Table 7.3. From the quantity-price data, the TR, AR and MR are computed. TR is computed in the third column as the product between quantity of seed transacted and price received. AR is computed in the fourth column by dividing the TR with quantity of seed transacted. The obvious point here is that, AR decreases with the increase in quantity of seed transacted. Moreover, AR is also equal to the price of seed for each quantity sold. For example, when the firm sells one unit of seed, it receives Rs. 1000 as AR and it is equal to the price of the seed *i.e.,* Rs. 1000. Similarly, if the firm sells 10 units of seed, it receives Rs. 550/unit as AR and it is equal to the price of the seed *i.e.,* Rs. 550/unit. So, AR is price and these two are one and the same.

Table 7.3: TR, AR and MR of a Monopoly Firm Selling Bt Cotton Seed

Quantity (units)	Price (Rs./unit)	TR (Rs.)	AR (Rs./unit)	MR (Rs./unit)
0	1050	0	—	—
1	1000	1000	1000	1000
2	950	1900	950	900
3	900	2700	900	800
4	850	3400	850	700
5	800	4000	800	600
6	750	4500	750	500
7	700	4900	700	400
8	650	5200	650	300
9	600	5400	600	200
10	550	5500	550	100
11	500	5500	500	0
12	450	5400	450	-100

MR is calculated by dividing the change in TR by the change in quantity of seed sold. For example, when the firm sells one unit of Bt cotton seed, it receives Rs. 1000 MR and if it sells 10 units of seed, it receives Rs. 100 MR. So, the MR decreases with the increase in quantity of seed sold by the firm. Further, the MR is less than the price (AR) of seed for each quantity sold. This is because, any decline in an average, which is most certainly happening to AR, is associated with a margin that is less than the average. That means, when AR is decreasing, MR must be less than AR. For example, the price at which three units of seed is sold is Rs. 900/unit, but the MR of the firm is only Rs. 800/unit. Similarly, the price at which ten units of seed is sold is Rs. 550/unit, but the MR of the firm is only Rs. 100/unit. Since, price is AR, MR is also less than AR. As shown through the Table 7.3,

☆ If the firm sets the price at Rs. 850/unit, then buyers (farmers) are willing to purchase four units of seed.

☆ If the firm wants to increase the quantity of sale from four units to five units, then it must lower the price from Rs. 850 to Rs. 800 per unit. But, the important aspect here is, that the firm must lower the price for all the five units now and not just the extra unit *i.e.*, 5th unit of seed.

☆ By decreasing the price to Rs. 800, now two forces influences the TR *viz.*, the revenue gained by selling extra unit of seed (*i.e.*, 5th unit only) and the revenue lost by lowering the price from earlier four units of seed. We have to work out these two forces separately, as MR is the net result of both.

❖ First, by lowering the price, the firm increases the quantity of seed sold from four to five units. This extra 5th unit generates an extra of Rs. 800 revenue, *i.e.* the price of the fifth unit of seed. This extra revenue of Rs. 800, the firm did not have at the higher price (*i.e.*, when the price/unit is Rs.850).

❖ Second, by lowering the price, the firm collects less revenue from the earlier four units of seed. For the earlier four units of seed, the firm would have collected Rs. 850 per unit of seed for a total of Rs. 3400, before the fall in price. With the lower price of Rs. 800, now the firm collects only Rs. 3200 for the earlier four units of seed *i.e.* a reduction of TR by Rs. 200 or Rs. 50 per unit of seed.

☆ That means, Rs. 800 gained by selling the extra fifth unit of seed is partially offset by the Rs. 200 lost from lowering the price for earlier four units of seed. On net, TR increases by only Rs.800-Rs. 200 = Rs.600. So, the total loss of revenue on the earlier four units of seed is the key reason that, MR is less than price.

The Table 7.3 further infers that, the rate of fall in MR is more compared to price or AR, and this gives more steepness to the slope of MRC compared to ARC (Figures 7.4 and 7.5). So, both AR and MR decreases with increase in quantity of seed sold by the firm, thereby, both ARC (demand curve) and MRC are negatively sloped. As the slope of MRC is steeper compared to ARC, it implies, ARC is more elastic compared to MRC. That means, if the price of seed falls in the market, MR falls more rapidly than AR, but the TR of the firm increases continuously and reaches maximum, when MR is equal to zero. Thus, ARC and MRC for the firm enjoying monopoly status look different when compared to perfect competition. For a monopoly firm, both ARC and MRC are negatively-sloped and the MRC lies below the ARC, which means that, MR is less than AR (and price) for any given quantity and larger quantities of output are sold only at lower prices, whereas under perfect market competition, MRC coincides

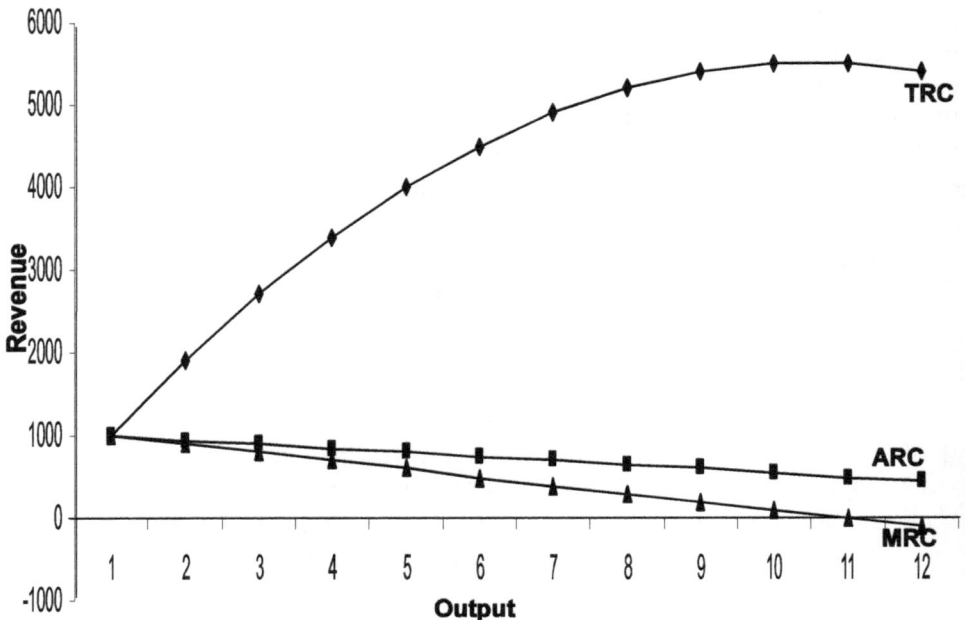

Figure 7.4: TR, AR and MR Curves of a Monopoly Firm Selling Bt Cotton Seed.

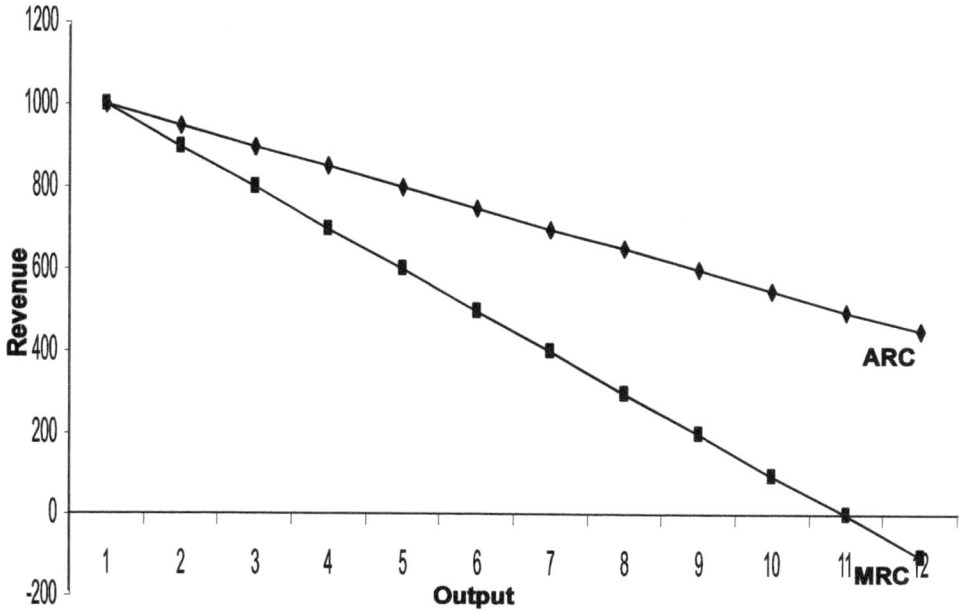

Figure 7.5: ARC and MRC of a Monopoly Firm Selling *Bt* Cotton Seed.

with ARC and price and they are perfectly elastic and even larger output is also sold at same price.

ii. Oligopoly Competition

Even in oligopoly competition, the ARC and MRC slopes downward from left to right and MRC lies below ARC. However, the interesting aspect is that, the ARC or demand curve will bear a kink such that, above the kink 'K', the ARC is more elastic for price rise and below kink, the ARC is less elastic for price fall (Figure 7.6). Due to differences in elasticities along the ARC, the MRC will show discontinuity below the kink.

iii. Monopolistic Competition

Let us assume, a retail firm (operating under monopolistic competition) selling fertilizer in the market and it offers various quantities of fertilizer for sale at different prices and the same are shown through Table 7.4. From the quantity-price data, the TR, AR and MR are computed. TR is computed in the third column as the product between quantity of fertilizer transacted and price received. AR is computed in the fourth column by dividing the TR with quantity of fertilizer transacted. The obvious point here is that, AR decreases with the increase in quantity of fertilizer transacted. Moreover, AR is also equal to the price of fertilizer for each quantity sold. For example, when the firm sells one unit of fertilizer, it receives Rs. 1040 as AR and it is equal to the price of the fertilizer *i.e.,* Rs. 1040. Similarly, if the firm sells 10 units of fertilizer, it receives Rs. 950/unit as AR and it is equal to the price of the fertilizer *i.e.,* Rs. 950/unit. So, AR is price and these two are one and the same.

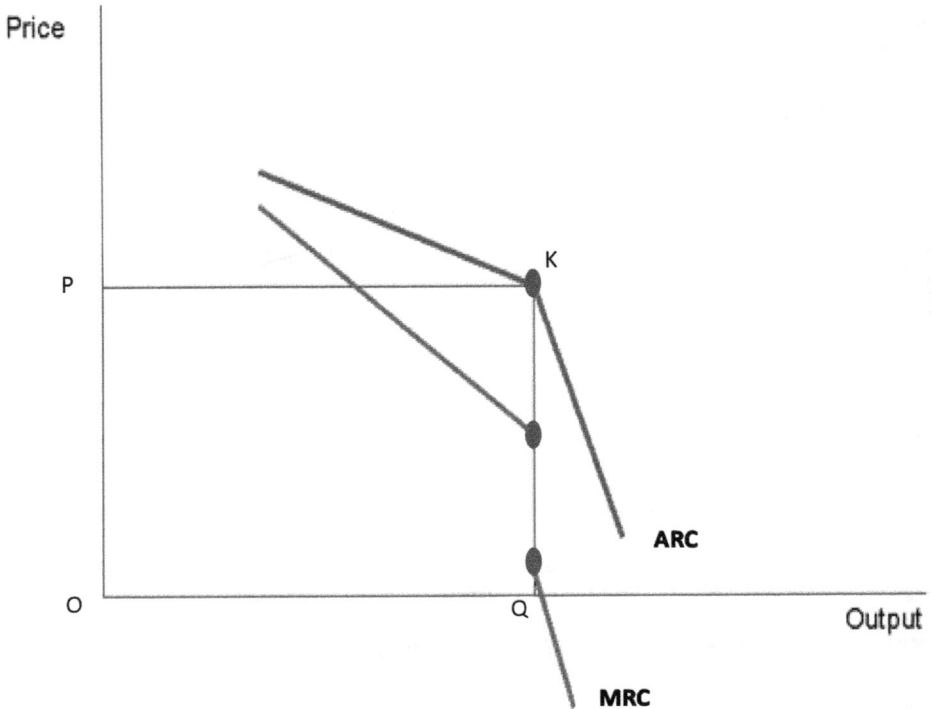

Figure 7.6: ARC and MRC of an Oligopoly Firm.

Table 7.4: TR, AR and MR of a Firm Selling Fertilizer under Monopolistic Competition

Quantity (units)	Price (Rs./unit)	TR (Rs.)	AR (Rs./unit)	MR (Rs./unit)
0	1050	0	—	—
1	1040	1040	1040	1040
2	1030	2060	1030	1020
3	1020	3060	1020	1000
4	1010	4040	1010	980
5	1000	5000	1000	960
6	990	5940	990	940
7	980	6860	980	920
8	970	7760	970	900
9	960	8640	960	880
10	950	9500	950	860

MR is calculated by dividing the change in TR by the change in quantity of fertilizer sold. For example, when the firm sells one unit of fertilizer, it receives Rs. 1040 MR and if it sells 10 units of fertilizer, it receives Rs. 860 MR. So, the MR decreases with the increase in quantity of fertilizer sold by the firm. Further, the MR is less than the price (AR) of fertilizer for each quantity sold. This is because, any decline in an average, which is most certainly happening to AR, is associated with a marginal that is less than the average. That means, when AR is decreasing, MR must be less than AR. For example, the price at which three units of fertilizer is sold is Rs. 1020/unit, but the MR of the firm is only Rs. 1000/unit. Similarly, the price at which ten units of fertilizer is sold is Rs. 950/unit, but the MR of the firm is only Rs. 860/unit. Since, price is AR, MR is also less than AR. As shown through the Table 7.4,

☆ If the firm sets the price at Rs. 1010/unit, then buyers (farmers) are willing to purchase four units of fertilizer.

☆ If the firm wants to increase the quantity of sale from four units to five units, then it must lower the price from Rs. 1010 to Rs. 1000 per unit. The important aspect here is, that the firm must lower the price for all the five units now and not just the extra unit *i.e.* 5th unit of fertilizer.

☆ By decreasing the price to Rs. 1000, now two forces influences the TR *viz.*, the revenue gained by selling extra unit of fertilizer (*i.e.*, 5th unit only) and the revenue lost by lowering the price from earlier four units of fertilizer. We have to work out these these two forces separately, as MR is the net result of both.

  ❖ First, by lowering the price, the firm increases the quantity of fertilizer sold from four to five units. This extra 5th unit generates an extra of Rs. 1000 revenue, *i.e.*, the price of the fifth unit of fertilizer. This extra revenue of Rs. 1000 twas not available to the firm at the higher price (*i.e.*, when the price/unit is Rs. 1010).

  ❖ Second, by lowering the price, the firm collects less revenue from the earlier four units of fertilizer. For the earlier four units of fertilizer, the firm would have collected Rs. 1010 per unit of fertilizer for a total of Rs. 4040, before the fall in price. But, with the lower price of Rs. 1000, now the firm collects only Rs. 4000 for the earlier four units of fertilizer *i.e.*, a reduction of TR by Rs. 40 or Rs. 10 per unit of fertilizer.

☆ That means, Rs. 1000 gained by selling the extra fifth unit of fertilizer is partially offset by the Rs.40 lost from lowering the price on earlier four units of fertilizer. On net, TR increases by only Rs. 1000-Rs.40 = Rs.960. So, the total loss of revenue on the earlier four units of fertilizer is the key reason that, MR is less than price.

The Table 7.4 further infers that, the rate of fall in MR is more compared to price or AR, and this gives more steepness to the slope of MRC compared to ARC (Figures 7.7 and 7.8). So, both AR and MR decreases with increase in quantity of fertilizer sold by the firm, thereby, both ARC (demand curve) and MRC are negatively sloped. As the slope of MRC is steeper compared to ARC, it implies, ARC is more elastic as compared to MRC. That means, if the price of fertilizer falls in the market, MR falls more rapidly than AR, but the TR of the firm increases continuously and reaches maximum, when MR is equal to zero. Thus, ARC and MRC for the firm under

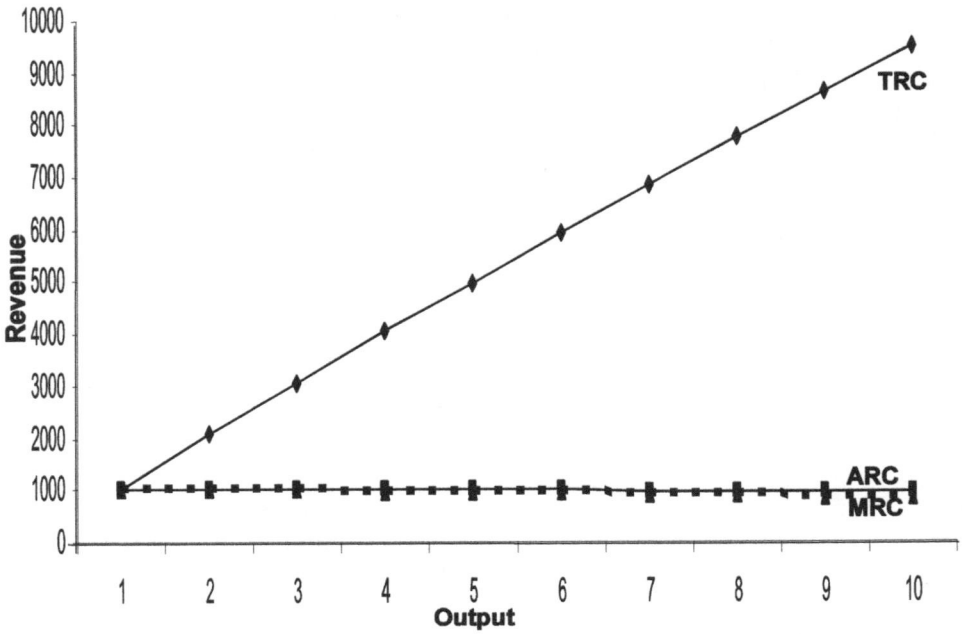

Figure 7.7: TR, AR and MR of a Firm Selling Fertilizer under Monopolistic Competition.

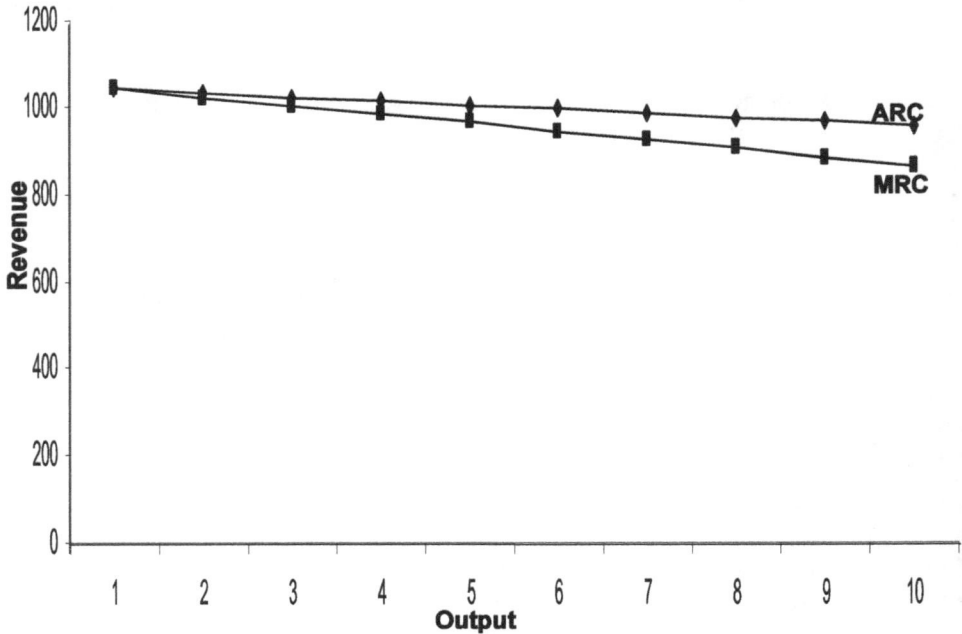

Figure 7.8: ARC and MRC of a Firm Selling Fertilizer under Monopolistic Competition.

monopolistic competition look different when compared to perfect competition and monopoly. For a firm operating under monopolistic competition, both ARC and MRC are negatively-sloped and the MRC lies below the ARC, which means that, MR is less than AR (and price) for any given quantity and larger quantities of output are sold only at lower prices. The same is the case under monopoly, but the AR and MR curves are more steeper compared to monopolistic competition. As the firm itself represents the industry under monopoly, the steepness of the slopes of AR and MR curves fetch higher price for the product, in case the firm wishes to maximize the profits through increasing the price of the product. However, under perfect market competition, MRC coincides with ARC and price and they are perfectly elastic.

III. Derivation of ARC and MRC from TRC

From the TRC, we can easily derive the ARC and MRC and the same is discussed through the Figure 7.9. On X- axis, quantity of output and on the Y-axis, revenue of the firm are taken. TRC rises upward from left to right from the point of origin, but it continues to flatter as it rises *i.e.*, with the increase in the quantity of output sold. That means, TR increases at diminishing rate with increase in quantity of output sold in the market.

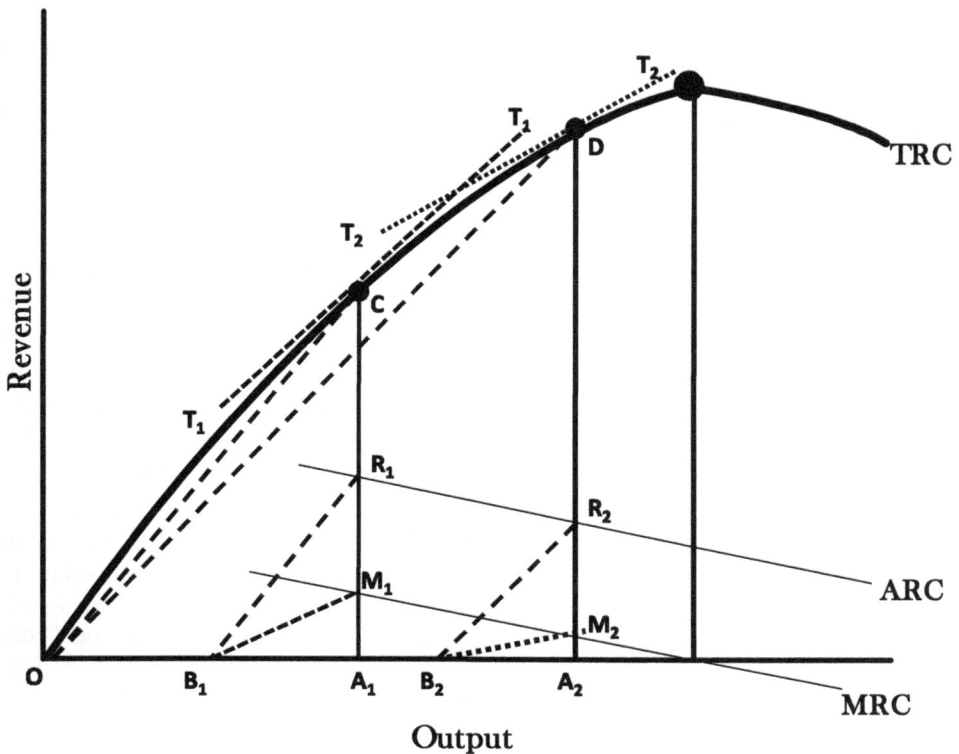

Figure 7.9: Derivation of ARC and MRC from TRC.

Derivation of AR

To derive ARC from TRC, consider a point C on the TRC. To this point draw a straight line (dotted line) OC from the origin and the slope of the straight line represent the AR. This is because, with reference to point C on TRC, TR is A_1C and total output is OA_1. So, A_1C/OA_1 gives the AR with reference to point C. So, the slope of the straight line OC represent the AR. Now, to derive the ARC, consider one unit output level from point A_1 on X-axis and it is B_1. From this point B_1 draw a line parallel to OC i.e, B_1R_1 and it touches the A_1C line at R_1. Since, the point B_1 is at one unit of output distance from point A_1, the slope of this line B_1R_1 represents AR per unit of output (as B_1R_1 is parallel to OC). So, with reference to B_1R_1 line, the AR is equal to A_1R_1/B_1A_1. Since, B_1A_1 represents one unit of output, the AR is equal to A_1R_1.

Derivation of MR

We know, the slope of TRC indicates MR of the firm. So, a tangent T_1T_1 is drawn with reference to point C on the TRC. Again, considering one unit output length from A_1 *i.e.*, B_1A_1, draw a line B_1M_1 parallel to T_1T_1 tangent and the line touches the A_1C line at point M_1. Since, the two lines *i.e.*, T_1T_1 and B_1M_1 are parallel to each other, the slope of the line B_1M_1 indicates the MR for an output B_1A_1. So, slope of line B_1M_1 *i.e.*, MR is given by A_1M_1/B_1A_1. Since, B_1A_1 represents one unit of output, the MR is equal to A_1M_1.

The same procedure for computation of AR and MR is repeated again with reference to point D on the TRC and accordingly we derive AR as A_2R_2 and MR as A_2M_2. So, when the points R_1R_2 are connected by a line, it represents ARC of the firm and the line connecting the points M_1M_2 represents MRC of the firm. Also notice that, when MR is equal to zero, TR is maximum.

IV. Relation between TR, AR and MR Curves

The following are the interesting relationships we can have between TR, AR and MR curves:

☆ When MRC is positive TRC increases, when MRC is zero TRC is maximum and when MRC is negative TRC falls (Figure 7.9).

☆ In case of perfect market competition, ARC is a straight line parallel to X-axis and thereby, MRC is also a straight line and coincides with ARC. That means, when ARC is constant, MRC must be constant (Figure 7.3).

☆ When ARC is a straight line and slope downwards from left to right as under imperfect competition, the MRC also is a straight line slopes downwards from left to right and lies below the ARC (Panel A of the Figure 7.10). The perpendicular drawn at any point from the ARC to the Y-axis will cut the MRC exactly at the mid-point of the perpendicular line. From point A on the ARC, a perpendicular line AY is drawn to Y-axis. This perpendicular line AY will cross the MRC at point E, thereby, MRC will lie at mid-point on the perpendicular line.

From Panel A of the Figure 7.10, we can also prove that, MRC lies exactly at half way between ARC and Y-axis. From Panel A,

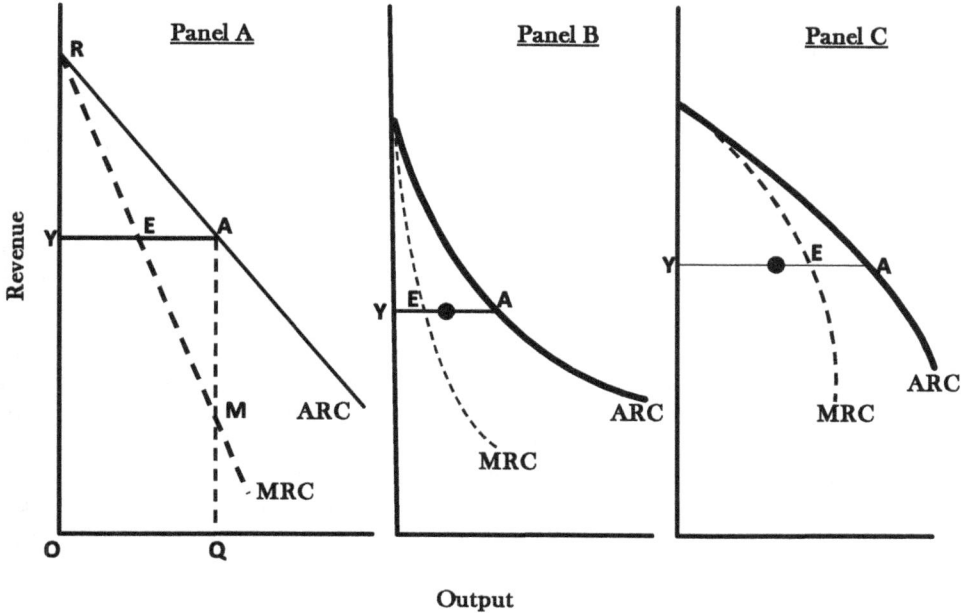

Figure 7.10: Geometric Relationships between ARC and MRC under Imperfect Competition.

☆ The TR of the firm can be computed in two ways *viz.*, from the AR and from the MR.

☆ *From the AR:* With reference to point A on the ARC, the TR can be computed as, TR=AR*output sold.

So, TR=QA*OQ=OYAQ   *Equation 7.1*

☆ *From the MR:* The summation of MRs at the given output gives the TR. So, the area below the MRC with reference to OQ level of output gives TR. This is given by area,

OREMQ   *Equation 7.2*

☆ So, we can write, Area OYAQ = Area OREMQ   *Equation 7.3*

☆ In the above two areas, the area OYEMQ is common. So, let us deduct this area OYEMQ from the above two areas i.e, OYAQ and OREMQ. By doing so, we will have

Area REY= Area MEA   *Equation 7.4*

☆ Since, the two areas REY and MEA are equal and similar (because, angle REY = angle MEA (being vertically opposite angles)), we can conclude that, when ARC is a straight line and downward sloping, MRC is also a straight line and downward sloping and lies below ARC at exactly half way distance between ARC and Y- axis, and as shown in the Panel A, YE=EA.

☆ When ARC is a curve, the corresponding MRC also traces a curve and lies below ARC.

❖ If ARC is convex (Panel B of Figure 7.10), MRC is also convex in shape. When ARC is convex to the origin, the perpendicular drawn from ARC to the Y-axis cuts the MRC at E *i.e.*, to the left of the mid-point of the perpendicular (AY) drawn.

❖ If the ARC is concave (Panel C of Figure 7.10), MRC is also concave in shape. When ARC is concave to the origin, the perpendicular drawn from the ARC to the Y-axis cuts the MRC at E *i.e.*, to the right of the mid-point of the perpendicular (AY) drawn.

☆ When ARC is more elastic, MRC is also elastic (but, comparatively less elastic) as in case of monopolistic competition (Figure 7.8). However, when the ARC is less elastic, MRC is still less elastic, as in the case of monopoly firm (Figure 7.5). This infers that, both MRC and ARC are more elastic in monopolistic competition compared to monopoly competition.

☆ When the slope of ARC shows different elasticities as in case of oligopoly market competition (Figure 7.6), the MRC shows discontinuity at the point, where the elasticity on the ARC curve changes.

The above discussion also infers an interesting aspect that, in the output–price analysis of the firm, we commonly use AR and MR curves and therefore TRC is superfluous for the purpose, as MR=MC is the optimality criterion and ARC indicates the price of the commodity.

V. Relationship between TR, AR, MR and Price Elasticity of Demand (E_p)

This concept of useful relationships between TR, AR, MR and E_p was extensively studied by Joan Robinson in her work *'The Economics of Imperfect Competition'*. In the Figure 7.11, DD' is the ARC or demand curve of the firm under imperfect market competition. So, the E_p at point 'A' on the DD' curve is given by (Point method),

$E_p = AD'/AD$ *Equation 7.5*

So, with this measure of E_p, we can formulate the relationship between TR, AR, MR and E_p as explained below.

☆ When ARC or demand curve slopes downward, MRC also slopes downward from left to right and lies below the ARC.

☆ From the point 'A' considered on the ARC or demand curve, draw a perpendicular to Y-axis as AB.

☆ The triangles AQD' and ABD are similar, as angle AD'Q and angle DAB are corresponding angles and angle AQD' and angle DBA are right angles. We know, the corresponding sides of these two similar triangles will have the same ratio, thereby, AD'/AD =AQ/DB. But, as per the Equation 7.5, E_p =AD'/AD. Therefore,

E_p =AD'/AD = AQ/DB   *Equation 7.6*

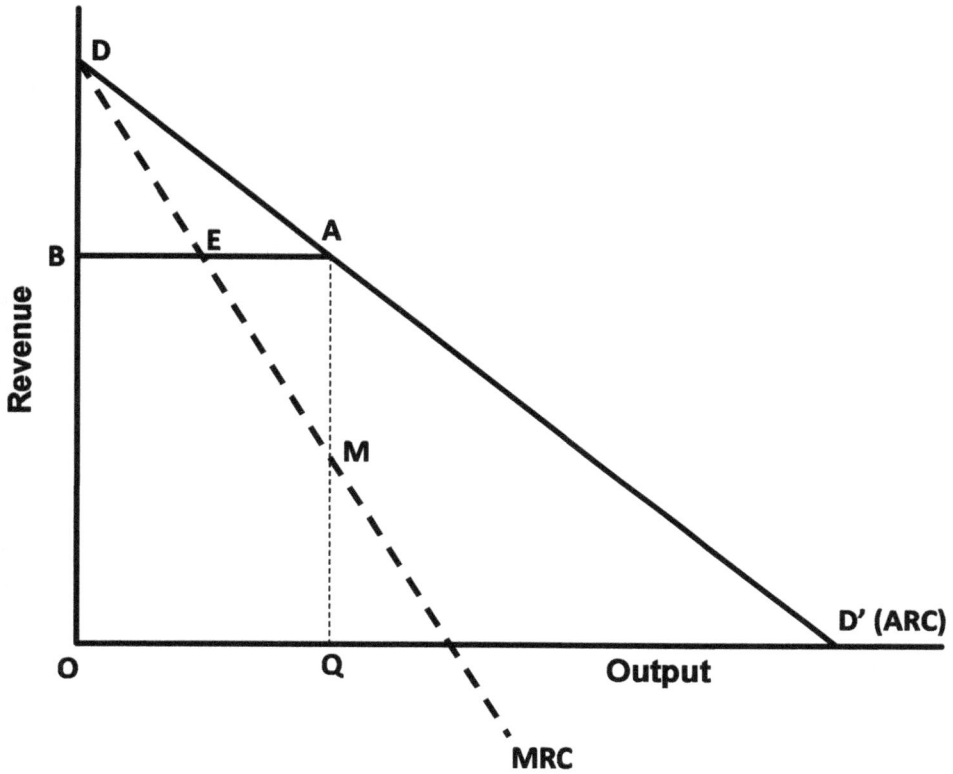

Figure 7.11: Relation between AR and MR Curves of a Firm under Imperfect Competition.

☆ In the Figure 7.11, the triangle DBE is equal/similar to triangle EAM in all aspects as per the Equation 7.4. So, DB=AM. Therefore, substitute DB as AM in Equation 7.6 above, we get,

$E_p = AD'/AD = AQ/DB = AQ/AM$ *Equation 7.7*

☆ In the Figure 7.11, AM =AQ-MQ. So, the above Equation 7.7 can be written as,

$E_p = AQ/(AQ-MQ)$ *Equation 7.8*

☆ E_p =Average Revenue/(Average Revenue-Marginal Revenue)
= AR/(AR-MR)   *Equation 7.9*

☆ The above Equation 7.9, can be rewritten to compute AR as,

$E_p(AR - MR) = AR$
$(E_p AR) - (E_p MR) = AR$
$(E_p AR) - AR = E_p MR$
$AR(E_p - 1) = E_p MR$
Therefore, $AR = E_p MR/(E_p - 1) = MR(E_p/(E_p-1))$ *Equation 7.10*

☆ From Equation 7.10, we can write, $MR = AR(E_p-1)/E_p = P(E_p-1)/E_p$

Equation 7.11

☆ The above Equations 7.10 and 7.11 infers that, given E_p, we can estimate the MR and AR relationship.

Case 1

Assume E_p of the firm's ARC is equal to one, then MR is given by,

As per the Equation 7.11, $MR = AR(E_p-1)/E_p = AR(1-1)/1 = 0$.

The above case is represented through Figure 7.12 with reference to point A on the ARC. So, when E_p of the firm's ARC is equal to one, MR is zero, *i.e.*, MRC touches the X-axis.

Case 2

Assume E_p of the firm's ARC is equal to 2, then MR is given by,

As per the Equation 7.11, $MR = AR(E_p-1)/E_p = AR(2-1)/2 = 0.5AR$

The above case is represented through Figure 7.12, with reference to point M on the ARC. So, when E_p of the firm's ARC is equal to two, it implies, MR will be half of the AR. Further, it also infers that, when E_p of the firm's ARC is more than one, MR is positive.

Case 3

Assume E_p of the firm's ARC is equal to 0.5, then MR is given by,

As per the Equation 7.11, $MR = AR(E_p-1)/E_p = AR(0.5-1/0.5) = -1AR$

The above case is represented through Figure 7.12, with reference to point N on the ARC. So, when E_p of the firm's ARC is less than one, MR is negative.

To sum up, as long as the E_p on the ARC is more than one, the MR of the firm will be positive at any output level. If the E_p on the ARC is equal to one/unitary, then MR of the firm will be zero. If the E_p on the ARC is less than one, the MR of the firm will be negative at any output level. So, the above methodology of estimating the relationship between MR and AR at different levels of output based on E_p of the firm's ARC or demand curve guides the firm in making profits under different types of market structures.

So far, we derived the relation between AR, MR and E_p of the firm's output. Now, we are in a position to formulate the relationship between TR, AR, MR and E_p and the same is explained through Figure 7.12. The Figure 7.12 shows the usual total-average-marginal relation as discussed under the concept of LDR. The inferences derived from the Figure 7.12 are summarized through Table 7.5.

Table 7.5: Relationship between TR, AR, MR and E_p

MR	E_p of the Firm's ARC	TR and AR
MR is Positive	>1	TR rises upward, AR is positive
MR is zero	=1	TR is maximum, AR is positive
MR is less than zero	<1	TR slopes downward, AR is positive. AR will be zero only, when TR is zero.

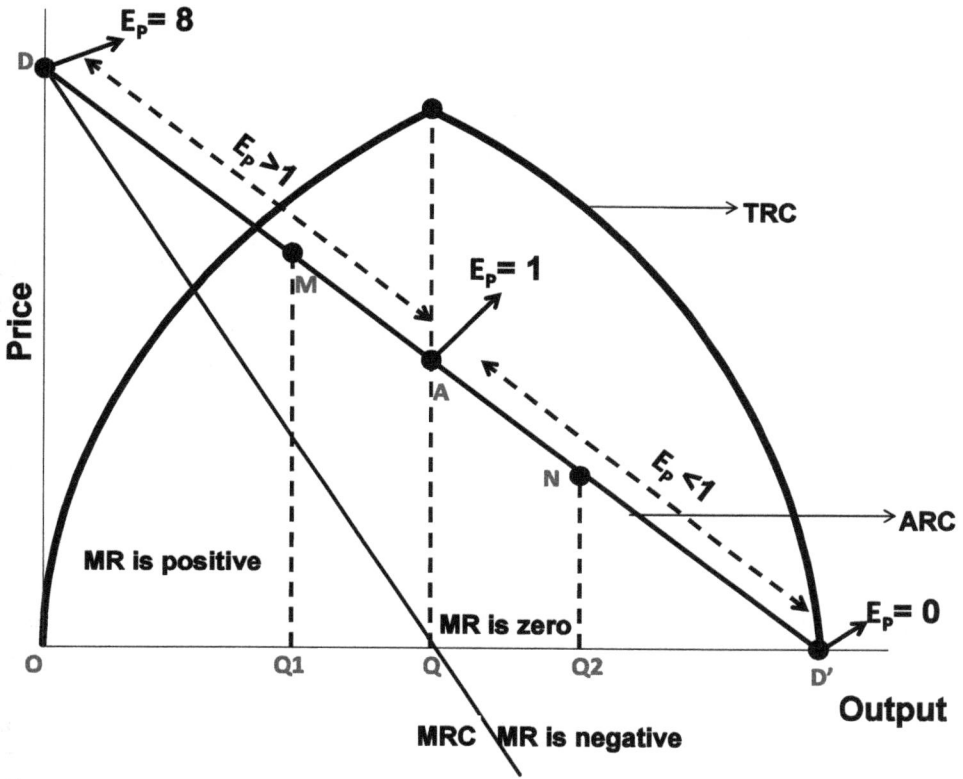

Figure 7.12: Relation between TR, AR, MR and EP.

VI. Determination of Firm's Equilibrium

After analyzing the concepts of TR, AR and MR under different forms of market competition, we now study different approaches to determine the firm's equilibrium. In Economics, a firm refers to a technical and managerial unit of production. In other words, it is an enterprise engaged in the production of a commodity. Considering the market conditions, the firm takes up the production activity to produce the commodity at lowest cost possible. In the words of Prof. Watson, *'a firm is a unit engaged in production for a sale at a profit and with the objective of maximizing the profit'*. So, a firm is considered as an income earning unit and it tries to maximize the income in the business. Once the point of profit maximization is reached, the firm will not disturb the production activity *i.e.,* it will neither expand nor contract the output. Such a stage in the production programme is referred as 'Equilibrium point'. So, in determining the firm's equilibrium, it is assumed that, the firm tries to attain profit maximization and this forms the basis for analyzing the equilibrium output in the production programme. The profits to the entrepreneur of the business firm comprises of three important elements *viz.,* normal profits, super-normal profits and sub-normal profits. In general, profits refer to the excess of TR over TC in the production programme.

Symbolically, $\pi = R - C$, where, 'π' is the Profits, R is the TR and C is the TC incurred in the production programme. When R>C, then the firm is said to be earning profits and when R<C, then the firm is said to be incurring losses. But, this is the accounting sense of interpreting the concept of 'profit'. But, in economic sense, the TC includes both explicit costs and implicit costs. So, Economists use three different notions of profits *viz.*, normal profits, super-normal profits and sub-normal profits.

i. Normal Profits

It is the amount of profits the business firm earns that is sufficient for the firm to stay in the industry. So, normal profits are the minimum reasonable level of profits that the farmer or entrepreneur must earn in the long run, so that, he is induced to continue the production programme in the present form. It is, otherwise, defined as the minimum level of profits required to keep the factors of production in their current use in the long run.

Normal profit is always regarded as a part of TC. Say, for example, farm manager labour, farm family labour are the important factor services employed in the crop production programme. The price paid for these factor services is the normal profit, but they are to be included as implicit costs while computing the TC. So, TC includes explicit costs + implicit cost (normal profit). That means, in economic sense, TC include normal profit. So, in computing firm's equilibrium, when we say, TR=TC, it implies, in economic sense, there is no pure business profit, but there is normal profit, which is already included as implicit cost in the TC. That means, normal profits occur when TR = TC or when the firm experiences Break Even Point (BEP).

It is important to note that, the entrepreneur desires to have a fixed amount of normal profits, irrespective of the level of output. This is because, normal profits includes a fixed implicit cost element. So, when the firm expands the output, like TFC, the implicit cost or normal profit will spread over a wide range of output. This inclusion of normal profit also has a bearing on the ATC curve of the firm. The same concept is explained through Figure 7.13.

ATC is the ATC curve excluding normal profit and ATC + NP is the ATC curve including normal profit/implicit cost of the firm. Consider two points A and B on ATC + NP curve and the movement from A to B indicates the gap between ATC and ATC + NP curve tends to become narrow. This implies that, as the output increases, the normal profits/implicit costs are spread over larger output, thereby, the gap between the two curves (normal profits or implicit costs) gradually decreases. But, the total profit at all levels of output remains same. This is because,

★ At OQ_1 level of output, the average normal profit is AC. So, the total profit is given by total output * average normal profit = $(OQ_1 = EA)*AC = EACH$.

★ At OQ_2 level of output, the average normal profit is BD. So, the total profit is given by, total output*average normal profit = $(OQ_2 = FB)*BD=FBDG$.

★ So, at output OQ_1, the total profit is EACH and at output OQ_2, the total profit is FBDG and EACH=FBDG.

It is important that, in economic theory, whenever ATC curve is drawn, it implies ATC + normal profit/implicit cost. Hence, ATC curve represents ATC + normal profit.

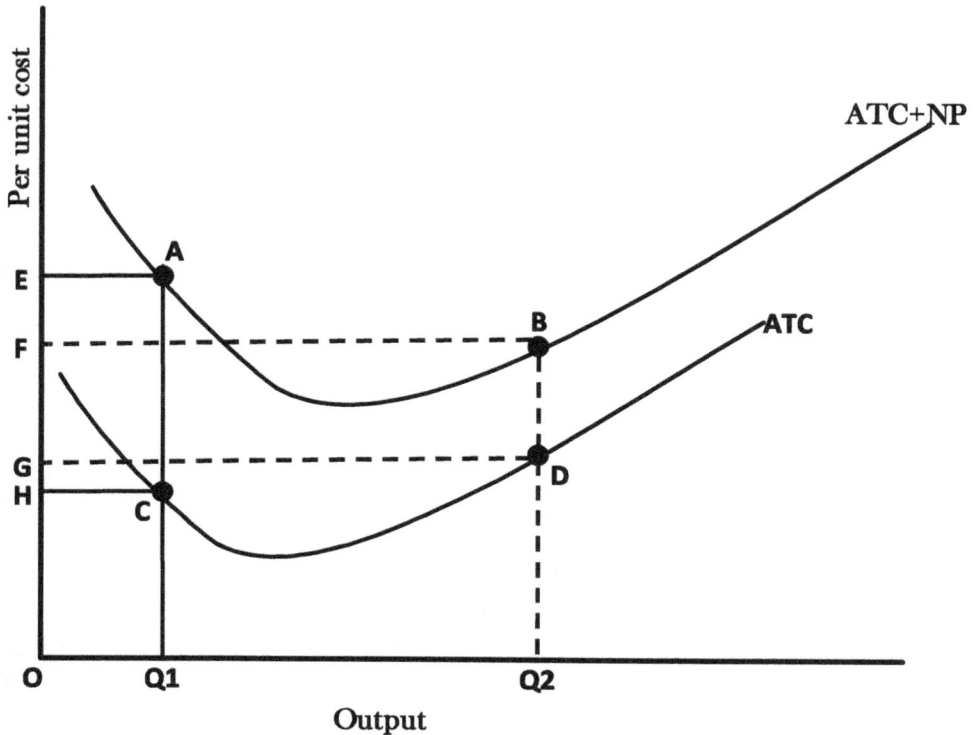

Figure 7.13: Normal Profit Independent of the Level of Output.

So, when the firm enjoys normal profits in the business (price=ATC), it implies, there are no pure business profits and the normal profits include only the implicit costs of the firm. Thus, when there are only normal profits, no new firms enter the industry and existing firms in the industry show no tendency to leave the industry. Note that, the output level at which normal profits occur, two conditions must be satisfied:

☆ MR = MC

☆ AR = ATC

ii. Super-Normal Profits

A business is said to be earning super-normal profits, when the TR > TC. That means, the super-normal profits are over and above the normal profits. Since, normal profits are included in the TC, when TR exceeds the TC, the business firm is said to be earning excess profits over normal profits. So, super-normal profits are also called as 'Pure business profits' or 'Excess profits' or 'Abnormal profits' or 'Economic profits'. When a business firm is earning super-normal profits, it implies, the entrepreneur has successfully managed all the risks and uncertainties and the resources are exploited efficiently. Since, super normal profits are over and above the normal profits, and if the firm enjoys super-normal profits, new firms get attracted to these profits and enter the industry. Note that, the output level at which super normal profits occur, two conditions must be satisfied:

☆ MR = MC

☆ AR > ATC

iii. Sub-Normal Profits

This is another important concept of profits of the business firm. As the name implies, the profits earned by the business firm are below normal profits. That means, the TR earned by the business firm fully covers the explicit costs plus only a part of the implicit costs, thereby, the profits are sub-normal profits. They are also called as 'Economic loss'. Note that, the output level at which economic losses occur, two conditions must be satisfied:

☆ MR = MC

☆ AR < ATC

A. Assumptions to Determine Firm's Equilibrium

The concept of the firm's equilibrium rests upon the following assumptions:

☆ The entrepreneur acts rationally and tries to maximise the profits in the production programme. If losses in the production programme are inevitable, he tries to minimise the losses.

☆ The firm produces only one commodity and its price is stable.

☆ The factor prices remains constant, thereby, the firm purchases the desired quantity of factors at a given price.

B. Methods to Determine the Firm's Equilibrium

As explained earlier, a firm is said to be in equilibrium, when it shows no inclination to change the output from the optimum level, thereby, it can maximize the profits or minimize the losses. This concept is applicable to all types of market competitions *i.e.*, perfect competition, monopoly, oligopoly and monopolistic competition. There are two complementary approaches to determine the conditions of profit maximization or equilibrium output of the firm and they include,

i. TR and TC approach

ii. MR and MC approach

Both the approaches are applicable in cases of perfect competition, pure monopoly, oligopoly and monopolistic competition.

i. TR and TC Approach

This methodology is simple to explain the concept of firm's equilibrium. We know, TR is the total income the firm earns through selling the output and TC is the total cost the firm incurs in producing the output. Profit is the difference between TR and TC. For a firm, the profits are maximized, when the difference between TR and TC is maximum. So, we have the firm's equilibrium by comparing the TR and TC at each level of output and the equilibrium output can be determined, where the positive difference between TR and TC is maximum or highest. The same principle can be studied under perfect and imperfect market competitions.

a. Firm's Equilibrium Based on TR and TC Approach under Perfect Competition

As explained earlier, under perfect competition, there will be an infinite number of buyers and sellers and no single seller or buyer can influence the price of the commodity, thereby, same price will prevail for the same commodity at the same time. Hence, the firm is only a price taker, as it cannot influence the price of the commodity. In the Table 7.6, at the prevailing price of paddy (Rs. 1000/quintal), the firm has to sell any quantity of paddy. The TC of producing the paddy increases with increase in the quantity of output and TR from the commodity increases with increase in the quantity transacted at the prevailing market price. It is evident that, by producing eight quintals of output, the firm can maximize the profits (Rs. 3300), as the difference between TR and TC is maximum at this level of output. The firm also maximizes the profits (Rs. 3300) even at seven quintals of output, but this indeterminacy is due to assumption of discrete data. If continuous data are considered, there is no such indeterminacy and only specific output level will be obtained, which contributes to maximum profit. The same concept is represented graphically (Figure 7.14), where TRC and TC curve are shown as continuous upward sloping curves from left to right. The following are the interesting points from the Figure 7.14:

☆ The TRC curve rises from the origin indicating that, at zero output level, there is no revenue to the firm. The rise in TRC as a straight line indicates that, the TR of the firm increases with increase in quantity of paddy transacted in the same ratio, as price of paddy remains same.

Table 7.6: TR and TC Approach for Determining Firm's Equilibrium under Perfect Competition

Output (Quintals)	Price (Rs/Quintal)	TR (Rs.)	TC (Rs.)	Profit (Rs.)	MC (Rs./Quintal)	MR (Rs./Quintal)
0	1000	0	1000	-1000	0	—
1	1000	1000	1600	-600	600	1000
2	1000	2000	2000	0	400	1000
3	1000	3000	2100	900	100	1000
4	1000	4000	2200	1800	100	1000
5	1000	5000	2500	2500	300	1000
6	1000	6000	3000	3000	500	1000
7	1000	7000	3700	3300	700	1000
8	1000	8000	4700	3300	1000	1000
9	1000	9000	6100	2900	1400	1000
10	1000	10000	8100	1900	2000	1000

☆ The TC curve of the firm also rises upward, but not as a straight line because, it rises rather slowly at the initial levels of output, as the production programme comprises of more of fixed factors and less of variable factors. So, when there is less amount of variable resource, they are properly

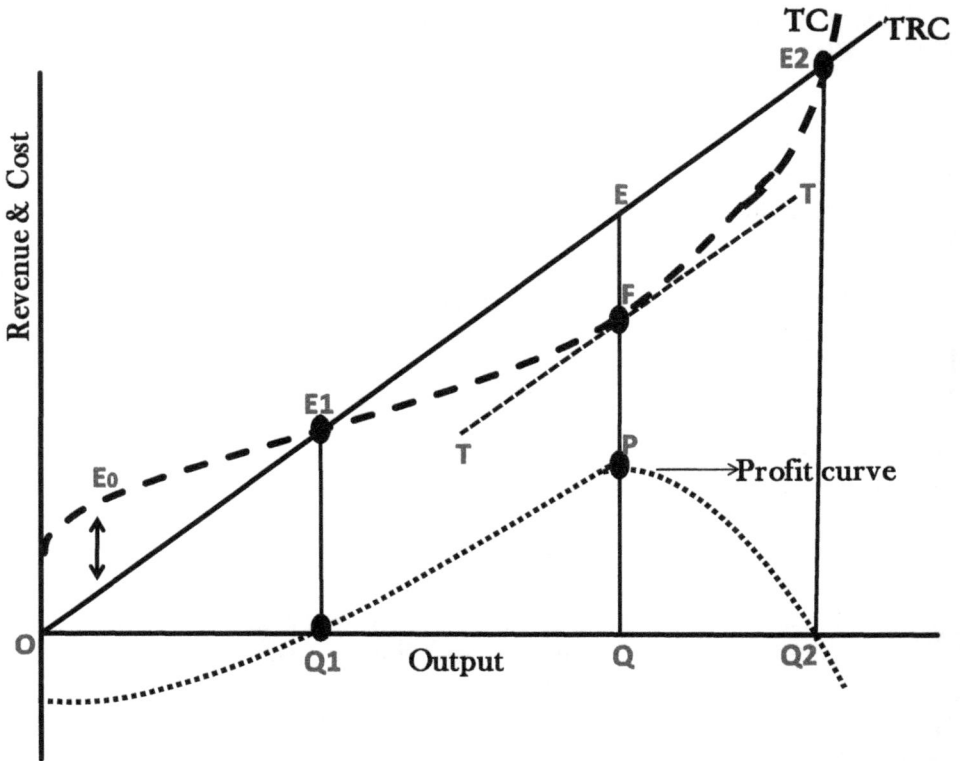

Figure 7.14: TR and TC Approach to Determine Firm's Equilibrium under Perfect Competition.

managed by the farm manager leading to higher resource use efficiency. So due to internal economies of scale, increasing returns or decreasing costs is experienced, thereby, the curve rises slowly. But with the gradual increase in output, the proportion of variable factors in relation to fixed factors will be more leading to diseconomies of scale, which results in diminishing returns or increasing costs and hence, the curve rises steeply at higher levels of output, thus giving an S shape to the TC curve. Further, TC curve originates above the origin, as TC includes TFC even at zero level of output.

☆ At 8 units of output (OQ), the gap between TR and TC is maximum (EF), thereby, the firm maximizes the profits (Rs. 3300).

☆ Below 8 units (<OQ) of output, two distinct phases are seen with reference to the behaviour of TR and TC curves.

   ❖ Up to OQ_1 level of output, the TC curve is higher than TRC indicating that, TC incurred are more than TR earned by the firm, thereby, the firm incurs losses. This is shown by the profit curve (dotted line curve) and its portion upto OQ_1 level of output lies below the X-axis indicating that, the firm incurs losses.

❖ At OQ_1 level of output, TC curve intersects TRC at point E_1, thereby, TR=TC and hence, it is the point of zero profits to the firm. It is otherwise called as 'BEP' of the business. At this point, profit curve touches the X-axis.

☆ Beyond OQ_1 level of output, TRC is higher than TC curve upto OQ_2 level of output. Between OQ_1 and OQ_2 levels of output *i.e.*, at OQ, the gap between TRC and TC curve is maximum by EF, thereby, at this OQ output level, the firm earns maximum profits, QP. So, if the farmer continues the production programme beyond OQ_1 (*i.e.*, after break even output), he can maximize the profits at OQ level of output.

☆ If the farmer still continues the production programme beyond OQ level of output, again the point of break even will be reached at OQ_2 level of output, where TR=TC at point E_2, but production beyond OQ level of output will reduce the profits.

☆ At the BEPs *i.e.*, at OQ_1 and OQ_2 output levels, TR covers all TC. So, there will be no economic profits and the farmer enjoys only normal profits. Between these two break even points, the farmer enjoys economic profits and it is maximum at the maximum gap between TR and TC curves *i.e.* at OQ output level.

☆ So, it is evident that, to maximize the profits in the production programme, the firm should produce and market the output such that, the gap between TR and TC is maximum. Geometrically, this is obtained when the slopes of both TRC and TC curve are equal. As shown in the Figure 7.14, the tangent drawn TT at point F on TC curve is parallel to TRC, indicating that, their slopes are equal, thereby, between E and F with reference to output OQ, the profits are maximum in the production programme. So, at output OQ, TR is QE and TC is QF, thereby, the profits is QE-QF=EF=QP. So, at this output OQ, the total profit is maximum, as indicated by QP with reference to the profit curve.

☆ At first BEP *i.e.*, at OQ_1 output, the farmer should produce more. The farmer should maintain the output, where there is maximum vertical distance between TR and TC curves *i.e.*, OQ, as he enjoys maximum economic profits. At second break even point *i.e.*, at OQ_2, the farmer should stop producing and reduce the quantity of output till OQ.

☆ The demerit of this TR and TC approach is that, the exact point at which profit is maximized is difficult to pinpoint from inspection, which is why the MR=MC method is superior. In MR and MC approach, the reason, why a profit-max point can be found is due to the LDR or increasing marginal costs and the same is discussed in the ensuing pages.

b. Firm's Equilibrium Based on TR and TC Approach under Imperfect Competition

1. Case of Profit Maximization

Unlike perfect competition, in imperfect competition, the firm has control on the price of the commodity. So, the entrepreneur is not a price taker, rather a price maker.

In accordance with the Law of demand, the firm can sell large quantities of output only at lower prices. So, under imperfect competition, the TRC also rises from left to right with increase in quantity of output sold, but the rate of rise of TRC falls with increase in quantity of output sold. Hence, TRC is not a straight line, as with the price fall only, the firm can transact large quantities of output in the market. As usual, the TC curve behaves as discussed under the perfect competition. The concept of profit maximization or firm's equilibrium as discussed under the perfect competition also holds good even under imperfect competition, but the only difference is that, the TRC is not a straight line. So, as shown in the Figure 7.15, the firm maximizes the profits (QP) at OQ level of output, where the gap between TR and TC curves is maximum. Geometrically, the tangents drawn at the two points F and E are exactly parallel to each other indicating that, the slopes of TR and TC curves are equal, thereby, the firm maximizes the profits QP, as indicated by the profits curve. As shown in the Table 7.7, the firm maximizes the profits at six units of output, where the gap between TR and TC is maximum *i.e.,* Rs. 1500. The firm also maximizes the profits (Rs. 1500) even at five units of output, but this indeterminacy is due to assumption of discrete data. If continuous data are considered, there is no such indeterminacy and only specific output level will be obtained, which contributes to maximum profit.

Table 7.7: TR=TC Approach for Determining Firm's Equilibrium under Imperfect Competition

Output (units)	Price (Rs./unit)	TR (Rs.)	TC (Rs.)	Profit (Rs.)	MC (Rs./unit)	MR (Rs./unit)
0	1050	0	1000	-1000	0	—
1	1000	1000	1600	-600	600	1000
2	950	1900	2000	-100	400	900
3	900	2700	2100	600	100	800
4	850	3400	2200	1200	100	700
5	800	4000	2500	1500	300	600
6	750	4500	3000	1500	500	500
7	700	4900	3600	1300	600	400
8	650	5200	4300	900	700	300
9	600	5400	5100	300	800	200
10	550	5500	6000	-500	900	100
11	500	5500	7000	-1500	1000	0
12	450	5400	8100	-2700	1100	-100

2. Case of Minimization of Losses

Sometimes, the firm may even undergo losses either due to fall in price of output in the market or due to rise in prices of factors. In such case, a rational producer will try to minimize the losses to the extent possible. So, the case of firm's equilibrium will be such that, the vertical gap between TR and TC curves should be minimum. In the Figure 7.16. as the firm is incurring losses TC curve is higher over TRC at each level of output. The gap between TC curve and TRC is minimum between C and R, thereby,

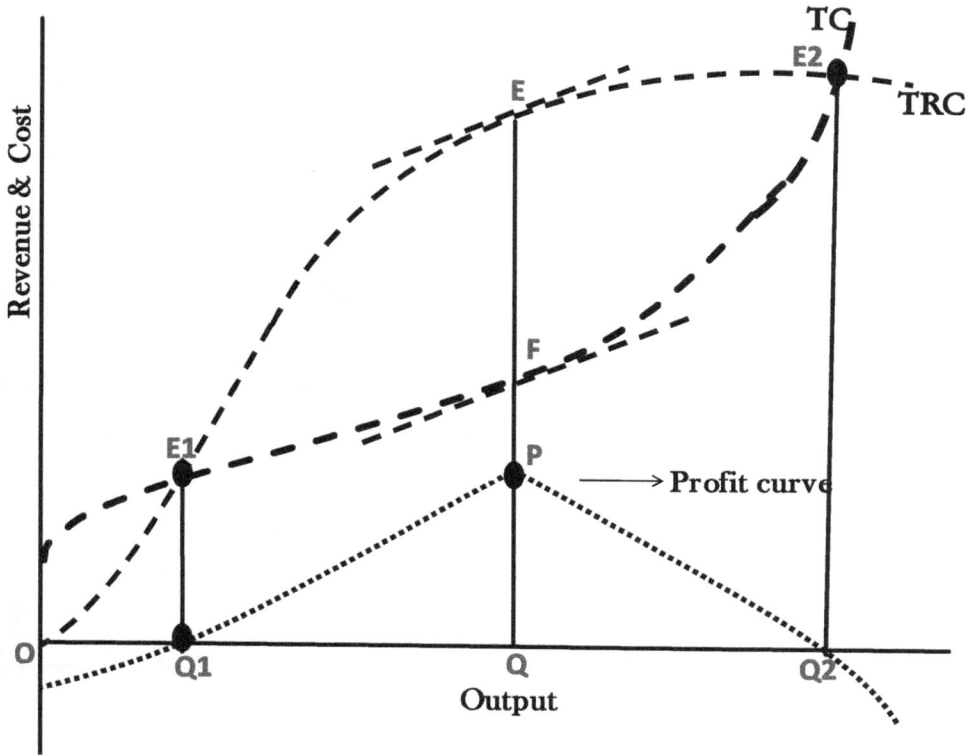

Figure 7.15: TR – TC Approach to Determine Firm's Equilibrium under Imperfect Competition – Case of Maximization of Profits.

producing at least OQ level of output, the firm can minimize the losses. Geometrically, the tangents drawn at the two points C and R are exactly parallel to each other indicating that, the slopes of TR and TC curves are equal, thereby, the firm minimizes the losses CR at OQ level of output. If the firm produces the output less than OQ or more than OQ, the gap between TC curve and TRC is widened, thereby, the losses in the firm will increase by C_1R_1 and C_2R_2 respectively.

Limitations of TR and TC Approach

Though the TR and TC approach is the simplest method to study the firm's equilibrium, it suffers from the following limitations:

☆ It is difficult to locate the maximum gap between TR and TC curves at a glance from the figure.

☆ Many tangents have to be drawn to locate the highest points of TR and TC curves.

☆ This approach will not directly indicate the cost per unit of output (MC) and revenue per unit of output (MR). This is a serious limitation because, if the firm enjoys economies of large scale, even the TC may be high, but cost

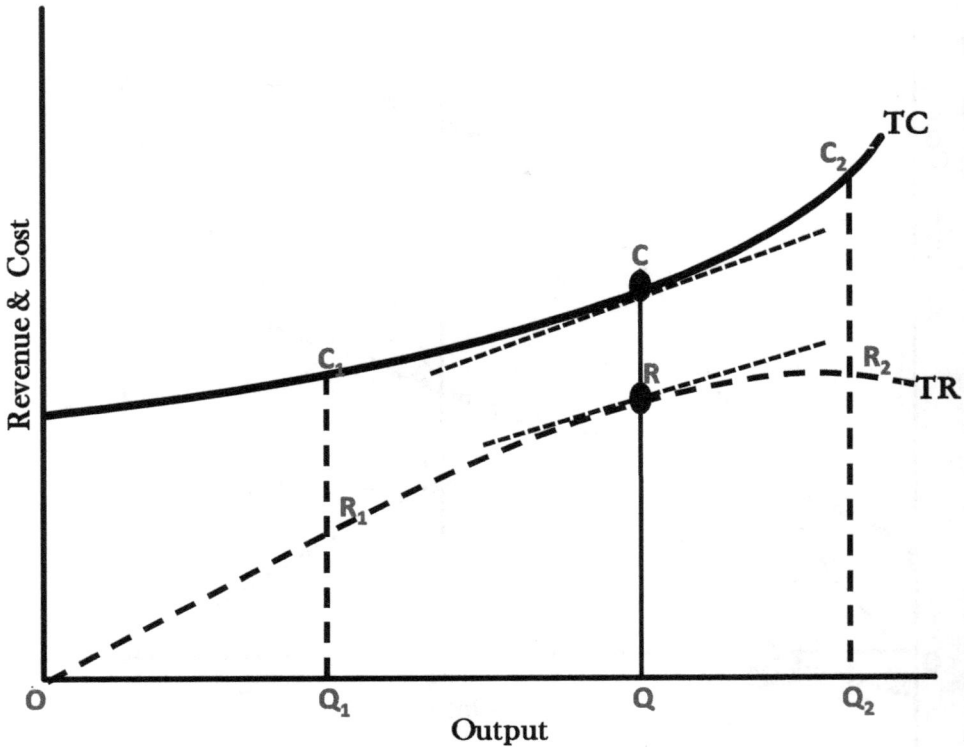

Figure 7.16: TR and TC Approach to Determine Firm's Equilibrium under Imperfect Competition – Case of Minimization of Losses.

per unit of output may be low due to higher levels of output. Similarly, even at higher levels of TR, revenue per unit of output may be low due to transacting large quantities of output. So, the maximum gap between TR and TC curves may not give the true picture of firm's equilibrium without considering MR and MC of the output.

So, considering the above limitations, the business firm generally employ MR and MC approach, as this method directly reveals the additional cost (MC) incurred in producing the additional unit of output and additional revenue (MR) the firm gets in selling additional unit of output, thereby, the firm can easily analyze optimum output and whether it is profitable for the firm to produce and sell additional unit of output.

ii. MR and MC Approach

This concept was proposed by Mrs. Joan Robinson. This approach is more informative and superior in computing the firm's equilibrium when compared to the earlier approach. As discussed earlier, the slopes of TR and TC curves will give MR and MC respectively and these two concepts _viz._, MR and MC will guide the firm to optimize the output or maximize the profits. MR indicates the additional revenue the firm gets in selling additional unit of output and MC indicates the additional cost incurred by the firm in producing the additional unit of output. The rules of thumb are:

☆ The firm attains equilibrium, when MR=MC

☆ When MR>MC, the firm should continue the production programme to increase the output, so that MC rises and thereby, the equality between MR and MC is ensured.

☆ When MR<MC, the firm has to reduce the output, so that MC falls and thereby, the equality between MR and MC is ensured.

The above rules of firm's equilibrium implies that, the firm will not produce an additional unit of output, which involves more MC compared to MR earned from the same. In other words, the firm will produce an additional unit of output, only when the MR earned from that unit is more than MC incurred in producing the same. So, the firm continues to produce more units of output and attains optimum level of output at the point, where MR = MC. According to Stonier and Hague, *'a firm will be in equilibrium when it is earning maximum money profits. But, the money profits of a firm will always be maximized when its marginal revenue equals the marginal cost'*. In the graphical illustration of the MR and MC approach, the equality between MRC and MC curve will not be the only sufficient condition for the firm's equilibrium, but the firm must also satisfy the second order condition *i.e.*, the MC curve should cut the MR curve from below, while MC curve is rising upward. Thus, the two important conditions for the firm's equilibrium include,

☆ *MR= MC*

☆ *MC curve should cut the MR curve from below, while MC curve is rising upward.*

This approach is applicable to study the firm's equilibrium both under perfect and imperfect market competitions. This simple rule (MR=MC) forms the basis for deciding the level of output that maximizes the profit. Let us derive this criterion from the following example: Assume a farmer sells his paddy output (Y) at price P_p. Then, the TR is given by: $TR=Y.P_p$. We also know that, profit realized by the farmer is given by: P = TR-TC. As per the TR and TC approach, the greatest profit the farmer realizes is when the difference between TR and TC is maximum (Figure 7.14). By superimposing these two curves *i.e.,* TR curve and TC curve, the vertical gap between TR and TC occurs at points, where the slopes of TR and TC are the same. There are two such points E_0 and E, where there exists gap between TR and TC curves (Figure 7.14). At the first point E_0, TC is above TR and hence, this point represents the point of minimum profits. The second point E is the desired point, where TR is above and at maximum distance from TC and hence, this is the desired point of maximization of profits. At this point of maximum profit, the slope of the profit function is equal to zero. Thus,

$d\pi/dY = dTR/dY - dTC/dY = 0$

In the above equation, Notice that dTR/dY represents the slope of TR, and dTC/dY is the slope of TC. The slope of TR is referred to as MR. The slope of TC is defined as MC. Hence, the above equation can be rewritten as:

MR - MC = 0

MR = MC

At this point of MR=MC, the firm realizes maximum profits in the production programme. Assuming perfect market competition, the price of output remains constant. So, each additional unit of output is sold at the same price and hence, MR=Price of the output. So,

MR=P=MC

Differentiating the above equation *i.e.*, MR - MC = 0, we get

$dMR/dY - dMC/dY = + \text{ or } -$ *Equation 7.12*

In the above equation, dMR/dY is the slope of MR. Since, under perfect market competition, MR is constant and lies parallel to X-axis, slope of MR is zero *i.e.*, dMR/dY is zero. Since, slope of MC *i.e.*, dMC/dY is not equal to zero, its value determines the profit maximization. That is, if the value (slope) of dMC/dY is negative, then the above equation is '+ve' thereby, it is the point of minimization of profits. On the other hand, if the value (slope) of dMC/dY is positive, then the above equation is '-ve' thereby, it is the point of maximization of profits. Thus, when the slope of MC curve is negative (*i.e.,* downward sloping), it corresponds to the positive value of the above equation (profit function) and when it intersects the MR curve, it is the point of minimization of profits. On the other hand, when the slope of MC curve is positive (*i.e.,* upward sloping), it corresponds to the negative value of the above equation (profit function) and when it intersects the MR curve, it is the point of maximization of profits. The same concept is discussed with reference to perfect and imperfect competitions here under.

a. Firm's Equilibrium Based on MR and MC Approach under Perfect Competition

As mentioned earlier, the MRC of the firm under perfect competition lies parallel to X-axis and coincides with ARC. As usual, the MC curve will first fall, reaches minimum and rises upward with gradual increase in the output. In the Figure 7.17, the MC curve intersects the MRC at two points *viz.*, E_1 and E_2. Considering the above two essential conditions of optimality, the firm's equilibrium will be at OQ_2 level of output, where the MR=MC at E_2. Even though, MR=MC at E_1, it is not the point of the firm's equilibrium because,

☆ At E_1, the MC curve cuts the MRC from above and not from below, thereby, the second-order condition is not fulfilled.

☆ If the firm expands the output beyond OQ_1, the MC is lower than MRC thereby, there is still scope for the firm to expand the output till MR=MC is ensured and this is at E_2, where OQ_2 is the optimum output produced by the firm.

☆ If the firm still expands the output beyond OQ_2, now the MC curve rises over MRC, thereby, the firm incurs losses.

So, we infer that, when the two essential conditions viz, MR = MC and MC curve should cut the MRC from below while rising are fulfilled, the firm attains equilibrium

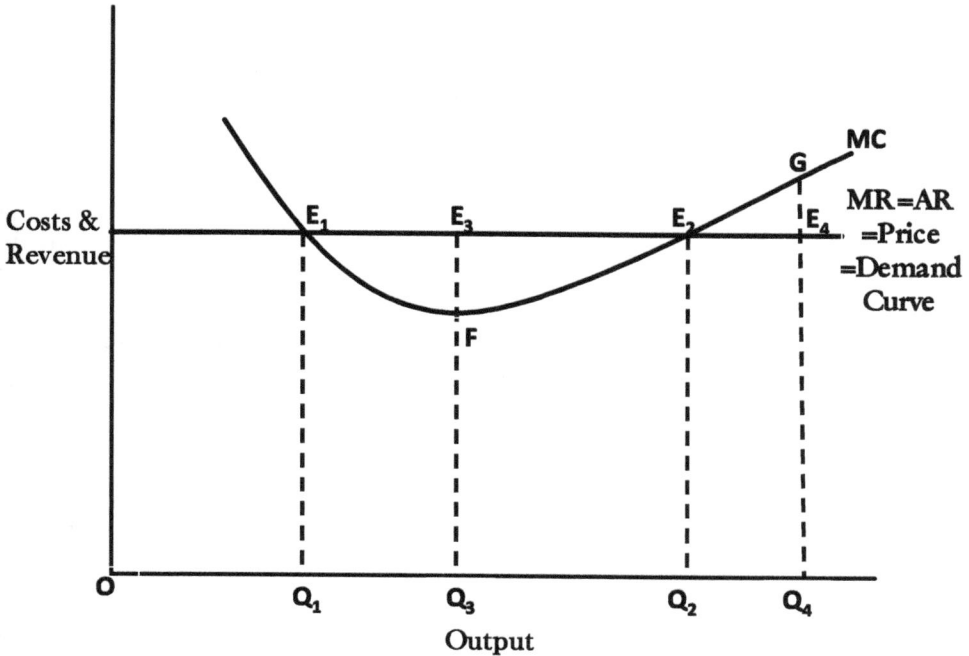

Figure 7.17: MR and MC Approach to Determine Firm's Equilibrium under Perfect Competition.

and it is at point E_2 with reference to OQ_2 level of output. Diagrammatically, the area under the MRC indicates the TR of the output and the area underlying the MC curve measures the TC incurred in producing the output. With reference to OQ_1 and OQ_2 levels of output, the area between MR and MC curves *i.e.*, $E_1E_3FE_2$ refers the profits gained by the firm due to increase in output from OQ_1 to OQ_2 and the profits are maximum at OQ_2 output. Say, if the firm increases the output from OQ_1 to OQ_3, the firm earns the profits E_1E_3F area, as MR>MC. Since, MR>MC, the firm can still increase the output from OQ_3 to OQ_2, where MR=MC, thereby, the profits are increased from E_1E_3F to $E_1E_3FE_2$ and are maximum at OQ_2 level of output. But, if the firm still increases the output beyond OQ_2, *i.e.*, upto OQ_4, now the firm experience losses to the extent of E_2GE_4, thereby, the firm has to reduce the output back to E_2 to ensure firm's equilibrium.

The second necessary condition *i.e.*, MC curve should cut the MRC from below, is considered essential to ensure firm's equilibrium and its importance is shown graphically through Panel A and Panel B of the Figure 7.18. In the Panel A, MC intersects MR at point 'E_1', but this is not the condition for firm' equilibrium because, here MC intersects MR from above rather than from below. But in Panel B, the necessary condition of firm' equilibrium is established at point 'E_2', as MC intersects MR from below. So, in Figure 7.16, OQ_2 is the optimum output produced by the firm to realize maximum profits in the business.

The above concept can also be illustrated through per unit cost curves. The Figure 7.19 is an extension of the Figure 5.13, but two more curves are added *viz.*,

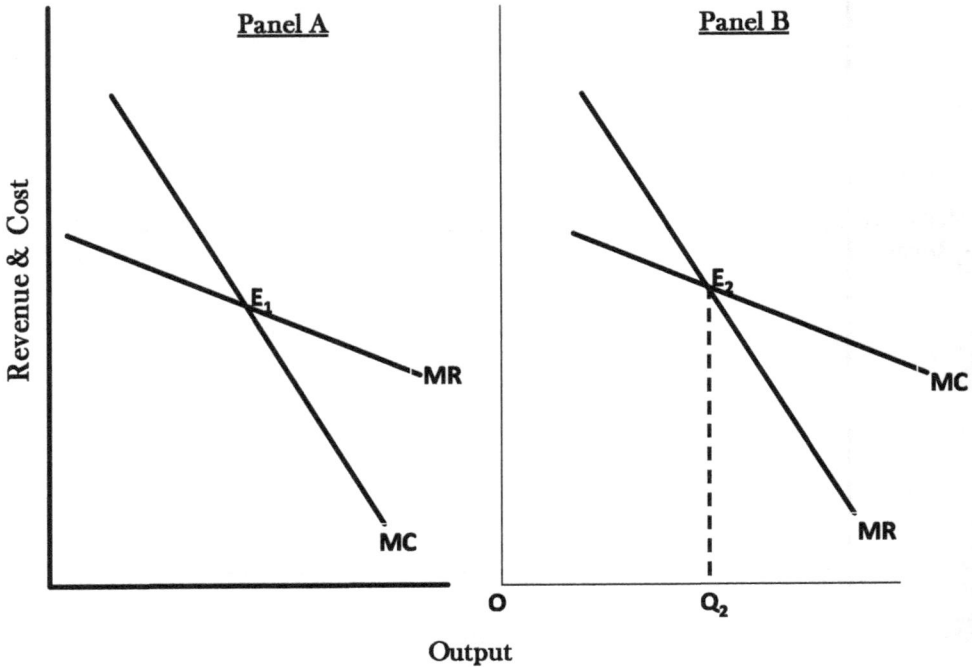

Figure 7.18: Second-Order Condition of MR and MC Approach to Determine Firm's Equilibrium.

MRC and Profit curve. In Panel B, MRC is shown as parallel to X-axis, as price of the product is assumed constant under perfect market competition. The point of equality of MR=MC _i.e.,_ at point E_2, when slope of MC curve is positive (or MC curve is rising), is the point of profit maximization. The same is shown by the profit curve at its peak in Panel C. At this point of equality of MR=MC, the gap between TRC and TC curve is maximum _i.e.,_ at point E in Panel A. The corresponding point of E also indicates the profit curve at its peak. At the initial vertical gap between TR and TC curves _i.e.,_ at point E_0 in Panel A, TC is above TR and hence, this point represents the point of minimum profits. The same is shown by the negative slope of MC curve at the point of intersection with MRC (in Panel B), which yields positive value as per the Equation 7.12. Accordingly, the profit curve lies below the X-axis indicating the minimum profits in the production programme.

b. Firm's Equilibrium Based on MR and MC Approach under Imperfect Competition

As discussed earlier, under monopoly, oligopoly and monopolistic competitions, ARC and MRC are not equal, as the firm sells more quantities of the output only at lower prices because, the firm is a price maker and not simply price taker as in perfect competition. ARC and MRC are downward falling curves from left to right and MRC lies below the ARC (Figure 7.20). As usual, ATC and MC are 'U' shaped curves. The point of optimality is MR=MC _i.e.,_ at 'E', with reference to OQ level of output and OP

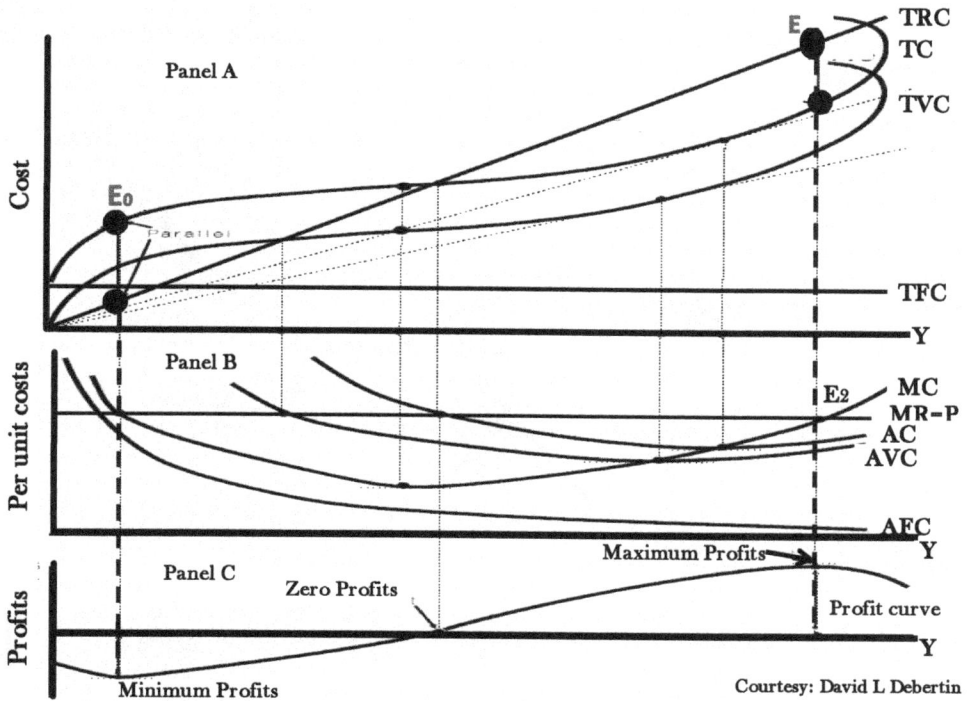

Figure 7.19: Estimation of Profit Function from Cost Functions in Perfect Competition.

level of price. So, TR to the firm will be total output * average price= OQ*QP=OQPC. The TC of producing OQ output is = total output*average cost= OQ*QA=OQAB. So, total profits of the firm is TR-TC, *i.e.*, OQPC- OQAB=PABC.

In the Figure 7.20, since the ARC lies above the ATC curve, the firm is enjoying profits (super-normal profits) *i.e.*, price is above the ATC. But, when the price < ATC or ARC< ATC curve, the firm experience losses in the business. The conditions for shut down of the business either temporarily or permanently will be in accordance with the relationship between price, ATC and AVC and they are already discussed through Table 5.1 of Chapter 5.

So, the explanation offered under MR and MC approach highlights the following aspects:

☆ It helps to compute TR of the firm in selling the optimum output.

☆ It helps to compute TC of the firm in producing the optimum output.

☆ It helps to compute profits of the firm in producing the optimum output.

So, the conclusions we derived from the MR and MC approach leads to the conclusions of earlier TR and TC approach, thereby, MR and MC approach of determining firm's equilibrium is a more superior approach. Note that, in drawing

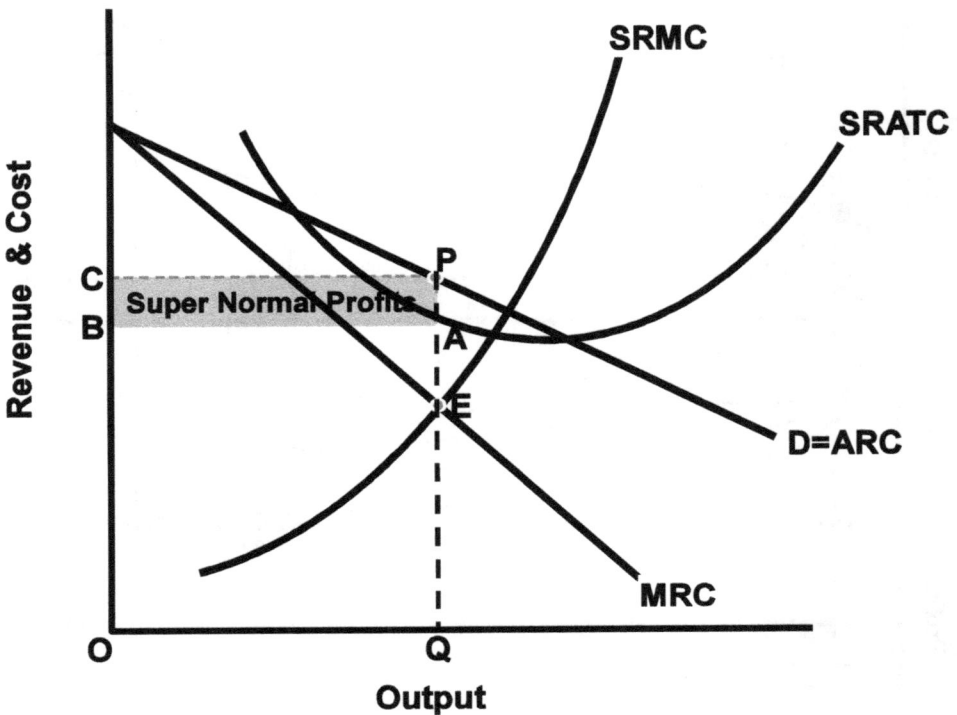

Figure 7.20: MR and MC Approach to Determine Firm's Equilibrium under Imperfect (Monopoly) Competition.

the MR and AR curves, for the linear function, the representation is simple: the MR curve is half the horizontal distance to the AR curve. For non-linear cost curves, however, drawing the SRMC curve so that, it corresponds to the SRATC (or *vice versa*) can be tedious. Too often, we simply sketch a SRMC curve that cuts the SRATC curve at its minimum point and assume that this is good enough for deciding profit maximization. Even some textbook authors commit this error fairly frequently. Failure to draw the curves consistently causes at least two inconsistencies. One is that, the quantity (output) at which MR curve equals SRMC will not be the quantity at which profit (*i.e.*, price less SRATC) times quantity is, in fact, maximized. The other is that, profit as defined above will not equal profit, defined as the area between the MR and SRMC curves.

VII. MR=MC Analysis in Markets with Linear Demand

We know, the equation for a linear demand curve is given by,

P=a-bY   *Equation 7.13*

Where, P is price of the commodity (paddy), Y is output, 'a' is the vertical intercept of the demand curve and 'b' is the slope of the demand curve. As studied earlier, the firm's equilibrium point is MR=MC. Since, we assumed linear demand curve (ARC),

MRC is also linear and has the same vertical intercept as the demand curve, but twice the slope of the demand curve. This is given by,

MR=a-2bY

As per the Panel A of the Figure 7.10, we already proved that, when demand curve (ARC) is a straight line and downward sloping, MRC is also a straight line and downward sloping and lies below ARC at exactly half way distance between demand curve and Y- axis. The following is another approach to prove the above statement:

We know, TR is the product between price and output and it is given by,

TR=P.Y=aY-bY² *(As per Equation 7.13)*

Assume, output increases from Y to Y + ΔY *i.e.*, by an amount ΔY. So, the new TR is given by,

TR=a(Y + ΔY) - b(Y + ΔY)²

The change in TR due to change in output is given by,

ΔTR = a(Y + ΔY) - b(Y + ΔY)²– (aY-bY)²

= aΔY – 2bYΔY – b(ΔY)²

We know that, MR is the change in TR due to per unit change in output. So,

MR=(ΔTR/ΔY) = [(aΔY – 2bYΔY – b(ΔY)²)/ΔY] = a – 2bY – bΔY

Since, output quantities can vary continuously, we will be interested in evaluating MR for very small changes in output. Assuming a very small change in output, then ΔY tends to be zero. So, MR is given by,

MR = a – 2bY

To find the profit-maximising output level, we should know MC of producing the output. Assume, MC is constant in producing additional unit of output *i.e.*, 'c' then, the following is true:

a – 2bY = c

2bY = a – c

Y = (a-c)/2b

To estimate the firm's best price for profit maximization, substitute the above output equation in the demand curve P=a-bY, gives a price

P = a-b((a-c)/2b)

Example 7.1

Suppose, a firm faces a linear demand curve of P = 2500 – 100Y, where 'Y' represents quintals of output and 'P' represents price/quintal. The firm faces a constant MC of Rs. 300. Estimate the firm's profit-maximising output and price.

Solution

We know, when demand curve (ARC) is linear (P = 2500 – 100Y), MRC will have the same vertical intercept as the demand curve, but with twice the slope.

So, MR is given by, MR = 2500 – 200Y.

The profit maximizing level of output is given by, MR = MC. So, given MC as Rs. 300, we can write,

2500 – 200Y = 300

So, firm's profit maximizing level of output, Y = 11quintals.

Inserting above Y in the demand equation, P = 2500 – 100Y, we can find firm's best price for profit maximization given by,

P = 2500 – 100(11) = Rs. 1400/quintal.

Example 7.2

Assume, the firm faces the same demand curve as above, P = 2500 – 100Y. The cost function of the firm is given by, C(Y) = 300Y + 2000. Estimate the firm's profit-maximising output and price.

Solution

From the above cost function, it implies that, MC continues to be equal to Rs.300/ quintal and the firm incurs a fixed cost equal to Rs. 2000. Following the same procedure as followed in the above example, we have firm's profit maximizing output level = 11quintals and firm's best price = Rs. 1400/quintal. This infers that, even in the presence of fixed costs, there has been no change in the firm's profit maximizing output level and firm's best price.

VIII. Break Even Point (BEP)

We know, maximization of profits is one of the traditional objectives of a firm. A farmer cannot achieve maximum profit and minimum cost at the same time. Similarly, profit maximizing output cannot be known in advance. Even if it is known, it cannot be achieved at the beginning of the programme because, in the process of production, the farmer will have to incur fixed cost even before the production starts. That is, even when output is zero, TFC will be there. But, when no unit of output is sold, then TR is zero. Thus, in the initial stages of production, SRTC remains higher than the TR. Therefore, the farmer has to bear some loss at the initial low levels of output. But, as more and more units of output are sold, TR starts increasing and it reaches to the point, where TR will cover SRTC *i.e.*, TR = SRTC. This point (at the volume or value of output), at which the TR is exactly equal to the SRTC is called BEP (Figure 7.21). So, at BEP in a farm business, there is no net profit or no loss to the farmer. It also refers to the volume of output in the farm business at which the net profit is zero. That means, the firm just 'breaks even'. BEP also refers to the volume of output, at which the farmer will be in dilemma regarding, whether he has to continue the business or not, as TR is equal to SRTC in the production programme. Note that, considering the rules presented through Table 5.1, it is advocated to the farmer to continue the production, when he faces with BEP in the business because, SRTVC<TR=SRTC. At BEP, the sales of the firm exactly cover its expenses *i.e.*, at BEP the firm sells enough units of its product to cover its expenses without making a profit or taking a loss. If it sells more beyond BEP, then it makes a profit and on the other hand, if it sells less than BEP, it takes a loss.

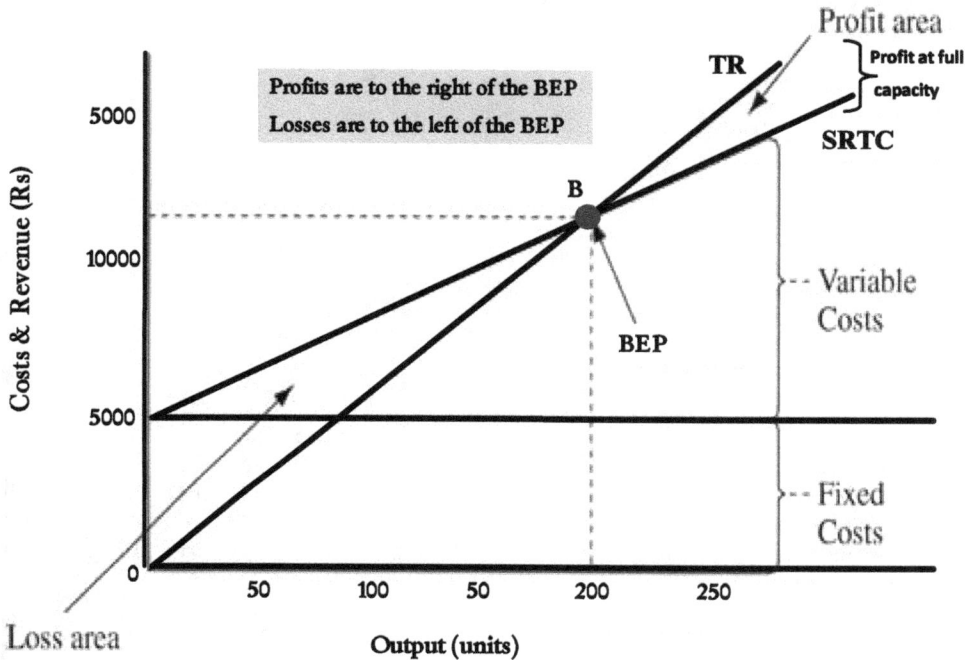

Figure 7.21: BEP in a Farm Business.

Methods of Computation of BEP

The point of beak even can be derived through the following three methods:

1. Graphical Method

Graphically, BEP is the point, where the SRTC curve meets the TR curve (Figure 7.21). Below the BEP 'B', TR<SRTC (*i.e.,* loss) and above the BEP, TR>SRTC *i.e.,* there is profit in the business and at BEP 'B', TR = SRTC (*i.e.,* no-profit and no loss).

Figure 7.21 also infers that, a business can be in any one of the following financial situations:

☆ *Loss:* This occurs, when TC exceed the TR of the business *i.e.,* up to BEP.

☆ *Break-even:* This occurs, when TR=TC in the business *i.e.,* BEP.

☆ *Profit:* This occurs, when TR exceed TC in the business *i.e.,* beyond the BEP.

2. Break-Even Formula

We know, at BEP, TR   = SRTC *i.e.,* TR – SRTC = 0

We also know, SRTC   = SRTVC + TFC

SRTVC   = Y * Variable Cost/unit

TR   = Y * Price/unit

SRTC$\qquad = (Y * \text{Variable Cost}/\text{unit}) + \text{TFC}$

At BEP, TR $-$ SRTC$\qquad = 0.$ So,

$(Y * \text{Price}/\text{unit}) - ((Y * \text{Variable Cost}/\text{unit}) + \text{TFC}) = 0$

So, $(Y * \text{Price}/\text{unit}) - (Y * \text{Variable Cost}/\text{unit}) = \text{TFC}$

So, $Y (\text{Price}/\text{unit} - \text{Variable Cost}/\text{unit}) = \text{TFC}$

Y (in terms of quantity)$\qquad = \text{TFC}/(\text{Price}/\text{unit} - \text{Variable Cost}/\text{unit})$

$\qquad\qquad\qquad\qquad\qquad = \text{TFC}/(\text{Sale price} - \text{SRAVC})$

So, Y (Break-Even Output)$\quad = \text{TFC}/(\text{SP} - \text{SRAVC})$

where, SP = Sale price/unit

$\qquad\qquad\qquad\qquad\qquad = \text{TFC}/(\text{S-V}) \qquad\qquad\qquad\qquad\qquad$ *Equation 7.14*

where, S = Selling price/unit, V = Variable cost/unit

In the above formula (Equation 7.14): the denominator S minus V, is called the Contribution Margin per unit or Unit contribution. It refers to the amount per unit of product sold, that the firm can contribute to paying its TFC. That is, any product that makes a positive contribution to the firm will help towards paying some of the fixed costs in the business.

So, BEP (in terms of quantity) = TFC/Contribution Margin per unit $\qquad$ *Equation 7.15*

Thus, BEP can alternatively be computed as the point where, Total Contribution Margin equals TFC. That is, at BEP

Total Contribution Margin = TFC

(Unit Contribution x Volume of output at BEP) = TFC $\qquad$ *As per Equation 7.15*

Volume of output at BEP (*i.e.,* Break even output) = TFC/Unit Contribution

The above Equation 7.14 also indicates that, to compute a firm's BEP in terms of quantity or volume of sales, we need to know the values of three variables. They include: TFC, SRTVC and selling price of the product. We already know, TFC are those, which do not change with the level of output or sales, but SRTVC do change with the level of output or sales volume. At BEP, price of the product equals the SRATC and so, above BEP, price covers both AFC and SRTVC. So, the price of the product has been set by the firm by looking at the SRATC (*i.e.,* AFC+SRAVC) and by marking it up. Contribution Margin Ratio (CMR) is the ratio between (S-V)/S. BEP can also be computed in terms of value (*i.e.,* Rupees) and it is given by:

BEP in terms of value (Rupees) = BEP (in terms of quantity) * Sale price per unit

or

$= \text{TFC}/\text{CMR}$

$= \text{TFC}/((\text{S-V})/\text{S})$

$= \text{TFC}/(1-(\text{V}/\text{S})) \qquad\qquad\qquad\qquad\qquad\qquad\qquad\qquad$ *Equation 7.17*

In the above Equation 7.17, V/S refers to Contribution Margin. So,

BEP in terms of value (Rupees) = TFC/(1- Contribution Margin)

Following are the other important formulae in break even analysis:

Break even sales (Rs.) = Fixed Cost/(P/V) ratio

where, (P/V) = Profit-Volume (P/V) ratio

Profit earned by the firm = Contribution – Fixed Costs

Contribution at BEP = Sales at BEP*(P/V) Ratio

Fixed costs = Sales at BEP - Contribution at BEP

Net Profit for a given value of sales = (Sales * (P/V) Ratio) – Fixed Costs

3. Tabular Method

This method uses a table to arrange data, so the BEP can be easily calculated. We already know that, at BEP, TR=SRTC. Let us assume that, a firm produces a processed food product with the following data particulars: TFC=Rs.5000, SRAVC=Rs.10/unit, Price per unit of product: Rs. 20. With this information, the following Table 7.8 is constructed to estimate the BEP. As per the definition, BEP will be at 500 units of output of the firm, as TR=SRTC and hence, there will be no profit and no loss to the firm in producing and selling that product.

Table 7.8: Computation of BEP for a Firm

Output (Units)	TFC	SRTVC	SRTC	TR	Profit (Rs.)
0	5000	0	5000	0	-5000
100	5000	1000	6000	2000	-4000
200	5000	2000	7000	4000	-3000
300	5000	3000	8000	6000	-2000
400	5000	4000	9000	8000	-1000
500	5000	5000	10000	10000	0
600	5000	6000	11000	12000	1000
700	5000	7000	12000	14000	2000

Since the BEP analysis explains the relationship between cost, production volume and returns in the business, this analysis is also known as Cost-Volume-Profit (CVP) analysis. The other names for this BEP analysis include: Break-Even Analysis, Break-Even Formula, Break-Even Model, Expense-Volume-Profit (EVP) analysis etc. However, the term CVP is more appealing because, the break-even technique can be used to determine the volume of sales needed to attain a specified amount of profits in the farm business. In performing this break even analysis, the following are the important assumptions:

☆ Sales price per unit of output is constant.

☆ Variable costs per unit are constant.

☆ TFC are constant.

☆ The behaviour of both costs and revenues is linear throughout the relevant range of activity.

☆ Everything produced by the firm is sold *i.e.* it assumes that the quantity of product produced is equal to the quantity of product sold.

☆ If the firm sells more than one product, they are sold in the same mix. That is, there is a constant product sales mix. If the sales mix changes say, from a high profit product to a low profit product, the BEP analysis must be adapted to accommodate this change.

☆ The cost function and revenue function are linear.

☆ The SRTC is divided into TFC and SRTVC.

☆ Prices of factors are constant.

☆ Productivity and efficiency remains unchanged.

Example 7.3

Assume a sugar factory with TFC = Rs. 10,000/year, SRAVC = Rs. 40/unit, Selling price = Rs. 50/unit. So, BEP (output) is given by:

We know: at BEP: $FC + VC * Y = SP * Y$

$$\text{BEP (Y)} = = \frac{TFC}{SP - SRAVC} = \frac{10000}{50 - 40} = 1000(units / year)$$

So, the entrepreneur must produce and sell at least 1000 units annually to cover TFC and SRTVC. He will have a profit after producing and selling more than 1000 units of output.

BEP in terms of value = BEP x Sale price per unit

= 1000 x 50 = Rs. 50000 or

= TFC/(1-(V/S)) = 10000/(1-(40/50)) = Rs. 50000.

Assume, the following are the sales of sugar from this factory:

Year 1: 750 units (behind 250 units)

Year 2: 1000 units (total 1750 units – still behind 250 units)

Year 3: 1250 units (total sales at the end of Year 3 = 3000 units or 1000 units per year, thus, here the factory is break even)

So, the factory will get break even at the end of the third year and would make profits after it sells 1000 units every year thereafter.

Example 7.4

Calculate the BEP in units and in sales (Rs.), when sales price per unit is Rs.35, variable cost per unit is Rs. 28 and TFC is Rs. 7000.

Solution

We know BEP (in terms of quantity)　　= TFC/Contribution Margin per unit

Contribution Margin per Unit　　= S-V = 35 – 28 = Rs. 7

So, BEP in terms of quantity is: $7000/7 = 1000$ units

Break-even Point in Rupees $=$ BEP x Sale price per unit or TFC/(1-(V/S))

$= 1000 \times 35$ or $[7000 \div (1-(28/35))] = $ Rs. 35,000

What Happens to the BEP, if Sales Change?

Say, if the economy is in a recession, the sales of the firm will drop. Then, the firm will not sell enough to make its BEP. That is, the new BEP will be less than the earlier BEP. Since, the new BEP is less now, the firm would not be able to pay all the earlier total costs. So, considering the formula for BEP discussed earlier, the entrepreneur will think about two possible solutions. First, it may either raise the price of its product and/or it find ways to reduce the TFC. So, re-writing the data in the above Example 7.3 by considering the above two possible solutions:

☆ *Lowering the Fixed Costs:* By lowering the fixed costs of the firm say, by Rs. 2000, then the TFC now becomes only Rs. 8000. So, the new BEP will now decline as given below:

$$\text{BEP (Y)} = \frac{TFC}{SP - SRAVC} = \frac{8000}{50-40} = 800 \, (units/\,year)$$

So, the new BEP is only 800 units/year. From this analysis, we can say that, if the firm reduce the TFC, it can lower the BEP without having to raise the price of the product. Note that, even by reducing the SRTVC without disturbing the TFC will also reduce the BEP, as fall in SRTVC also lead to fall in SRAVC and thereby, BEP will decrease.

☆ *Raising the price of the product:* By raising the price of the product say, by Rs.5 (without disturbing the TFC), then the price now becomes to Rs. 55. So, the new BEP will now decline as given below:

$$\text{BEP (Y)} = \frac{TFC}{SP - SRAVC} = \frac{10000}{55-40} = 667 (units/\,year)$$

So, the new BEP is only 667 units/year. From this analysis, we can see that, if the firm raise the price of the product, it can lower the BEP without disturbing the cost structure of the product.

Margin of Safety

The margin of safety is the excess of output (or value) of the firm over the break-even output (or value). Thus, the margin of safety can be expressed either in quantity of output or in value terms (*i.e.,* in Rupees) and also in percentage forms. The following are the formulae:

Margin of safety (quantity) = Actual quantity of output – Break even output

Margin of safety (quantity) = Level of demand – Break even output

Margin of safety (value) = Actual value of output (Rs/-) – Value of Break even output (Rs/-)

$=$ Actual sales (Rs/-) – Sales at BEP (Rs/-)

= Net Profit (Rs/-)

= Profits/(P/V) ratio

where, (P/V) refers to ratio of profit and volume of a firm

Margin of safety (per cent) = (Margin of safety in terms of quantity/Actual output in terms of quantity) x 100 or

= [(Actual output – Break even output)/Actual output] × 100 or

= [Margin of safety in terms of value/Actual output in terms of value]*100

Students must note that, through graphically, margin of safety can be studied only in terms of physical quantity, as volume of output is shown on the X-axis (Figure 7.22) and not the value of that output (Figure 7.35). Margin of safety represents the strength of the business. It enables a business firm to know, what is the exact amount it has gained or lost and whether they are over or below the BEP *i.e.,* it indicates how safer the business is compared to the break even output. The larger the positive difference between actual output and output at BEP, the safer the firm will be in terms of earning profits, especially if there are adverse changes in the production process or marketing process or both. A positive margin of safety (or safety margin) means that, the firm makes a profit, whereas a negative safety margin means the firm makes a loss in the business.

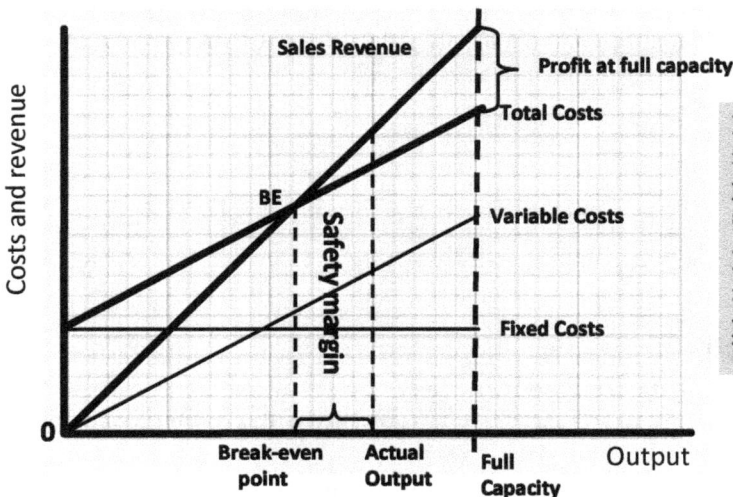

If margin of safety is positive, production is above break even.

If margin of safety is negative, production is below break even.

Margin of Safety is the amount by which the actual output exceeds the break even output. If output falls below this level, a loss will occur in the business.

Figure 7.22: Margin of Safety in a Farm Business.

Example 7.5

The ratio of profit and volume of a company is 50 per cent, while its margin of safety is 40 per cent. The sales volume is Rs. 50 lakhs. Find out its BEP and the net profit.

Solution

Given Sales = Rs. 50,00,000

Margin of Safety = 40 per cent *i.e.,* 40 per cent of Rs. 50,00,000) = Rs. 20,00,000

So, breakeven sales (BEP) = Rs. 30,00,000

We know, Margin of Safety = Profit/(P/V) ratio

Rs. 20,00,000 = Profit(50 per cent)

So, Profit = 20,00,000 * 50 per cent = Rs. 100,000

We can also compute profit of the firm in the following way,

Breakeven Sales = Fixed Cost/(P/V) Ratio

Rs. 30,00,000 = Fixed Cost/50 per cent

So, Fixed cost = Rs. 30,00,000 * 50 per cent = Rs. 15,00,000

Contribution = (P/V) ratio * Sales volume = 50 per cent * 50,00,000 = Rs. 25,00,000

So, Profit = Contribution – Fixed Cost

= Rs. 25,00,000 – 15,00,000 = Rs. 10,00,000

Example 7.6

From the following information of a vermicompost unit, calculate the BEP and turnover required to earn a profit of Rs. 36,000.

☆ Fixed costs: Rs. 1,80,000

☆ Selling Price: Rs. 20

☆ Variable Cost Per Unit: Rs. 2

If the company is earning a profit of Rs. 36,000, express the margin of safety available to it.

Solution

a. Breakeven Point: We know, Contribution Per Unit = S – V = Rs. 20/unit – Rs. 2/unit = Rs.18

Given, Fixed costs = Rs.1,80,000

Breakeven Point = Fixed costs/Contribution Per Unit = 1,80,000/18 = 10,000 units

In terms of sales (Rs.) = 10000*20 = Rs. 2,00,000

b. Turnover required to earn a Profit of Rs. 36,000 = (Fixed costs + Profit)/ Contribution Per Unit

= (1,80,000 + 36,000)/18 = Rs. 2,16,000

= 12,000 units (=12000*20 = Rs. 240000 sales)

    c. Margin of Safety = Actual output (units) – Break even output (units) = 12000 – 10000 = 2000

    = Actual sales (Rs.) – Break even sales (Rs.) = 240000-20000 = Rs.40000

    So, Margin of Safety is equal to Net Profit of the firm.

Example 7.7

The Profit-Volume (P/V) ratio of a pesticide company is 50 per cent and the margin of safety is 40 per cent. Find out the BEP and the net profit, if the sales volume is Rs. 50 lakhs.

Solution

    a. BEP = Sales - Margin of Safety

    Given Margin of Safety = 40 per cent of sales volume = (40/100)*50 = 20 lakhs

    So, BEP = 50 – 20 = 30 lakhs

    b. Contribution at BEP = Sales at BEP*(P/V) Ratio = 30 x 50 per cent = Rs.15 lakhs

    c. Fixed costs = Sales at BEP - Contribution at BEP = 30 – 15 = Rs.15 lakhs

    d. Net Profit, if the Sales Volume is Rs. 50 lakhs: Profit = (Sales * (P/V) Ratio) - Fixed Costs

    = (50 * 50 per cent) – 15 = Rs. 10 lakhs

Importance of Analyzing BEP

The following points indicate, why a business firm looks at the BEP in taking up the business:

    ☆ The entrepreneur can decide the margin of safety of the business and this guides him to plan the sales volume, price of the product and other transaction costs.

    ☆ BEP help the entrepreneur to gain an insight about TR from selling the output and his ability to recover the relevant production costs of that particular product,

    ☆ BEP is also helpful to the entrepreneurs in making important decisions in business like application for loans, setting prices for the products, drawing comparative picture with the rivalry firms etc.

    ☆ We know, break even output covers both TFC and SRTVC. This helps the managers to plan output both in short run and even used to evaluate the future demand. If, in case, the BEP lies above the estimated demand, it guides the entrepreneur to take various decisions like discontinuing the product (if the loss is very high) or planning for advertising strategies or re-pricing the product to increase demand in the market.

    ☆ We know, at BEP, there is no profit and there is no loss in the business. So, BEP is important for the entrepreneur, as it serves as the lower limit of profit, when prices are set and margins are determined.

☆ The concept of break-even analysis can be applied to a product, an investment or the entire firm's operations.

☆ As discussed earlier, break-even analysis is a useful tool to study the relationship between fixed costs, variable costs and returns. So, this analysis helps the business manager to plan the volume of production at which price of the product necessarily covers SRATC or fix a price for the product (by using mark-up) over SRATC to achieve profits.

☆ As the break-even analysis explains the relationship between cost, production volume and returns in the business, the same can be extended to show, how changes in TFC-SRTVC relationships or commodity prices or revenues will affect profit levels and BEPs.

☆ Break-even analysis is most useful when used with partial budgeting or capital budgeting techniques. The major benefit to using break-even analysis is that, it indicates the lowest amount of business activity necessary to prevent losses.

☆ If the entrepreneur has to plan and fix the price of the product, he must know how to calculate BEP.

☆ The BEP tells the farmer, how much money he needs to invest in the business before it starts earning actual profits. For instance, if the expenses are Rs 1,000 per month and revenue is Rs.1,000 per month, then the farmer is at the BEP in the business. This is where, the business is making enough money to cover the total expenses, but it isn't making a profit. To increase profits in the business, the farmer must increase the contribution margin unit (say, by decreasing the SRTVC) and this decreases the BEP.

☆ BEP analysis provides a dynamic view of the relationships between costs, volume of output and profits. A better understanding of BEP say, if expressed break-even sales as a percentage of actual sales, it helps the entrepreneur to understand when to expect to break even in his business say, in few months or in years.

☆ BEP analysis is important for planning and decision making, particularly in the short run. Trade-offs of fixed for variable costs or changes in variable or fixed costs and sales volume can be analyzed by using BEP analysis.

☆ Break-even is often a key objective of new and unestablished firms, as their viability in the future depends upon the achievement of minimum break even sales.

☆ BEP analysis helps to compare the profit margin of different firms.

☆ The concept of break even analysis provide useful answers to the following questions posed by himself by the entrepreneur:

❖ A person starting a new business (say, food processing firm) often asks, 'At what level of sales will my firm make a profit?'

❖ Manager of an established firm that had suffered through some rough years might have a similar question: *'At what point of sales, will I be able to draw a fair salary from my firm?'*

The analysis of BEP will provide a thought process that may help the entrepreneur to answer the above questions and also provide useful insight as to how profits change as sales increase or decrease.

Limitations of BEP Analysis

BEP analysis suffers from the following limitations:

☆ In general, costs and revenue functions are non-linear and hence, the BEP analysis is more complicated.

☆ CVP is a short run marginal analysis *i.e.,* it assumes that, unit variable costs and unit revenues are constant. But, in the long run, all costs are variable. For longer-term analysis that considers the entire life-cycle of a product, one therefore often prefers activity-based costing.

☆ Achieving break-even output in the current production programme does not return the losses occurred in the past. Also it does not build up a reserve for future losses. And finally it does not provide a return on your investment (the reward for exposure to risk).

☆ It is best suited to the analysis of only one product at a time.

☆ Sometimes, predicting a precise amount of sales or profits is nearly impossible due to a firm's many products (with varying degrees of profitability), many customers (with varying demands for service), and the interaction between price, promotion and the number of units sold. These and other factors will complicate the break-even analysis.

☆ Break-even analysis is only a supply side concept (*i.e.,* costs only) and is not related on the demand side *i.e.,* it will not tell about, what sales are actually likely to be for the product at its various prices.

☆ It assumes TFC remains constant in the production programme, as it based on short run analysis. But, an increase in the scale of production in the long run is likely to cause fixed costs to rise.

☆ Break-even analysis is based on certain assumptions, which are assumed to be constant. So, it is not applicable to the dynamic situation.

☆ BEP analysis fails to explain the impact of technological change, better management, division of labour, improved productivity and other factors, which influences profits.

☆ It assumes horizontal demand curve with the constant price. It is possible only in case of perfect competition. But, this is not true in case of monopoly, oligopoly and monopolistic competitions.

☆ The break even analysis does not consider elements of uncertainty due to tax structure.

☆ Not all variable costs increase directly with output.

☆ Not all costs can be categorized into fixed or variable costs; some are semi-variable.

☆ It is unlikely that, fixed costs will not change at various output levels.

The students must note that, BEP analysis must not be mistaken for the Pay Back Period (PBP), as the latter simply indicates the time taken by the firm to recover its investment from its annual returns.

Exercises

1. For a competitive firm, TFC, SRTVC and SRTC information is shown in the table below. Assume the following:

   a. Suppose, the firm can sell all the output it desires at the market price of Rs9.10. Compute the firm's TR and its profit or loss for the potential output choices shown in the table. What output level maximizes the firm's profits (or minimizes its losses)?

   b. Repeat above question, by assuming the price of output has fallen to Rs.7.10

Output (Units)	TFC (Rs.)	SRTVC (Rs.)	SRTC (Rs.)
0	9.00	0.00	9.00
1	9.00	8.00	17.00
2	9.00	15.00	24.00
3	9.00	21.00	30.00
4	9.00	26.00	35.00
5	9.00	32.00	41.00
6	9.00	39.00	48.00
7	9.00	47.00	56.00
8	9.00	56.00	65.00
9	9.00	66.00	75.00
10	9.00	77.00	86.00

2. For a competitive firm, price of the output and SRTC information are shown in the table below. Find the level of output at which profits are maximum?

Output (Units)	Price (Rs./unit)	SRTC (Rs.)	TR (Rs.)	MR (Rs.)	MC (Rs.)	Profits (Rs.)
0	5	9				
1	5	10				
2	5	12				
3	5	15				
4	5	19				
5	5	24				
6	5	30				
7	5	45				

3. Find the BEP of production in terms of units and in terms of value, if the price of the product is Rs 250 per unit; variable cost is Rs 150 per unit and the fixed cost is Rs 1,50,000.

4. If the product's demand is price-inelastic, the firm raises the price of the product from Rs 250 to Rs 300 with the same average variable cost of Rs 150 and the unchanged fixed cost of Rs 1,50,000. Will the BEP change from that when it remains unchanged?

5. If fixed cost is Rs 50,000, average variable cost is Rs 15 per unit and sales price is Rs 20 per unit, find out BEP in terms of number of units and value.

6. Find the margin of safety, if the actual sales amount to Rs 90,000 and the BEP sales amount to Rs 50,000.

7. A firm produces two products, A and B. The TFC is Rs 50,000. The AVC and sale price per unit is Rs 3 and Rs 5 respectively for Product A and Rs 4 and Rs 6 for Product B. Both of the products are produced in equal proportions. Find out the BEP.

8. A company produces three products *viz.*, A, B and C. The combined (non-separable) fixed cost is Rs 10 lakh to be allocated in the ratio of 2:3:5 respectively to A, B and C. The respective sale price is Rs 50, Rs 60 and Rs 90 with AVC of Rs 30, Rs 40 and Rs 50. The separable fixed cost is respectively Rs 3 lakh, Rs 3 lakh and Rs 4 lakh for Products A, B and C. Find out the break-even point in terms of quantity for each of the products.

9. For the given data:

   Fixed cost   = Rs. 100,000

   AVC   = Rs. 1 per unit

   Selling Price   = Rs. 5 per unit

   Maximum capacity output   = 200,000 units per year

   Calculate, Contribution per unit, Break even output, Margin of safety and Profits at maximum output

10. Given the equations…

    Demand (D): P   = 50-Y and

    Total Cost (TC): P $= 80+20Y+\dfrac{Y^2}{2}$

    Find the profit-maximizing quantity and price as well as the total profit of this monopolistic firm. Illustrate in graphs.

11. Assume a processor incurred TFC of Rs. 2,500 per month. SRAVC are known to be Rs. 10 per product, with each selling price for Rs. 30. Calculate the BEP and Unit Contribution.

12. Calculate the missing figures in the following table:

Break-even quantity (units)	400	600
Output (units)	800	——
Margin of safety (units)	——	300
Margin of safety (per cent)	100	——

13. A company makes a Rs.50 profit, with TFC as Rs. 20 and SRTVC of Rs.480. How much output to be produced to achieve BEP in the business (Hint: $P_Y.Y=TFC+SRTVC$)

14. How many units of product the firm is required to sell, if it want to earn Rs.4000, TFC=Rs.500, SRAVC=Rs.5, price=Rs. 10?

15. What is the level of profit for the firm, if the price of the product is Rs. 20, SRAVC is Rs.8, Total quantity of product sold is 700 Units and TFC is Rs.4500

(Hint: Total Contribution = Y x (Selling price – AVC), Profit = Total Contribution – Total Fixed Cost)

(Ans. Rs. 3900)

8

Profit Analysis

We know, the entrepreneur will receive remuneration in the form of profits, as he is one among the factors of production employed in the business. According to Prof. Taussig, this concept of profits has become a '*mixed and vexed one*'. We know that, the entrepreneur performs several functions *viz.*, planning, organization, direction, control, monitoring, coordination etc., in the business. Further, he will own the capital in the business. However we cannot decisively say, for which function is he receiving the payment. thereby, profits have become a mixed income for the entrepreneur. Further, there is no unanimity among the Economists in defining 'profits', thereby, it has become a vexed one. So, Prof. Knight pointed out that *'no term or concept in economic discussion is used with a more bewildering variety of well established meaning than profit'*. Several Economists have defined 'profits' in different ways and the following are the popular definitions:

'Profits may be considered a reward for making innovations, a reward for accepting risks and uncertainties and the result of imperfections in the market structure'.

(Henry Grayson)

'The residual payment, what is left to the producer's income after all other payments have been met'.

(Hansen)

'The surplus of current income over past cost is profit'.

(Drucker)

'The average remuneration necessary to bring into existence and to keep in existence, a sufficient supply of entrepreneurs'.

(Marshall)

'Profit is a determinate return for a production function performed by the entrepreneur with a superior ability than others'.

(Walker)

From the above definitions, we can have the following meanings for the term 'profit':

☆ Profit is the remuneration received by the entrepreneur for performing managerial functions.

☆ Profit is the reward earned by the entrepreneur for bearing the risk in the business.

☆ Profit is the residual income for entrepreneur after paying off to other factors.

☆ Profit is the difference between total sales proceeds obtained and total expenses incurred in the production programme.

Thus, there are different ways of interpreting the term 'profit' and all the interpretations explain the profits in relation to the functions performed by the entrepreneur.

8.1. Distinguishing Features of Profits

Profit differs from the remunerations paid to other factors of production like rent for land, wages for labour and interest for the use of capital on the following aspects:

☆ Unlike rent, wages and interest, profits can be negative.

☆ Compared to the other remunerations of factors of production like rent, wages and interest, profits in the business fluctuate widely.

☆ This form of remuneration is totally uncertain, unlike rent, wages and interest. That is, rent, wages and interest are decided or fixed in advance whereas, the receipt of profits is only an expectation on the part of the farmer and this expectation may become true or may not become true.

☆ Unlike rent, wages and interest, (economic) profit is not a part of cost.

8.2. Different Types of Profits

The term 'profit' is used in different senses and they are discussed here under.

1. Economic Profit and Accounting Profit

Economic profit refers to the difference between TR and total expenditure. In economic sense, the total expenditure includes both explicit costs and implicit costs. Thus,

Economic profit = TR – Total expenditure

= TR – (Total explicit cost + Total implicit costs)

But, in accounting sense, profits refer to the difference between TR and total explicit costs. So, while computing accounting profits, implicit costs are not considered. Thus, Accounting profit = TR – Total explicit costs.

2. Gross Profit and Net Profit

Gross Profit

The term 'profit' generally refer to 'gross profit'. That means the excess of income earned by the entrepreneur over the total expenses incurred in the production programme refers to gross profit. But, this 'gross profit' will include several items, which are not profits in the strict sense and they are discussed here under.

a. Remuneration for the Factors of Production Contributed by the Entrepreneur Himself

During the course of production programme, the entrepreneur himself contributes his owned land, owned labour and owned capital. So, the implicit returns like implicit rent, implicit wages and implicit interest earned by the entrepreneur will get included in the gross profit. These implicit earnings should be deducted from the gross profits to compute net profits.

b. Depreciation and Maintenance Charges

During the process of production, the machinery will get depreciated and thereby, the entrepreneur has to pay repairs and maintenance charges on the depreciated machinery. So, these costs should be deducted from gross profits to arrive at net profits.

c. Extra-Personal Profits

The entrepreneur may get some extra profits in the business in the form of monopoly profits due to inflationary rise in prices, due to external causes like wars etc., and all these chance profits should be deducted from the gross profits to arrive at net profits because, these profit elements are not related to the entrepreneurial ability in the strict sense.

The above three elements included in gross profit are relatively stable even in the long run and hence, any significant variation in the gross profit is due to significant variation in the net profit.

Net Profits

Net profit is the exclusive reward paid to the entrepreneur for the functions performed by him in the production programme. The entrepreneur has to perform several functions like planning, organization, coordination of the factors of production, risk and uncertainty bearing, making innovations in the production programme etc., with a view to minimize the cost or maximize the profits in the production programme. So, for executing all the above functions, the entrepreneur is rewarded with 'net profits'. It is essential to note that, in the modern days of business, the entrepreneur will insure the business with an insurance company against various risk factors thereby, risk taking is not the function of the entrepreneur, but by the insurance company. So, uncertainty bearing is one of the important functions borne by the entrepreneur and not risk taking.

From the formulae given below, we can easily differentiate gross profit and net profit accrued to the entrepreneur in conducting the business:

Gross profit = Net profit + implicit rent + implicit wages + implicit interest + depreciation and maintenance charges + non-entrepreneurial profits.

Net profit = Gross profit – (Implicit rent + implicit wages + implicit interest + depreciation and maintenance charges + non-entrepreneurial profits).

So, net profit refers to economic profit or pure business profit, as it is the reward exclusively paid for executing the entrepreneurial functions.

From the above discussion, we can infer the following interesting points:

☆ Gross profit includes net profit.

☆ Gross profit includes implicit costs whereas, net profit does not includes such costs.

☆ Net profit may be positive or negative. Being a residual income, if TC exceeds TR, gross profits will be negative, thereby, net profits will also be negative *i.e.*, loss. Thus, among the four factors of production, only the entrepreneur has the chance of getting the negative reward *i.e.*, losses.

☆ Net profit cannot be pre-determined, as it is influenced by the level of output, costs incurred and price of the product in the future. Further, the output in agriculture is influenced by climatic factors, which are not predictable accurately.

☆ Net profit is not a fixed remuneration, as it varies with the output, cost structure and price of the output. Thus, this remuneration fluctuates widely.

☆ Net profit is a residual surplus *i.e.*, the entrepreneur is rewarded after meeting the remunerations of all the other three factors of production.

☆ Net profit is an end payment *i.e.*, it is paid to the entrepreneur after selling the output and after realizing the TR from the business.

☆ Net profit is not earned in the long run under perfect competition and the profits earned in the long run include only normal profits (implicit costs).

☆ Loss in the business firm is computed with reference to net profits and not in terms of gross profits.

8.3. Modern Theory of Profits or Determination of Profits under Perfect Competition

According to this theory, 'profits' as the reward for entrepreneurs is determined by the interaction between 'demand for' and 'supply of' entrepreneurs under perfect competition.

A. Demand for Entrepreneurs

It is interesting that, in case of land, labour and capital, we can compute the MRP of the factor for a firm. But, in case of entrepreneur as a factor of production, for each firm, there will be only one entrepreneur, thereby, it is difficult to compute the MRP of the entrepreneur at firm level. However, at industry level, we can compute the MRP of the entrepreneurs and as usual, MRP curve of the entrepreneurs will slope downwards from left to right (Figure 8.2), indicating that, with the increase in number of firms in the industry, the number of entrepreneurs will increase, output increases, supply of the product into the market increases, price per unit of the output will fall, thereby, profits per entrepreneur too will fall. The demand for entrepreneurs in the industry depends upon the following factors:

☆ Extent of development of the industry

☆ Element of uncertainty in the business

☆ Scale of production

☆ MRP of the entrepreneur

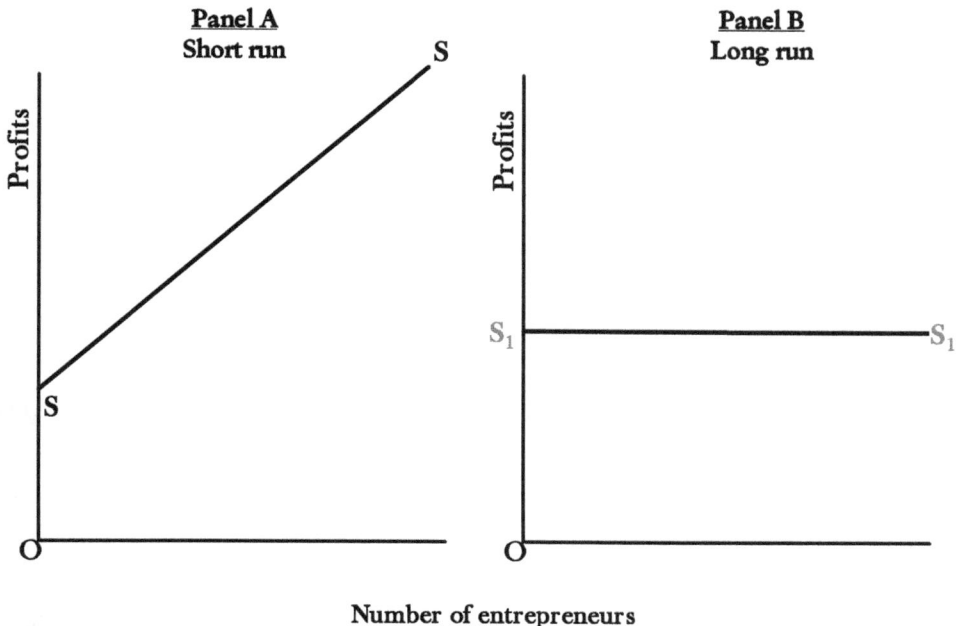

Figure 8.1: Supply of Entrepreneurs in the Industry.

All the above four factors directly influence the demand for entrepreneurs in the industry and among these four, MRP of the entrepreneur is the important factor. As explained above, MRP curve (demand curve) of the entrepreneurs at the industry level will slope downward from left to right (Figure 8.2).

B. Supply of Entrepreneurs

The supply of entrepreneurs to the industry depends upon the following factors:

- ☆ Availability of capital
- ☆ Availability of managerial and technical personnel
- ☆ Size of population
- ☆ Number of entrepreneurs
- ☆ Element of uncertainty in the industry
- ☆ Distribution of income
- ☆ Industrial experience
- ☆ Conditions in the society like political stability etc.

In general, profits of the industry directly influence the supply of entrepreneurs to the industry in the short run, and thereby, supply curve of entrepreneurs (SS) will rise upwards (Panel A of the Figure 8.1). But, in the long run, under the assumption of perfect competition, the supply curve of entrepreneurs ($S_1 S_1$) will be horizontal and parallel to X-axis, as all the entrepreneurs are homogenous and of equal efficiency

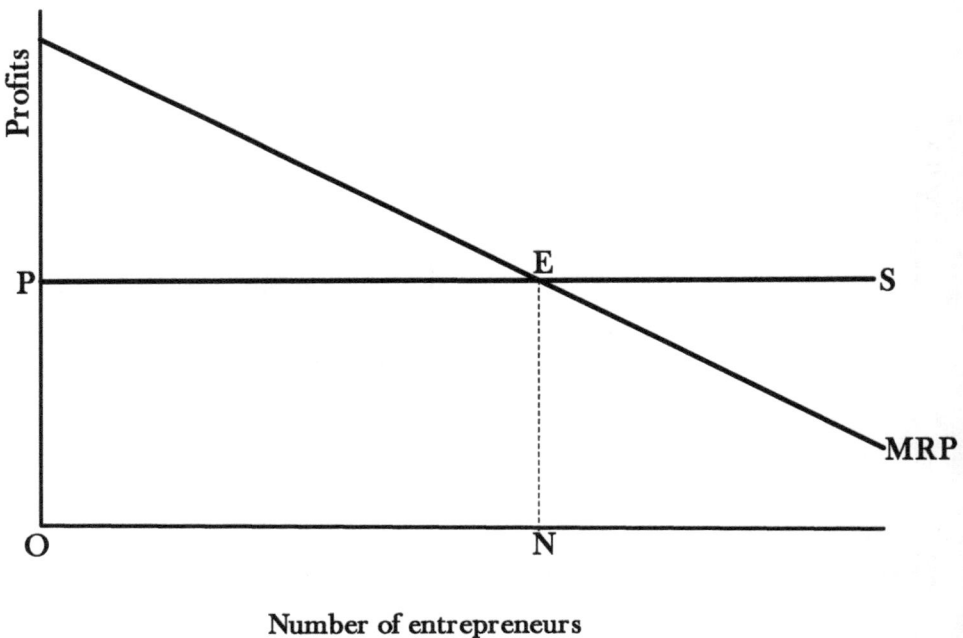

Number of entrepreneurs

Figure 8.2: Determination of Normal Profits by the Entrepreneurs in the Long Run in the Industry Assuming Perfect Competition.

(Panel B of the Figure 8.1). This infers that, in the long run, all the entrepreneurs will earn only normal profits equal to that of transfer earnings. So, if the entrepreneur in one industry could not earn even the minimum transfer earnings in the long run, he will quit that industry and move to some other industry to earn normal profits.

C. Determination of Entrepreneurial Profits in the Long Run in the Industry Assuming Perfect Competition

Profits are determined at the point, where the demand curve and the supply curve of the entrepreneurs will intersect and this is explained through Figure 8.2.

☆ The MRP curve (demand curve) of the entrepreneurs intersect the supply curve of entrepreneurs (S) at E and it implies that, the industry employs ON number of entrepreneurs and each entrepreneur will derive OP level of profits in the long run.

☆ This OP level of profits represents the normal profits earned by the entrepreneurs in the long run equal to their transfer earnings.

☆ All the entrepreneurs earn same level of normal profits OP because, under perfect competition all the entrepreneurs are considered homogeneous in terms of their efficiency.

☆ But, in the short run, the entrepreneurs may earn super normal profits. However, these super normal profits are competed away in the long run due to the entry of new firms into the industry (assuming perfect competition).

D. Determination of Entrepreneurial Profits in the Long Run in the Industry Assuming Imperfect Competition

In practicality, imperfect competition is more common in the market and thereby, the entrepreneurs can earn super normal profits even in the long run. The same is illustrated through Figure 8.3.

☆ In the Figure 8.3, DD is the demand curve and SS is the supply curve of entrepreneurs.

☆ These two curves intersect at point E and this indicates that, ON number of entrepreneurs are employed in the industry and each entrepreneur will earn OP super normal profits.

☆ In the Figure 8.3, OP_1 is the minimum profit the entrepreneur should get to stay in the industry and if he gets the profits less than OP_1, he will leave the industry. The entrepreneur who gets this OP_1 profits in the industry is called 'Marginal entrepreneur'.

☆ The triangle PEP_1 represents the rent element in the profits gained by intra-marginal entrepreneurs.

☆ The gain of OP profits represents the super normal profits earned by the entrepreneurs even in the long run and this is due to less elastic supply of entrepreneurs. If the supply of entrepreneurs is perfectly elastic (perfect competition) as discussed under Figure 8.2, they earn only normal profits

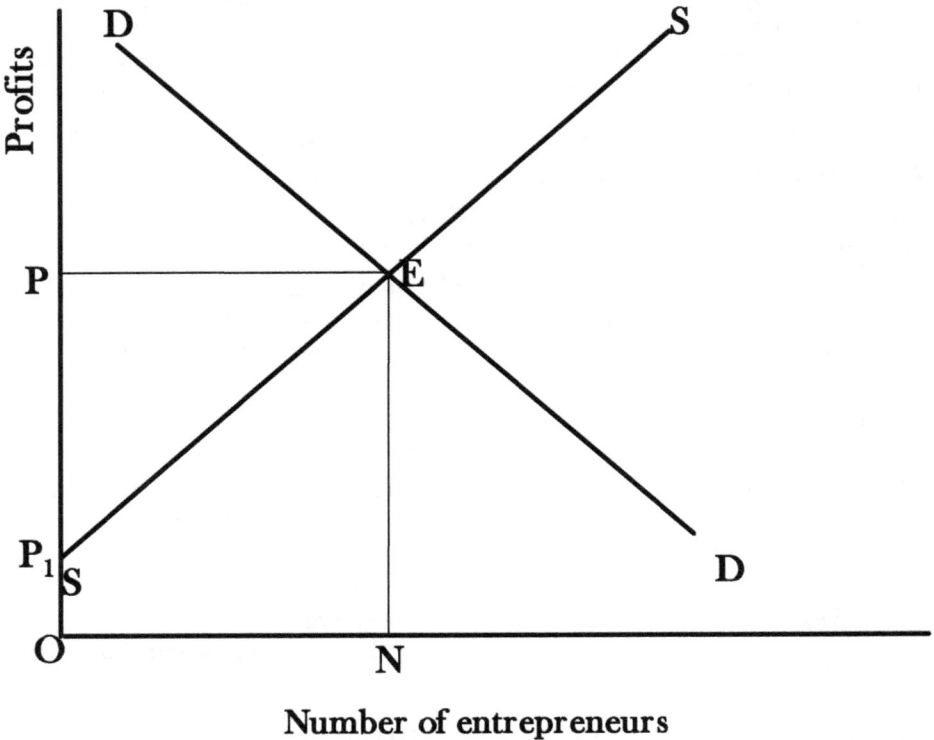

Number of entrepreneurs

Figure 8.3: Determination of Super Normal Profits by the Entrepreneurs in the Long Run in the Industry under Imperfect Competition.

equal to their transfer earnings. However, perfect competition does not really exist, thereby, the entrepreneurs can earn super normal profits even in the long run.

8.4. Profit Maximizing Criteria

The criteria for profit maximization under short run and long run production programmes are given here under.

A. Case: Perfect Competition

1. Short Run

☆ If SRMC=MR=Price is greater than SRATC, then the firm receives positive economic (super normal) profits by producing the profit maximizing output.

☆ If SRMC=MR=Price is equal to SRATC, then the firm receives normal profits by producing the profit maximizing output.

☆ If SRMC=MR=Price is greater than SRAVC, but less than SRATC, then the firm suffers from losses. But, the firm can still continue its production as long as MR>SRMC, as the extent of losses to the firm are less than TFC.

☆ If SRMC=MR=Price is less than SRAVC, then the firm suffers from losses and it should stop the production temporarily, as the losses in the business are to the extent of more than TFC.

☆ Profits when output is zero = (- TFC).

2. Long Run

☆ If LRMC=MR=Price is equal to LRATC, then the firm receives normal profits by producing the profit maximizing output.

☆ If LRMC=MR=Price is less than LRATC, then the firm suffers from losses and must shut down the business permanently.

B. Case: Imperfect Competition (Monopoly)

1. Short Run

☆ If AR (when SRMC=MR) is greater than SRATC, then the firm receives positive economic (super normal) profits by producing the profit maximizing output.

☆ If AR (when SRMC=MR) is equal to SRATC, then the firm receives normal profits by producing the profit maximizing output.

☆ If AR (when SRMC=MR) is greater than SRAVC, but less than SRATC, then the firm suffers from losses. But, the firm can still continue its production as long as MR>SRMC, as the extent of losses to the firm are less than TFC.

☆ If AR (when SRMC=MR) is less than SRAVC, then the firm suffers from losses and it should stop the production temporarily, as the losses in the business are to the extent of more than TFC.

☆ Profits when output is zero = (- TFC).

2. Long Run

☆ If AR (when LRMC=MR) is greater than LRATC, then the firm receives positive economic (super normal) profits by producing the profit maximizing output.

☆ If AR (when LRMC=MR) is less than LRATC, then the firm suffers from losses and must shut down the business permanently.

8.5. Maximization of Profits at the Point of Equality of MC=MR

Among the two approaches that are discussed earlier *viz.,* TR and TC approach and MR and MC approach, the latter approach is proved to be more meritorious over the former (as discussed in Chapter 7) in analyzing the firm's equilibrium of making maximum profits. The students must note that, mere equality between MR and MC under perfect and imperfect market competitions will not contribute to profit maximizing output, as the realization of profits depends upon the point of equality of MC=MR in relation with the position of per unit cost curves in the short run and long run production programmes. Let us go through the following cases with respect to perfect competition and imperfect (monopoly) competition to analyze the concept of profits both in short run and long run production programmes.

A. Concept of Equality of MR=MC in Perfect Competition

In case of perfect market competition, the concepts of firm's equilibrium and industry equilibrium can be studied both in short run (SRMC=MR) and long run (LRMC=MR) production programmes. So, we can divide our analysis into two following components:-

1. Equilibrium of firm and industry under perfect competition in the short run.

2. Equilibrium of firm and industry under perfect competition in the long run.

1. Equilibrium of Firm and Industry under Perfect Competition in the Short Run

We know, in a short run production programme, some factors are fixed and some are variable. If the firm wishes to increase the production or output, it can change only the variable factors, the quantity of fixed factors cannot be changed. The firm can increase the output by allocating more of variable resources, overworking of the plant or machinery etc. No new machinery can be installed in the production programme. New firms cannot enter the industry in the short period. The price of the commodity is determined by total demand and total supply at the industry level and this price is passed on to the individual firms. So, the two market forces, which determine the price of the commodity under perfect competition are demand and supply at the industry level. So, under perfect competition, each firm is a price taker and not a price maker. On this given price, the firm plans its output policy considering its cost conditions. We can discuss the equilibrium of the firm and industry under perfect competition in the short run considering two cases *viz.*, identical cost conditions and varying cost conditions.

a. Equilibrium of the Firm and Industry in the Short Run under Identical Cost Conditions

When we assume identical cost conditions, it implies, all the factors of production are homogenous, thereby, all the firms will incur same costs in producing the given output. So, there will not be any shift in the cost curves with respect to all the firms. As discussed earlier, each firm under perfect market competition is only a price taker, thereby, first the price is determined based on total demand and total supply forces at the industry level and the same price is passed on to the individual firms.

Case 1

In panel A of the Figure 8.4, DD is the initial demand curve for paddy in the industry, which slopes downward from left to right and SRS is the Short Run Supply (SRS) curve of the industry representing the total quantity of paddy supplied into the market in short run production programme. The DD demand curve intersects the SRS supply curve at point 'E', which indicates OQ is the equilibrium quantity of paddy supplied and demanded in the market at OP equilibrium price. This equilibrium price OP is passed on to the individual firms, as they are simply price takers in the market.

In Panel B of the Figure 8.4, a single firm is taken as a representative, as cost structure remains same across the firms under identical cost conditions. So, for the

Panel A
Industry

Panel B
Firm

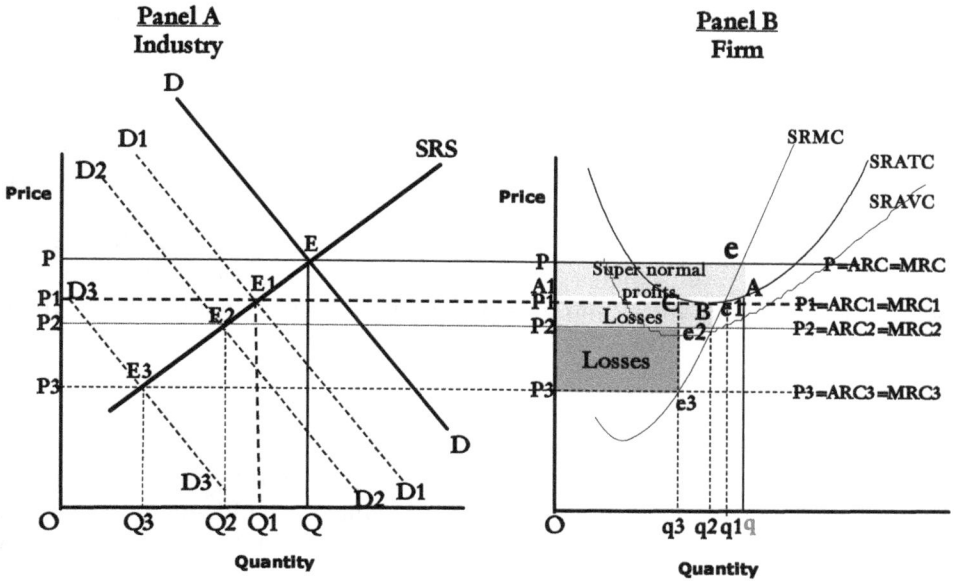

Figure 8.4: Equilibrium of Firm and Industry under Perfect Competition in the Short Run under Identical Cost Conditions.

firm, the price of paddy is OP. We know, for a firm under perfect competition, the AR and MR curves are parallel to X-axis and MRC coincides with ARC. As usual, the per unit cost curves *viz.*, SRAVC, SRATC and SRMC are 'U' shaped and there is no shift in these cost curves, as cost structure remains same across the firms. The price OP passed on from the industry to the individual firm is represented as a horizontal line parallel to X-axis and under perfect competition, price line coincides with AR and MR curves.

The firm is in equilibrium when SRMC=MRC and it is at point e, where Oq quantity of paddy is transacted in the market at OP price. This price OP is higher than SRATC curve by eA, thereby, the firm earns eA profits per unit of output. So, total super normal profits = total output sold by the firm x average profit per unit of output = Oq x eA = PeAA$_1$

As the firm earns price more than SRATC, PeAA$_1$ refers to super-normal profits realized by the firm. So, in the short run, the firm can earn super normal profits under perfect competition. These super normal profits are earned by all the firms in the industry, each by producing and selling Oq quantity of output at OP level of equilibrium price. Attracting to these super-normal profits, new firms show the tendency to enter the industry in the long run, thereby in the long run, these super-normal profits gets eroded and it is discussed in the ensuing pages.

Case 2

Let us suppose that, the demand for the commodity is decreased in the market, thereby, the new demand curve D$_1$D$_1$ moves towards the origin (Panel A). It intersects the original supply curve (SRS) at point E_1, which indicates OQ_1 is the equilibrium quantity of paddy supplied and demanded in the market at OP_1 equilibrium price. This equilibrium price OP_1 is passed on to the individual firms, as they are simply price takers in the market.

In Panel B, the equilibrium price OP_1 is represented as a horizontal line parallel to X-axis and it coincides with ARC_1 and MRC_1. The firm is in equilibrium when $SRMC=MRC_1$ and it is at point e_1, where Oq_1 quantity of paddy is transacted by the firm in the market at OP_1 price. This price OP_1 is equal to SRATC, thereby, the firm earns only normal profits. In this situation, the industry is also in equilibrium, as no new firms enter the industry and the existing firms show no tendency to leave the industry.

Case 3

Let us suppose that, the demand for the commodity is further decreased in the market, thereby, the new demand curve D_2D_2 moves towards the origin. It intersects the original supply curve (SRS) at point E_2, which indicates OQ_2 is the equilibrium quantity of paddy supplied and demanded in the market at OP_2 equilibrium price. This equilibrium price OP_2 is passed on to the individual firms, as they are simply price takers in the market.

In Panel B, the equilibrium price OP_2 is represented as a horizontal line parallel to X-axis and it coincides with ARC_2 and MRC_2. The firm is in equilibrium when $SRMC=MRC_2$ and it is at point e_2, where Oq_2 quantity of paddy is transacted by the firm in the market at OP_2 price. This price OP_2 lies below the SRATC, but above SRAVC inferring that, the firm is incurring losses to the extent of less than fixed costs incurred in the business. This is shown as an area between SRATC and SRAVC curves *i.e.*, $P_1P_2e_2B$. Thus, total loss $P_1P_2e_2B$ is given by,

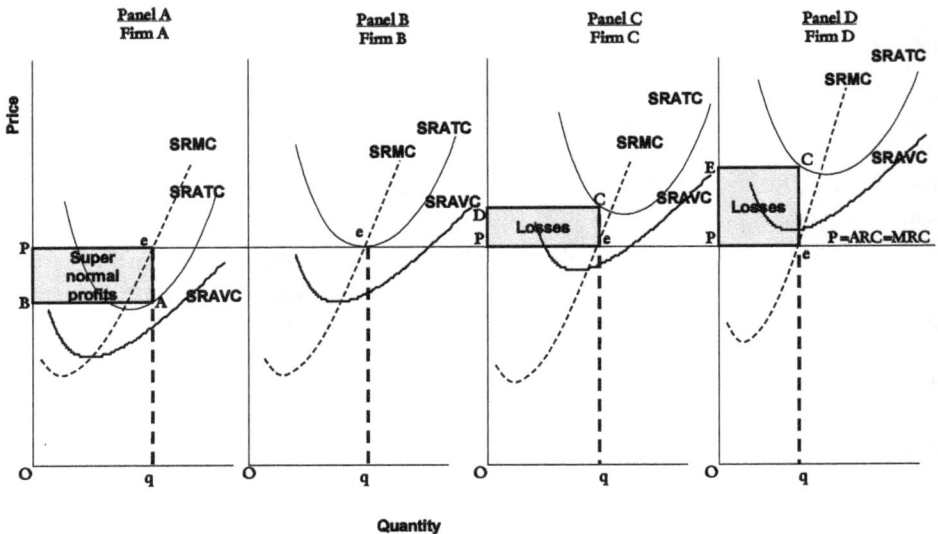

Figure 8.5: Equilibrium of Firms under Perfect Competition in the Short Run under Varying Cost Conditions.

Total loss = Total output sold by the firm x Average loss per unit of output

$$= Oq_2 \times e_2B = P_1P_2e_2B$$

In this situation, the industry is not in equilibrium because, when the firms experience losses, some of the firms will quit the industry. So, the total supply of the commodity by the industry into the market decreases, thereby, price will rise in the market. So, the remaining firms will gradually recover their losses and start earning normal profits at OP_1 price and the equilibrium output of the firm will be restored at Oq_1. As explained earlier, when the price of the commodity at least covers SRAVC (Table 5.1), the firm can continue the production programme temporarily because,

☆ The firms incur the losses only to the extent of less than fixed costs incurred.

☆ The variable costs or explicit costs incurred by the firm are recovered from the returns of the business firm.

Case 4

Let us suppose that, the demand for the commodity is still decreased in the market. As a result of this, the new demand curve D_3D_3 moves towards the origin. It intersects the original supply curve (SRS) at point E_3, which indicates OQ_3 is the equilibrium quantity of paddy supplied and demanded in the market at OP_3 equilibrium price. This equilibrium price OP_3 is passed on to the individual firms, as they are simply price takers in the market.

In Panel B, the equilibrium price OP_3 is represented as a horizontal line parallel to X-axis and it coincides with ARC_3 and MRC_3. The firm is in equilibrium when $SRMC=MRC_3$ and it is at point e_3, where Oq_3 quantity of paddy is transacted by the firm in the market at OP_3 price. This OP_3 price lies below the SRATC at a gap e_3C, inferring that, the firm is incurring huge losses to the extent of TFC and even some of the SRTVC. This total loss is shown by the area, $P_3e_3CP_1$ and it is given by,

Total loss = Total output sold by the firm x Average loss per unit of output

$$= Oq_3 \times Ce_3 = P_3e_3CP_1$$

In this situation, the firms will shut down their business, as even their SRTVC are not recovered besides TFC from the returns of the business.

b. Equilibrium of the Firm in the Short Run under Varying Cost Conditions

In majority of the cases, the factors of production are heterogeneous, thereby, the cost of production vary across the firms. We know, under perfect competition, price is determined at the industry and the same is passed on to the individual firms, as they are simply price takers. That means, the firms have to sell their output at the given price. As a result, the firms, which produce the output at low cost of production (price>SRATC) enjoy super-normal profits, some firms for which the price equals to SRATC enjoy only normal profits and some firms for which price<SRATC and price<SRAVC, suffers from losses. The same concept is explained through Figure 8.5, where the firms with different cost structures are shown due to heterogeneous nature of factors of production. Assume OP as the price determined for paddy in the industry and the same is passed on to the individual firms. Figure 8.5 highlights the

comparative picture with reference to the extent of profits earned and extent of losses experienced by the different firms at a given price.

In Panel A, the firm A is in equilibrium, when SRMC=MR *i.e.*, at 'e', which indicates that, the firm transacts 'Oq' quantity of paddy at OP level of price. As the price OP is above the SRATC by eA, the firm earns super normal profits given by,

Total profits = Total output sold by the firm x Average profit per unit of output

= Oq x eA = PeAB

In Panel B, the firm 'B' is in equilibrium, when SRMC=MR *i.e.*, at 'e', which indicates that, the firm transacts 'Oq' quantity of paddy at 'OP' price. A close examination of the Panel B reveals that, its cost structure is higher compared to firm 'A'. As the price OP is equal to the SRATC, the firm B earns only normal profits.

In Panel C, the firm C is in equilibrium, when SRMC=MR, *i.e.* at 'e' which indicates that, the firm transacts 'Oq' quantity of paddy at 'OP' price. On comparison, the cost structure of the firm 'C' is higher than firm B and firm A. As the price OP is less than SRATC, but higher than SRAVC, the firm can continue the business temporarily, as the extent of losses to the firm are less than TFC. The total loss is given by,

Total loss = Total output sold by the firm x Average loss per unit of output

= Oq x eC = PeCD

Though the firm experience losses, since the price OP covers at least SRAVC, the firm can continue production programme temporarily.

In Panel D, the firm D is in equilibrium, when SRMC=MR, *i.e.*, at 'e' which indicates that, the firm transacts 'Oq' quantity of paddy at 'OP' price. The cost structure of firm D is higher compared to earlier three firms A, B and C, thereby, firm 'D' is the least efficient firm. As the price OP is less than SRAVC, the firm experience greater losses (compared to firm C) *i.e.*, PeCE, as it could not recover TFC and even some of the SRTVC. So, the firm will shut down the production programme and wait for better times.

The above discussion clearly infers that, since the cost structure varies across the firms, some firms will enjoy profits and some firms experience losses in the industry. So, the industry under different cost conditions will not be in stable equilibrium in the short run and the industry will be in stable equilibrium only in the long run. In the words of Ferguson and Kreps, *'in the short run, the number of firms in an industry cannot be changed. Each firm attempting either to maximize profit or minimize loss, produces that output, for which marginal cost equals the market equilibrium price. At this point, the firm may earn a pure economic profit, it may earn a pure economic loss or it may happen to break even'.*

2. Equilibrium of Firm and Industry under Perfect Competition in the Long Run

As discussed earlier, in the long run, all the factors are variable and no factor is fixed in the production programme. That means, if the firm wishes to expand or contract the output, it can vary all the factors and the firm can move from one plant to another plant. When the firms earn super-normal profits, as discussed under Panel B of the Figure 8.4, new firms gets attracted to these super normal profits and enter the industry. The entry of new firms into the industry will be continued till the super-normal profits are wiped out or till all the firms enjoy at least normal profits. So, the firms will continue in the business as long as their ARC or MRC or price is above LRATC or at least equal to LRATC, but not less than LRATC. Similarly, when the firms experience losses in the long run (when price<LRATC), they will leave the industry. When some firms leave the industry, the Long Run Supply (LRS) into the market decreases, thereby, the price of the commodity will gradually rise. So, for the firms who remain in the industry, their price is equal to LRATC and they earn normal profits. So, the process of entry and exit of firms into the industry continues in the long run till the price equals to LRATC.

a. Equilibrium of the Firm in the Long Run

As discussed in the earlier Chapter 7, the superior approach to determine the firm's equilibrium is MR and MC approach. So, in the long run, under perfect competition, the first-order condition that is required for the firm's equilibrium is LRMC=MR. Since, MRC coincides with ARC under perfect competition, the first-order condition can also be written as LRMC=MRC=ARC. Besides this first-order condition, the second order condition that is necessary for the firm to be in equilibrium is that the LRMC must cut the MRC from below, while rising upward. That means, the LRMC should be rising at the point of determination of firm's equilibrium output. If MR>LRMC, it implies, the firm can still expand the output till the point of MR=LRMC and if MR<LRMC, it implies, the firm must reduce the output till the point of MR=LRMC and at the point of MR=LRMC, the firm will be in equilibrium.

b. Equilibrium of the Industry in the Long Run

An industry is said to be in equilibrium, when all the firms in the industry are in equilibrium. That means, at the point of equilibrium in the industry, no new firms show the tendency to enter the industry and no firms in the industry show the tendency to leave the industry. This is because, at the point of equilibrium in the industry in the long run, all the firms earn only normal profits. That means, the possibility of earning super-normal profits in the long run is completely wiped out and all the firms experience only normal profits. This is because, when the firms experience super-normal profits in the short run, new firms gets attracted to these super-normal profits and enter the industry, thereby,

☆ Competition increases for the employment of factors of production in the long run, thereby, factor prices increases and this reduces profits for all the firms in the long run.

☆ When large number of firms enters the industry, the existing market is to be shared among all the firms in the industry, thereby, profits share declines and hence, only normal profits are experienced instead of super-normal profits.

☆ With the entry of new firms, the supply of the product into the market increases, thereby, price decreases and hence, all the firms will enjoy only normal profits instead of super normal profits.

Thus, in the long run, all the firms in the industry experience normal profits only instead of super-normal profits and thereby, at the point of equilibrium, no new firms shows the tendency to enter the industry and existing firms in the industry show no tendency to leave the industry. So, normal profits are the profits for a firm in the industry in the long run, which are just sufficient to induce the firm to continue in the industry and do not induce new firms outside the industry to enter the industry. So, when all the firms in the industry experience normal profits only in the long run, the point of equilibrium is LRMC=MR=AR=Price=LRATC.

As in short run, we can study the equilibrium of the firm and industry under perfect competition in the long run under two conditions *viz.*, identical cost conditions and varying cost conditions.

i. Long Run Equilibrium of the Firms and Industry under Identical Cost Conditions

As discussed earlier, when we assumed identical cost conditions, it implies all the factors of production are homogenous thereby, all the firms will incur same costs in the industry to produce a given output. Thus, there will not be any shift in the cost curves with respect to all the firms. We know, each firm under perfect market competition is only a price taker, thereby, first the price is determined based on total demand and total supply of paddy in the industry and the same price is passed on to the individual firms.

In Panel A of the Figure 8.6, DD is the initial demand curve of the industry for paddy and SS is the initial supply of paddy in the industry in the long run production programme. The demand curve DD intersects the supply curve SS at point E, where

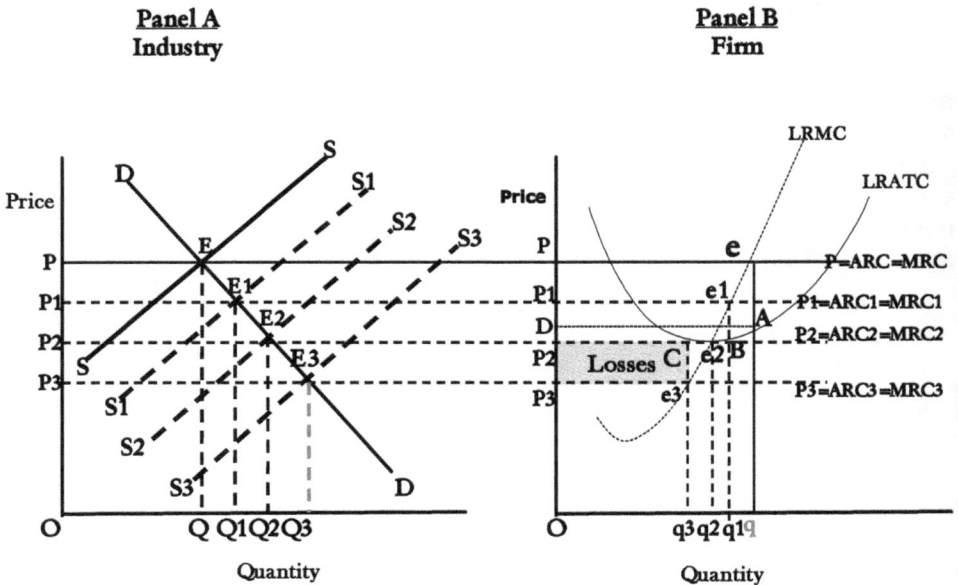

Figure 8.6: Equilibrium of Firm and Industry under Perfect Competition in the Long Run under Identical Cost Conditions.

OQ quantity of paddy is supplied and demanded in the industry at OP long run equilibrium price. This price OP is passed on to the individual firms, as they are simply price takers in the market.

In Panel B of the Figure 8.6, a single firm is taken as a representative, as cost structure remains same across the firms under identical cost conditions. So, for the firm, the price of paddy is OP. We know, for a firm under perfect competition, MRC and ARC curves are parallel to X-axis and MRC coincides with ARC. As usual, the per unit cost curves LRATC and LRMC are 'U' shaped and there is no shift in these cost curves, as cost structure remains same across the firms. The price OP passed on from the industry to each individual firm is represented as horizontal line parallel to X-axis, as under perfect competition, price line coincides with ARC and MRC. The firm will be in equilibrium when the LRMC=MRC(=ARC=OP) and it is at point 'e', where Oq is the quantity of paddy transacted by the firm at OP long run equilibrium price. This price OP is higher than LRATC by eA, thereby, each firm will earn super-normal profits, PeAD. But, this is not the point of stable equilibrium. This is because, attracted to these super-normal profits, new firms will enter the industry and thereby, the total supply of paddy into the market by all the firms will increase. Accordingly S_1S_1 is the new (increased) supply curve for paddy in the market with the entry of new firms (Panel A).

With increase in supply of paddy in the industry, the new S_1S_1 supply curve will intersect the original demand curve DD at E_1, where, OQ_1 quantity of paddy supplied and demanded in the industry at OP_1 long run equilibrium price. This price OP_1 is passed on to the individual firms, as they are simply price takers in the market. The OP_1 price is shown as a horizontal line parallel to X-axis and it coincides with MRC_1 and ARC_1 for the firm under perfect competition. The point of equilibrium is when $LRMC=MRC_1(=ARC_1=OP_1)$ and it is at point e_1, where Oq_1 is the quantity of paddy transacted by the firm at OP_1 long run equilibrium price. Again, this price OP_1 is higher than LRATC by e_1B, thereby each firm will earn super-normal profits, $e_1BP_1P_2$. But again, this is not the point of stable equilibrium, as new firms gets attracted to these super normal profits and enter the industry, thereby, the total supply of paddy into the market by all the firms will increase from S_1S_1 to S_2S_2 (Panel A).

With the increase in supply, the new supply curve S_2S_2 shifts towards right side and intersects the original demand curve DD at E_2, where OQ_2 quantity of paddy supplied and demanded in the industry at OP_2 long run equilibrium price. This price OP_2 is passed on to the individual firms, as they are simply price takers in the market. The OP_2 price is shown as a horizontal line parallel to X-axis and it coincides with MRC_2 and ARC_2 for the firm under perfect competition. The point of equilibrium is when $LRMC=MRC_2(=ARC_2=OP_2)$ and it is at point e_2, where Oq_2 quantity of paddy is transacted by the firm at OP_2 long run equilibrium price. This price OP_2 is equal to the minimum of LRATC of the firm, which implies each firm will now earn only normal profits in the long run. So, at the point of firm's equilibrium *i.e.* 'e_2' in the long run, when all the firms earn normal profits, the equilibrium condition is $LRMC=MRC_2=ARC_2=OP_2=LRATC$. At this equilibrium condition, all the firms will earn only normal profits only and the industry will also be in stable equilibrium. So, to generalize, the long run (stable) equilibrium for the firm (when all the firms experience normal profits only) is given by, LRMC=MRC=ARC=Price=LRATC. This general equilibrium condition in the long run prevails only, when the price equals the LRATC of the firm. So, the firm in the long run must produce the output at minimum LRATC.

Several central properties can be derived from this perfect competitive long run equilibrium (price=LRATC) and they are important from the normative economics point of view. They include,

☆ This equilibrium price is efficient, as it is equal to the LRATC at its lowest point. That means, at this point of equilibrium, the long run cost of production of paddy is at its lowest level and there is no other way to produce the same commodity that is cheaper. That is, there is no wastage of resources in the production programme.

☆ All the firms enjoy normal profits only, thereby, consumer welfare is maximized, as they pay only production costs.

☆ Social Surplus (SS) *i.e.* Producer Surplus + Consumer Surplus is maximized.

It is essential to note that, all the above properties are positive for the society and they are not achieved due to the actions of Central Planning Authority in the economic system. Only the free market forces are solely responsible for these positive aspects in the society and Adam Smith has rightly quoted them as *'Invisible Hand'*. However, any market intervention in the form of fixing ceiling price or floor price by the Government or by the formation of monopolies or collusive oligopolies will lead to reduction in the SS and the amount by which the SS or total welfare is reduced refers to deadweight loss.

If by miscalculation, new firms enter the industry even at price OP_2, then the total supply of paddy in the market increases and it is shown by S_3S_3 supply curve (Panel A). This S_3S_3 supply will intersect the original demand curve DD at E_3, where OQ_3 quantity of paddy supplied and demanded in the industry and OP_3 long run equilibrium price. This price OP_3 is passed on to the individual firms, as they are simply price takers in the market. The price OP_3 is shown as a horizontal line parallel to X-axis and it coincides with MRC_3 and ARC_3 for the firm under perfect competition. The point of equilibrium is when $LRMC=MRC_3(=ARC_3=OP_3)$ and it is at point e_3, where Oq_3 quantity of paddy is transacted by the firm at OP_3 long run equilibrium price. This price OP_3 is less than LRATC, thereby, the firm will incur loss to the extent of e_3C per unit of output, thereby, it will shut down the production programme permanently. We know, no firm can stay in the production programme in the long run, if it makes losses. So, the new firms will not enter the industry, when the industry is in equilibrium, where OP_2 price is equal to minimum of LRATC for all the firms *i.e.*, when all the firms enjoy the normal profits only.

ii. Long Run Equilibrium of the Firms under Varying Cost Conditions

In general, the cost of production varies across the firms, as the factors of production are heterogeneous. We know, price of the commodity is determined by the industry based on the interaction between total demand and total supply of the commodity and this equilibrium price is passed on to the firms, as they are simply price takers. So, the firms can determine the level of output in the long run considering the price offered by the industry. Depending upon the level of price offered by the industry, the firm can achieve normal profits in the long run in relation to its cost structure. That is, if the price offered by the industry equals the LRATC of the firm, the firms experience normal profits only. It is essential to note that, the firms experiencing losses (price<LRATC) in the long run, will quit the industry.

In Panel A of the Figure 8.7, let us assume, OP is the price offered by the industry and hence, firm A accepts this price. This price OP is represented as a horizontal straight line parallel to X-axis, as for the firm under perfect competition, the price=ARC=MRC. As usual, the LRATC and LRMC are 'U' shaped curves and the point of firm's equilibrium is LRMC=MR, which is at point 'e', where Oq quantity of paddy is transacted by the firm in the market at OP long run equilibrium price. Since, OP price < LRATC, the firm experiences losses PeAB. That means, if the firm has higher cost structure because of inefficient management, it suffers from losses in the long run production programme.

In Panel B, the cost structure of firm B is lower compared to firm A. So, at the same long run equilibrium price OP, the firm B experiences normal profits, as LRMC=MRC=ARC=Price=LRATC. This firm that enjoys normal profits in the long run is called 'Marginal firm', as it is the first firm to leave the industry, if price falls below OP. So, a marginal firm is a firm that enjoys higher cost structure, where its LRATC = Price and thereby, enjoys only normal profits. We already know, under perfect competition, super normal profits that enjoyed by the firms in short run are eroded in the long run and the firms enjoy only normal profits.

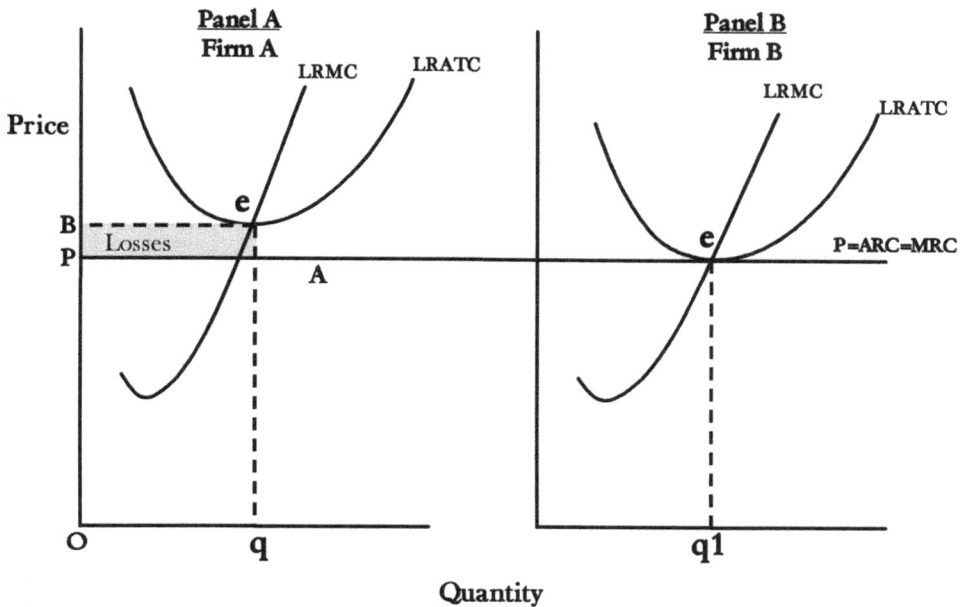

Figure 8.7: Equilibrium of Firm and Industry under Perfect Competition in the Long Run under Varying Cost Conditions.

B. Concept of Equality of MR=MC in Imperfect (Monopoly) Competition

In case of monopoly competition, the concepts of firm's equilibrium and industry equilibrium can be studied both in short run (SRMC=MR) and long run (LRMC=MR) production programmes. So, we can divide our analysis into two components:-

1. Equilibrium of monopoly firm or industry in the short run
2. Equilibrium of monopoly firm or industry in the long run

Even under imperfect competition, the point of equality between MR=MC determines the point of profit maximization of a (monopoly) firm. The point of intersection between MR and MC curves and the perpendicular drawn from this intersection of MR and MC curves onto the ARC, determines the price of the product (as ARC is nothing but, demand curve). It implies that, in monopoly, price > MC=MR, as MRC lies below ARC. This concept of profit maximization of a monopoly firm in short run and long run is based on the following assumptions:

☆ There is one firm in the production of a product.

☆ The product is homogenous without substitutes.

☆ Monopolist is rational with an objective of profit maximization or cost minimization.

☆ Prices of factors and product remain same.

☆ The monopolist exercises full market power in fixing the market price and block the entry of rivalry firms.

1. Equilibrium of Monopoly Firm or Industry in the Short Run

Case 1: TR>SRTC or Price>SRATC

In the Figure 8.8, on X-axis, output and on Y-axis, revenue and costs are taken. ARC and MRC are downward sloping curves, the ARC is a higher level sloping down curve and MRC is a lower level sloping down curve. SRMC curve cuts the MRC at point 'E'. So, the monopolist is in equilibrium at 'E' and produces OQ quantity of output by fixing the price of the product at OC=QP. At this price and output, the monopolist realizes super-normal profits shown by the shaded rectangle PABC. This is because, at OQ level of output, QP=OC price is above SRATC curve by PA portion between ARC and SRATC curve. Beyond OQ level of output, MR<SRMC and below OQ level of output, MR>SRMC. So, to derive maximum profits, the monopolist has to produce the output OQ, where MR=SRMC.

Estimation of Profits

The output OQ is supplied in the market at price OC=QP. At this level of output, the difference between ARC and SRATC is PA *i.e.* average profit. So,

Total profit = Average profit x Output = PA x OQ = PABC

Case 2: TR=SRTC or Price=SRATC

In the Figure 8.9, on X-axis, output and on Y-axis, revenue and costs are taken. ARC and MRC are downward sloping curves, the ARC is a higher level sloping down curve and MRC is a lower level sloping down curve. SRMC curve cuts the MRC

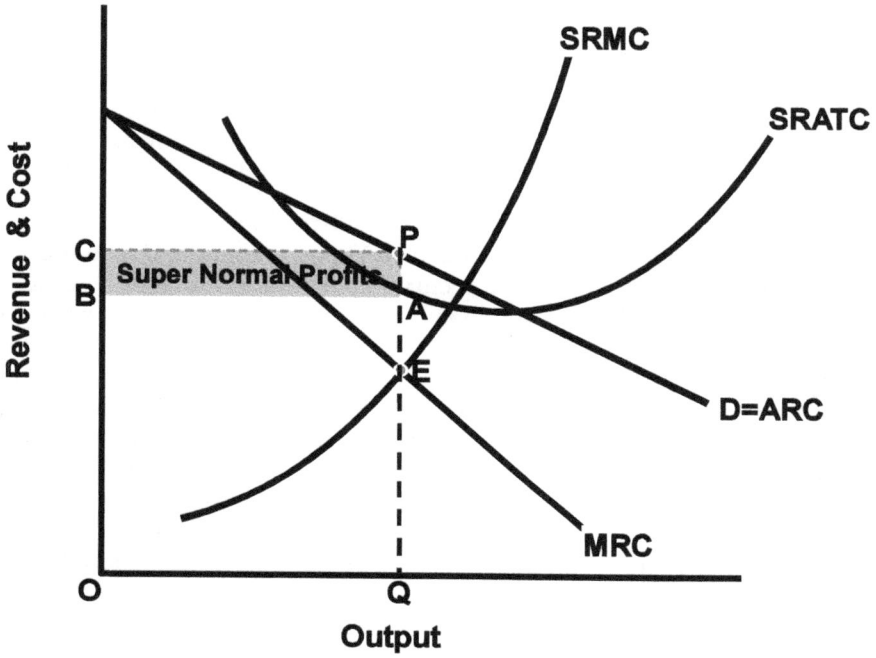

Figure 8.8: Price Determination of Monopoly Rirm in Short Run (Case: TR>SRTC or Price > SRATC).

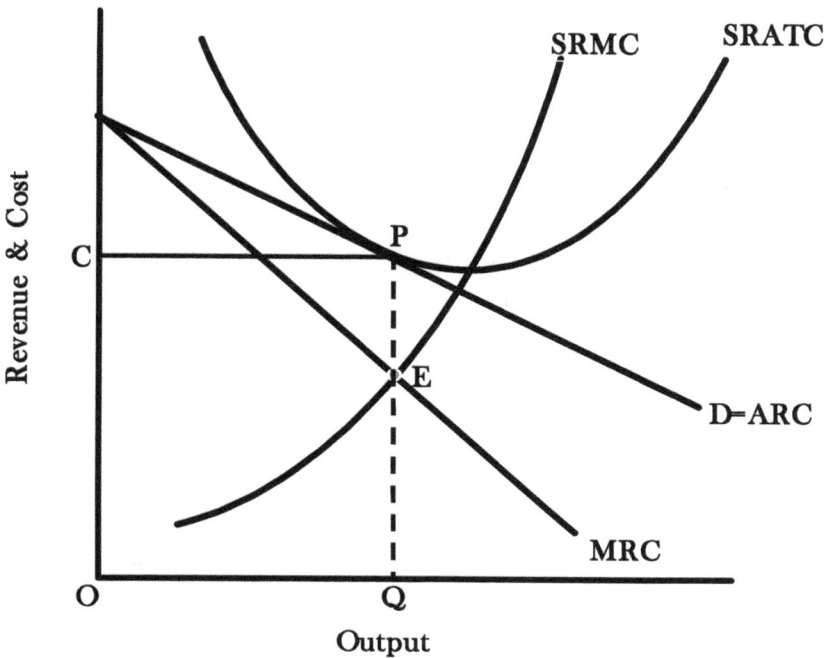

Figure 8.9: Price Determination of Monopoly Firm in Short Run (Case: TR=SRTC or Price = SRATC).

at point 'E'. So, the monopolist is in equilibrium at 'E' and produces OQ quantity of output by fixing the price of the product at OC=QP. At this price and output, the monopolist realizes normal profits or the firm becomes break even, since price=SRATC. Beyond OQ level of output, MR<SRMC and below OQ level of output, MR>SRMC and at OQ output, MR=SRMC and the firm derives only normal profits, as price=SRATC.

Case 3: SRTC>TR>SRTVC or SRATC>Price>SRAVC

In the Figure 8.10, on X-axis, output and on Y-axis, revenue and costs are taken. ARC and MRC are downward sloping curves, the ARC is a higher level sloping down curve and MRC is a lower level sloping down curve. SRMC curve cuts the MRC at point 'E'. So, the monopolist is in equilibrium at 'E' and produces OQ quantity of output by fixing the price of the product at OC=QP. At this price and output, the monopolist incurs losses as shown by the shaded rectangle PABC. This is because, at OQ level of output, QP price is below SRATC curve by PA portion between SRATC curve and ARC. Here, price QP covers only SRAVC, but not SRATC. In the short run, the monopolist can continue the business temporarily, as price per unit of output covers at least SRAVC and not SRATC thereby, the losses are less than the extent of TFC. However, if the price of the product falls below SRAVC, the monopolist better stop the business temporarily because, he is incurring huge losses, as even explicit costs (SRAVC) are also not recovered. Beyond OQ level of output, MR<SRMC and hence, the firm should not produce output beyond OQ.

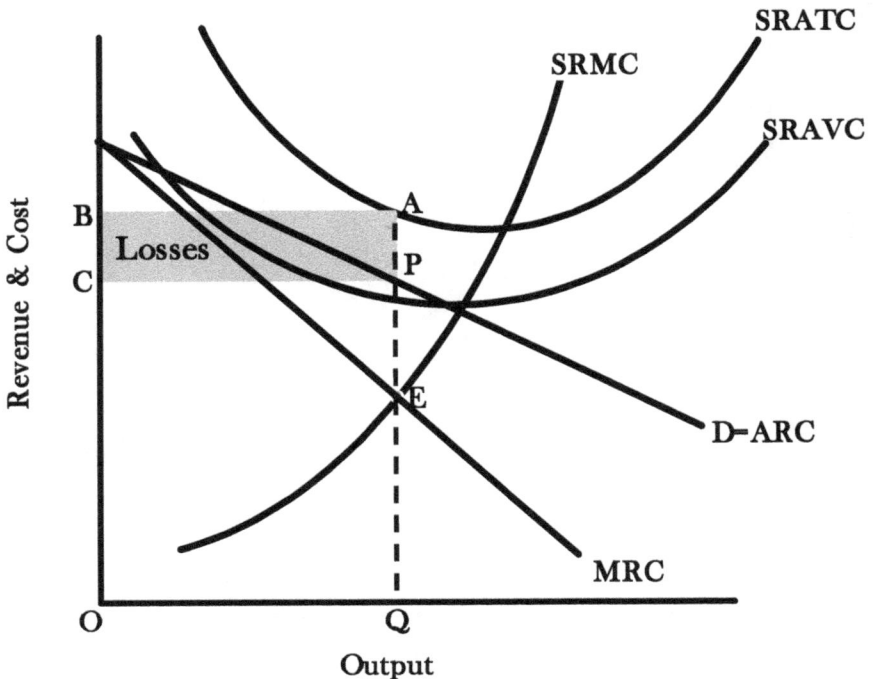

Figure 8.10: Price Determination of Monopoly Firm in Short Run (Case: SRTC>TR>SRTVC or SRATC > Price > SRAVC).

Estimation of Losses

The output OQ is supplied in the market at price OC=QP. At this level of output, the difference between ARC and SRATC is PA *i.e.*, average loss. So,

Total loss = Average loss x Output = PA x OQ = PABC

Case 4: TR<SRTVC or Price<SRAVC

In the Figure 8.11, on X-axis, output and on Y-axis, revenue and costs are taken. ARC and MRC are downward sloping curves, the ARC is a higher level sloping down curve and MRC is a lower level sloping down curve. MC curve cuts the MRC at point 'E'. So, the monopolist is in equilibrium at 'E' and produces OQ quantity of output by fixing the price of the product at OC=QP. At this price and output, the monopolist incurs huge losses, as shown by the shaded rectangle PABC. This is because, at OQ level of output, QP price is below SRAVC curve. So, the price QP could not cover even SRAVC and hence, the monopolist better stop the business temporarily because, even explicit costs are also not recovered besides TFC.

Estimation of Losses

The output OQ is supplied in the market at price OC=QP. At this level of output, the difference between ARC and SRATC is PA *i.e.*, average loss. So,

Total loss = Average loss x Output = PA x OQ = PABC

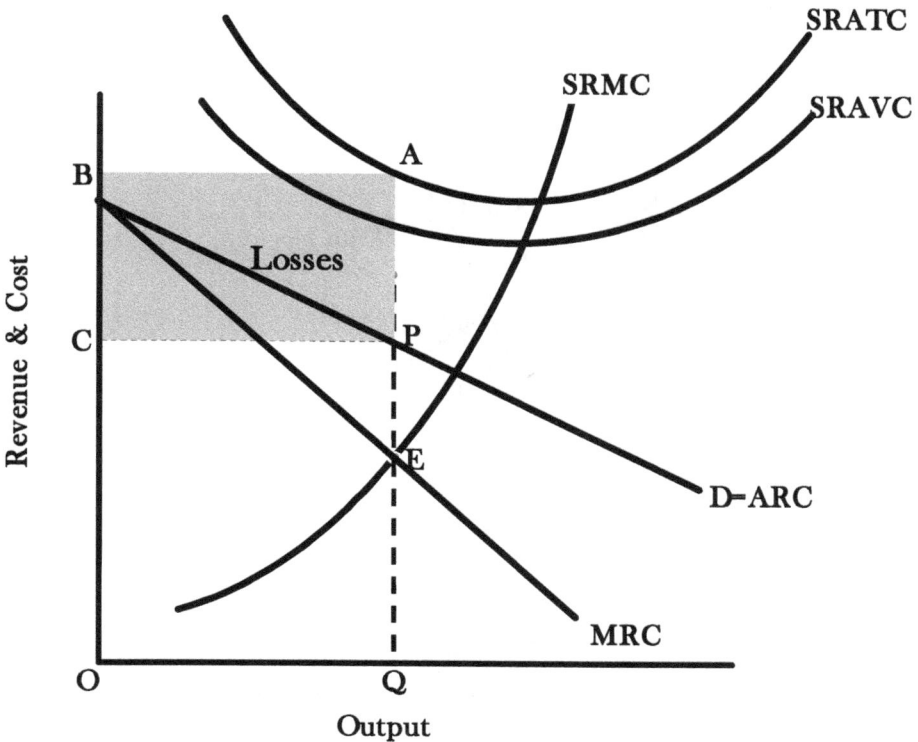

Figure 8.11: Price Determination of Monopoly Firm in Short Run (Case: TR < SRTVC or Price < SRAVC).

2. Equilibrium of Monopoly Firm or Industry in the Long Run

In the long run, the monopolies can remain in the business only, if the firm is able to earn super normal profits (Price>LRATC). This is explained through the following cases:

Case 1: TR>LRTC or Price>LRATC

In the Figure 8.12, on X-axis, output and on Y-axis, revenue and costs are taken. ARC and MRC are downward sloping curves, the ARC is a higher level sloping down curve and MRC is a lower level sloping down curve. LRMC curve cuts the MRC at point 'E'. So, the monopolist is in equilibrium at 'E' and produces OQ quantity of output by fixing the price of the product at OC=QP. At this price and output, the monopolist realizes super-normal profits shown by the shaded rectangle PABC. This is because, at OQ level of output, QP price is above LRATC curve by PA portion between ARC and LRATC curve. Beyond OQ level of output, MR<LRMC and below OQ level of output, MR>LRMC. So, to derive maximum profits, the monopolist has to produce the output OQ, where MR=LRMC.

Estimation of Profits

The output OQ can be sold in the market at price OC=QP. At this level of output, the difference between ARC and LRATC is PA *i.e.*, average profit. So,

Total profit = Average profit x Output = PA x OQ = PABC

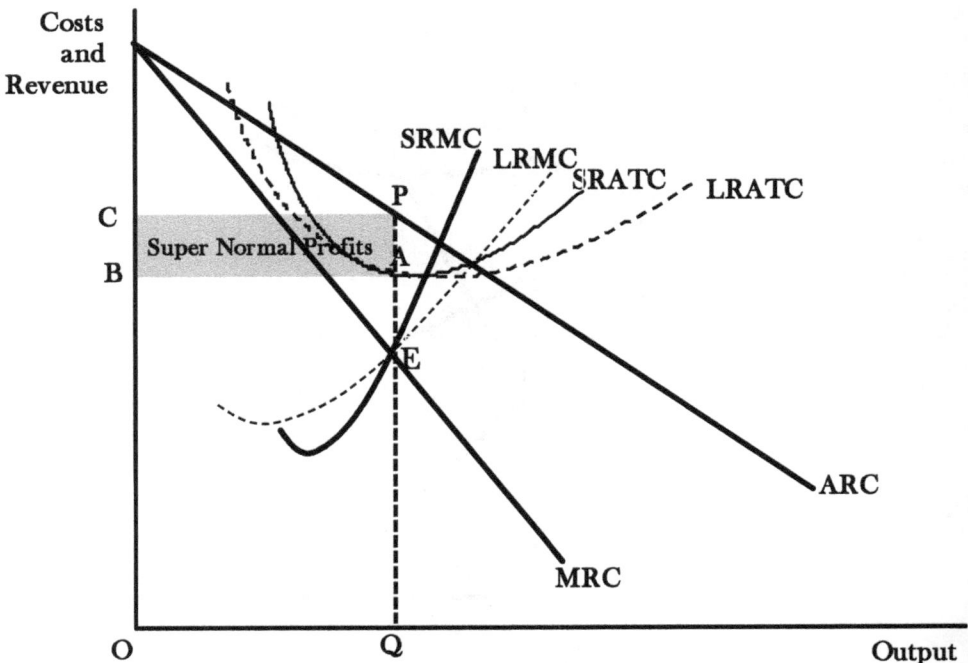

Figure 8.12: Price Determination of Monopoly Firm in Long Run (Case: TR>LRTC or Price>LRATC).

Case 2: TR<LRTC or Price<LRATC

In the Figure 8.13, on X-axis, output and on Y-axis, revenue and costs are taken. ARC and MRC are downward sloping curves, the ARC is a higher level sloping down curve and MRC is a lower level sloping down curve. LRMC curve cuts the MRC at point 'E'. So, the monopolist is in equilibrium at 'E' and produces OQ quantity of output by fixing the price of the product at OC=QP. At this price and output, the monopolist incurs losses as shown by the shaded rectangle PABC. This is because, at OQ level of output, QP price is below LRATC curve by PA. So, the price QP could not cover LRATC and hence, the monopolist better stop the business permanently because, he is incurring huge losses.

Estimation of Losses

The output OQ is supplied in the market at price OC=QP. At this level of output, the difference between ARC and LRATC is PA *i.e.*, average loss. So,

Total loss = Average loss x Output = PA x OQ = PABC

In the earlier Figures 8.10 and 8.11, since price could not cover SRATC and even SRAVC respectively in the short run, the monopolist incurs losses and when the price falls below SRAVC, the monopolist has to stop the production programme temporarily. But, in the long run, the monopolist has enough time to make changes in the existing plant, so as to overcome the losses and to realize profits. With the entry of

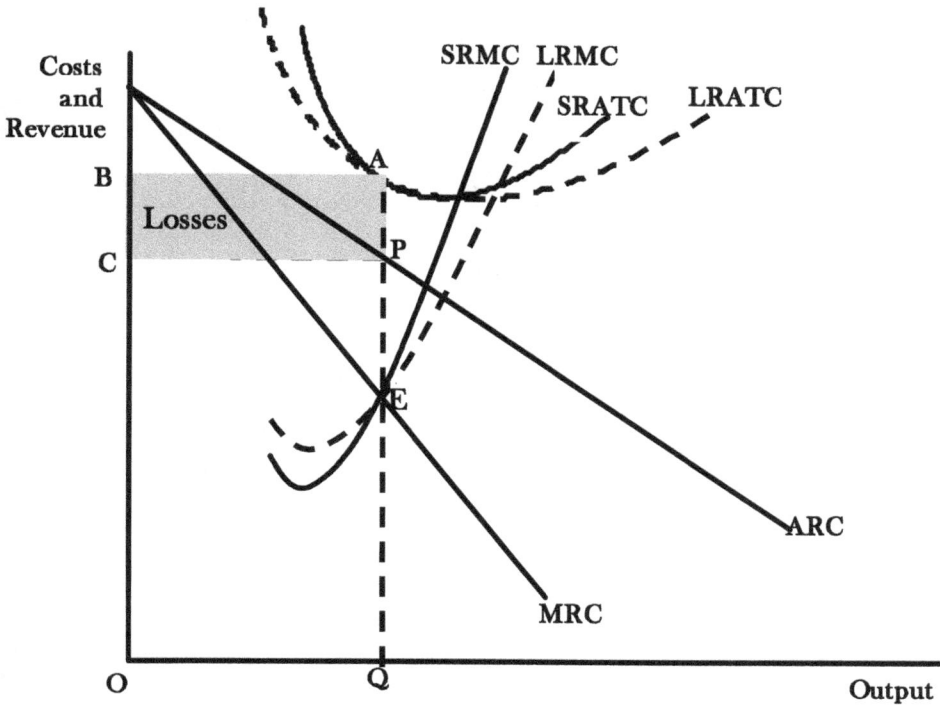

Figure 8.13: Price Determination of Monopoly Firm in Long Run (Case: TR<LRTC or Price<LRATC).

new firms is completely ruled out in monopoly market situation, the monopolist can install a smaller than optimum scale plant or an optimum scale plant or a larger than optimum scale plant in the long run, depending upon the size of the market for the product he wishes to produce. The following conditions must be satisfied to ensure the profitable level of output in the case of each plant:

☆ LRMC curve=MRC and SRMC curve must pass through this point, and

☆ LRATC curve must lie tangent to the SRATC curve at this level of output.

Case 1: Smaller than Optimum Size Plant

SRMC and SRATC are the short run per unit cost curves of the firm (Figure 8.14). To earn super normal profits in the long run, if the size of market is small, the monopolist installs smaller than optimum size plant and the monopolist maximizes the profits, where LRMC=MRC=SRMC and LRATC is tangent to SRATC with reference to that output level. This is shown at point E and it infers that, when monopoly firm is in equilibrium in long run, it is also in equilibrium in short run. The corresponding point of E on ARC is P and it implies that, at OC=QP level of price, the firm earns super-normal profits, PABC, as ARC>LRATC in the long run by PA. So,

Total profit = Average profit x Total output =PA x OQ =PABC

The plant is, however, of less than optimum size. In the Figure 8.14, the LRMC curve cuts the LRATC curve at its lowest point L implying that at L, the LRATC is

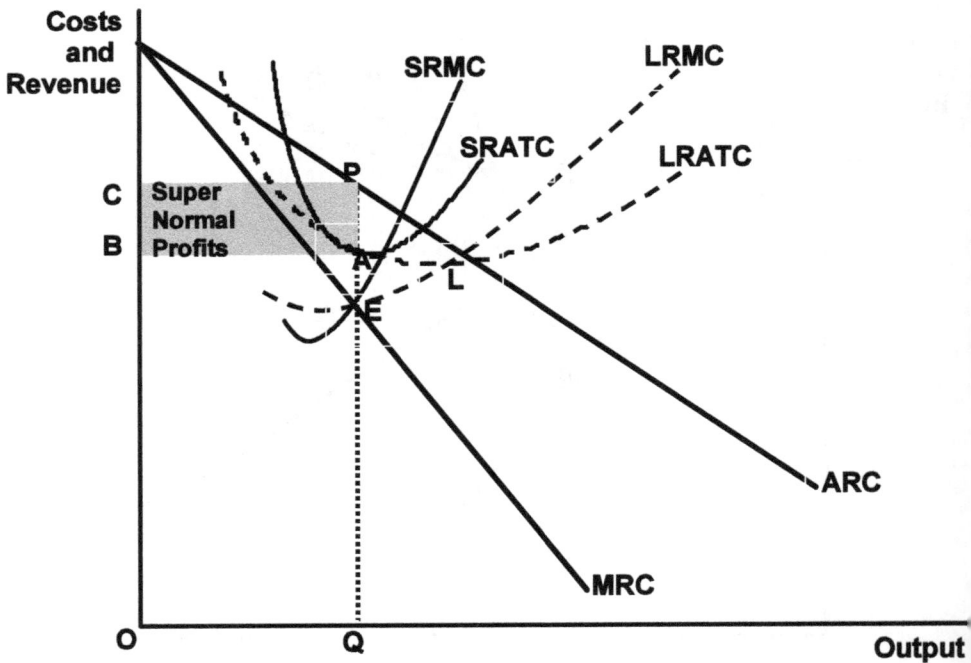

Figure 8.14: Price Determination of Monopoly firm in Long Run (Case: Smaller than Optimum size plant).

minimum for the product. But, the profits are not studied at this lowest point 'L' on the LRATC curve. This is because, the plant is of less than optimum size, thereby, the firm is not in a position to take full advantage of economies of large scale due to small size of the market. Hence, profits are studied even before the minimum point of 'L' of LRATC curve., *i.e.*, at point 'A' on LRATC. So, the corresponding point of E (LRMC=MRC=SRMC) with reference to LRATC is A and with reference to ARC is P and this infers the firm earns super normal profits PABC. (If profits are studied with reference to lowest point L of LRATC curve, then the profits will be much higher).

Case 2: Optimum Size Plant

If the size of the market is big, the monopolist installs a plant of optimum size. SRMC and SRATC are the short run per unit cost curves of the firm (Figure 8.15). To earn super normal profits in the long run, if the size of market is big, the monopolist installs optimum size plant and he maximizes the profits, where LRMC=MRC=SRMC=SRATC=LRATC. This is with reference to point E and it infers that, when monopoly firm is in equilibrium in long run, it is also in equilibrium in short run. The corresponding point of E on ARC is P and it implies that, at OC=QP level of price, the firm earns super-normal profits, PEBC, as ARC>LRATC in the long run by EP. So, Total profit = Average profit x Total output =PE x OQ =PEBC

In the Figure 8.15, the plant is of optimum size. This is because, LRMC cuts the LRATC at its minimum point L and at this minimum point, L=E, where LRMC=MRC=SRMC=SRATC=LRATC and profits are studied with reference to

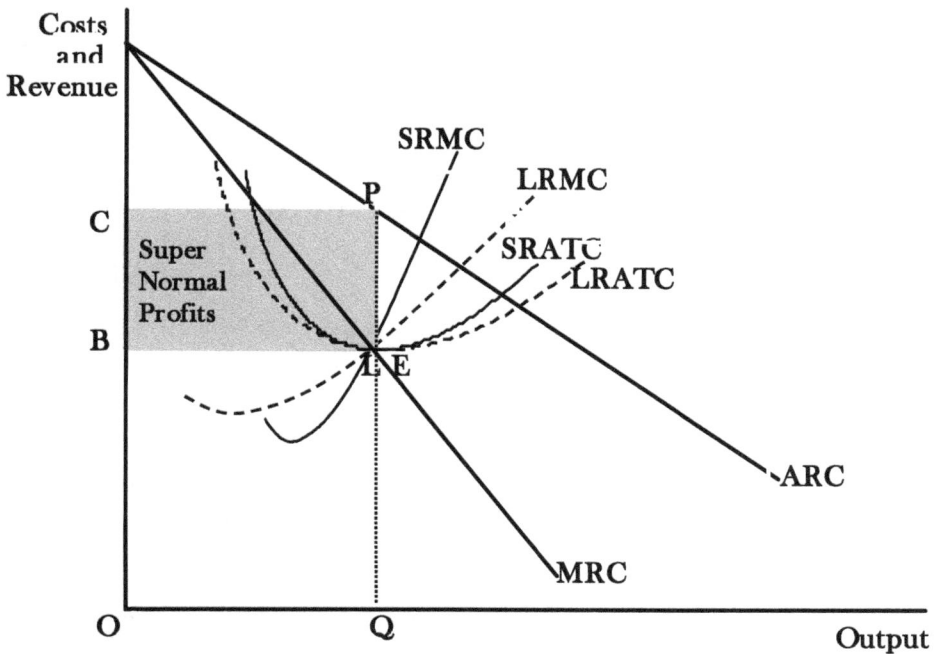

Figure 8.15: Price Determination of Monopoly Firm in Long Run (Case: Optimum size plant).

minimum point L=E on LRATC. We can say the firm is operating at its optimum size, as the profits are studied with reference to the lowest point of LRATC and hence, the firm maximizes the super-normal profits, PEBC.

Case 3. Larger than Optimum Size Plant

If size of the market is very big, the monopolist installs a plant of larger than optimum size. He will earn more by producing the output beyond the minimum point of LRATC. But it leads to over utilization of the plant, thereby, bringing in diseconomies of production, *i.e.*, per unit cost of output is high.

SRMC and SRATC are the short run per unit cost curves of the firm (Figure 8.16). To earn super normal profits in the long run, if the size of market is very big, the monopolist installs a plant of larger than optimum size and the monopolist maximizes the profits, where LRMC=MRC=SRMC and LRATC is tangent to SRATC with reference to that output level. This is shown at point E and it infers that, when monopoly firm is in equilibrium in long run, it is also in equilibrium in short run. The corresponding point of E on ARC is P and it implies that, at OC=QP level of price, the firm earns super-normal profits, PABC, as ARC>LRATC in the long run by PA. So,

Total profit = Average profit x Total output =PA x OQ =PABC

The plant is, however, of more than optimum size and it is over utilizing its capacity. In the Figure 8.16, the LRMC curve cuts the LRATC curve at its lowest point L implying that at L, the LRATC is minimum for the product. But, the profits are studied to the right side of the lowest point 'L' of LRATC curve *i.e.*, at 'A', indicating

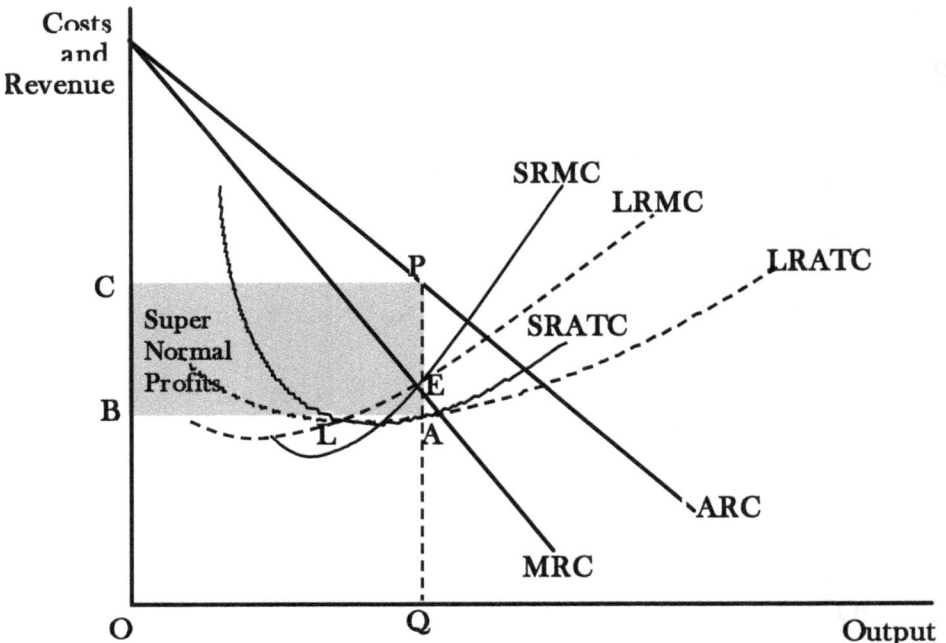

Figure 8.16: Price Determination of Monopoly Firm in Long Run (Case: Larger than optimum size plant).

that, costs are slightly more at point A when compared to at point 'L'. This is because, since the plant is more than optimum size, to meet the needs of big size market, it is over utilized above its capacity. This will lead to diseconomies of large scale, thereby, the profits will be declined compared to the firm operating at optimum size. That means, had the profits studied at lowest point L on the LRATC curve, the profits will be much higher, as we studied in earlier Case 2 (Figure 8.15), when the plant is of optimum size. So, the corresponding point of E (LRMC=MRC=SRMC) with reference to LRATC is A and with reference to ARC is P and this infers that, the firm earns super-normal profits PABC.

To sum up, in the long run production programme, with the entry blocked to other firms in monopoly market situation, the firm meets the market demand by installing less than optimum or optimum or more than optimum plant sizes in accordance with the market size and tries to attain super-normal profits. On the other hand, in case of perfect competition, in the long run, the firm must operate with an optimum plant size at the lowest point of LRATC and derive only normal profits.

8.6. Profit Function

We know, Profit (π) $= TR - TC$. The same can be written as

$\pi \qquad = Y.P_Y - (P_1 X_1 + P_2 X_2 + P_3 X_3 + \ldots\ldots\ldots + P_n X_n + TFC)$

Where, π = Profits of the firm, Y = Output, P_Y = Price of output, $P_1, P_2, P_3, \ldots\ldots P_n$ = Prices of inputs $X_1, X_2, X_3, \ldots\ldots X_n$, TFC = Total Fixed Cost

Let us differentiate the above equation with respect to $X_1, X_2, X_3 \ldots\ldots X_n$, we get,

$\partial\pi/\partial X_1 = (\partial Y/\partial X_1) P_Y - P_1$

$\partial\pi/\partial X_2 = (\partial Y/\partial X_2) P_Y - P_2$ and so on for other inputs $X_3, X_4, X_5 \ldots\ldots X_n$

For profit maximization, $\partial\pi/\partial X_1, \partial\pi/\partial X_2 \ldots\ldots$etc. should be equal to zero. Therefore,

$(\partial Y/\partial X_1) P_Y - P_1 = 0$

$(\partial Y/\partial X_1) P_Y = P_1$

$(\partial Y/\partial X_1) = P_1/P_Y$

$(\partial Y/\partial X_1) (P_Y/P_1) = 1$

We already know, $(\partial Y/\partial X_1) P_Y = MVP_{X1}$ or VMP_{X1}

So, $MVP_{X1}/P_1 = 1$

Similarly, we can write: $MVP_{X2}/P_2 = 1$, $MVP_{X3}/P_3 = 1$ etc. Therefore,

$MVP_{X1}/P_1 = MVP_{X2}/P_2 = MVP_{X3}/P_3 = \ldots\ldots\ldots\ldots = MVP_{Xn}/P_n = 1$

The above equation is the profit maximizing criteria, when the farmer faces with limited variable factors that are to be applied to a given level of fixed factors, so as to achieve profit maximization.

As discussed in chapter 7, assume that the firm is aiming for profit maximization and thereby,

$\pi = TR - TC$

$\pi = P_Y.Y - C(Y)$

To maximize profits, take the first derivative of the above profit function with respect to Y and set this equal to zero. This will give the quantity (Y) that maximizes profits, assuming of course that the firm has already taken steps to minimize costs.

So, $(\partial\pi/\partial Y) = (\partial TR/\partial Y) - (\partial TC/\partial Y) = 0$

$= MR - MC = 0$

So, MR = MC

The above equality can be defined as the additional revenue gained by selling one additional unit of output should be equal to the extra cost incurred to produce an extra unit of output. The second order condition or the condition on the second derivative here is that, the second derivative of profit with respect to quantity of output must be less than zero *i.e.,* $\partial^2\pi/\partial Y^2 < 0$ for profit maximization.

8.6.1. Important Formulae

Before solving the numerical problems, the students must note the following important formulae:

☆ Profit function $\pi = P_Y.Y - (wL + rK)$

So, $\pi = P_Y.Y - wL - rK$

☆ Profit function = TR – TC

☆ Marginal profit = MR – MC

☆ Marginal profit is the first derivative of given profit function (π)

☆ Average profit = π/Y

☆ Marginal average profit is the derivative of average profit function.

Example 8.1

Imagine that, a firm has costs given by $TC(Y)=120 + 2Y^2$ and revenue given by $TR(Y)=100Y$, equivalent to saying that, the firm sells the product at a market price of Rs.100. The profit maximizing quantity is given by:

$\pi = TR-TC$

$= 100Y-(120+2Y^2) = 100Y-120-2Y^2$

To get the profit-maximizing output (quantity), take the first derivative of the profit function and set it equal to zero.

So, $d\pi/dY = 100-4Y=0$

So, Y=25units

Example 8.2

Imagine that, a firm has costs given by $TC(Y)=420 + 3Y + 4Y^2$ and revenue given by $TR(Y)=100Y - Y^2$. The profit maximizing quantity is given by:

$\pi = TR-TC$

$= 100Y - Y^2 - (420 + 3Y + 4Y^2) = 100Y - Y^2 - 420 - 3Y - 4Y^2 = 97Y - 5Y^2 - 420$

So, $d\pi/dY = 97 - 10Y = 0$

So, $Y = 9.7$ units

Example 8.3

Suppose that a business firm has estimated its profit (π) function (based on production and marketing studies) as follows: $\pi = 2Y - 0.1Y^2 - 3.6$, where π is profit (in thousands of rupees) and Y is units of output (in thousands of units). At what level of output, the firm can maximize the profits.

Answer

Considering the given profit function: $\pi = 2Y - 0.1Y^2 - 3.6$, substitute each level of output and compute the profit.

Output (Y)(000)	Profit (Rs'000)
0	–3.6
2	0.0
4	2.8
6	4.8
8	6.0
10	6.4
12	6.0
14	4.8
16	2.8
18	0.0
20	–3.6

The above table guide to draw the profit function and it all looks inverted U shaped curve as in Figure 8.17. Thus, a firm's profit function shows its maximal profits as a function of the output that the firm produces. The profit function shows the relationship between the firm's decision variable (output, Y) and its objective (profits) (π). That is why, we can call profit function as the Objective function. Profit is maximized at the quantity Y* (Figure 8.17) and is lower at all other quantities. The curvature of the profit function is consistent with a negative second derivative and results in Y* being a quantity of maximum profit.

From the Figure 8.17, it is clear that, the slope of the profit function is zero at its maximum point. So, the first derivative of the profit function with respect to output will be zero at output (Y*). But, the problem is, how do we know we have a maximum instead of a minimum? So, go for second derivative of profit function and it must be less than zero *i.e.* $(d^2\pi/dY^2) < 0$ to have profit maximum (See Example 8.4). From the profit function, we can also compute Marginal Profit, which is nothing but the slope of the tangent to the profit function. So, $(\Delta\pi/\Delta Y)$ gives the marginal profit. That is, marginal profit, $(\Delta\pi/\Delta Y)$ = Marginal revenue – Marginal cost.

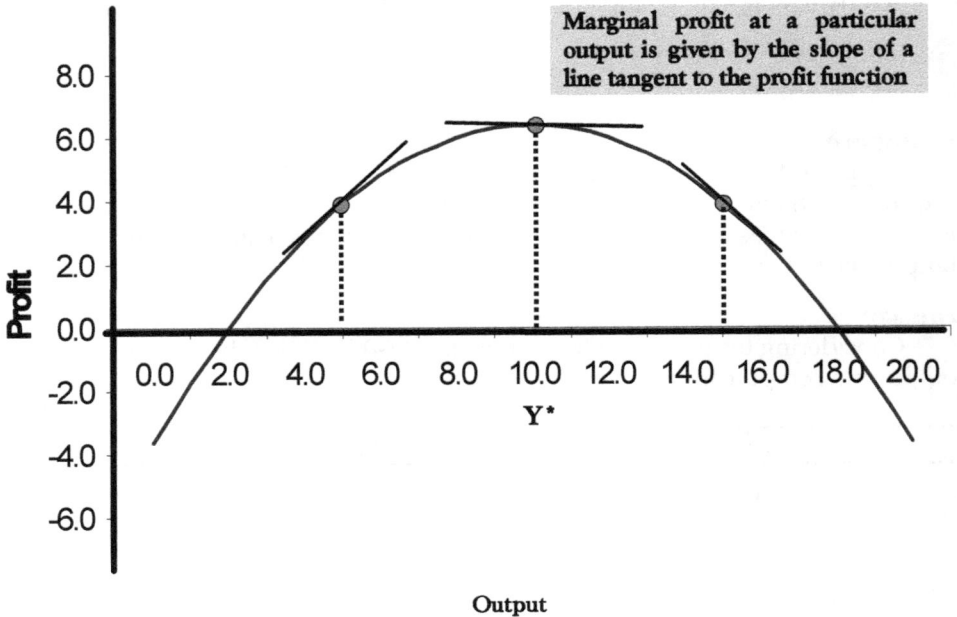

Marginal profit at a particular output is given by the slope of a line tangent to the profit function

Figure 8.17: Profit Function Curve.

Example 8.4

Given the cost function $TC(Y) = 500 + 3Y + 0.01Y^2$ and the demand function $P(Y) = 10$, find the number of units to be produced in order to have maximum profit.

Answer

We know, π = TR-TC. We also know, $TR = Y.P_Y$. So,

$$\pi = Y(10) - (500 + 3Y + 0.01Y^2)$$

$$= 7Y - 500 - 0.01Y^2$$

$$d\pi/dY = 7 - 0.02Y = 0$$

So, Y= 350. Thus, producing 350 units will lead to maximum profit. To prove this, let us apply Second Derivative Test: *i.e.* $d^2\pi/dY^2 = (-0.02)$. Since, second derivative $d^2\pi/dY^2$ is negative *i.e.*, (-0.02) the above calculated 350 units of output will contribute to maximum profits.

Example 8.5

A firm determines that the demand function for the product is: $P = 1000/\sqrt{Y}$, where Y is the number of units of product demanded at a given price, P. The cost of producing Y product is given by the following cost function: $TC(Y) = 10Y + 100\sqrt{Y} + 10000$. Determine the MC, MR and marginal profit $(M\pi)$ at Y = 100 units of product.

Answer

MC is given by:

$\Delta C/\Delta$ = $10+0.5*100Y^{-0.5}$

= $10+(50/\sqrt{Y})$

Given Y = 100. So,

MC = $10+(50/\sqrt{100})$=Rs. 15

That means, to produce one extra unit of product, it costs Rs. 15 for the firm. That is, the cost of 101st unit of product is Rs. 15.

To compute MR, first workout TR as given below.

TR = P_Y*Y

= $(1000/\sqrt{Y})*Y$

= $(1000/\sqrt{Y})(\sqrt{Y}/\sqrt{Y})*Y = 1000\sqrt{Y}$

So, MR = $dTR/dY=0.5*1000Y^{-0.5}$

= $500/\sqrt{Y}$

Given Y = 100. So,

MR = $500/\sqrt{100}$=Rs.50

Thus, the MR from selling the extra unit (101st) of the product is Rs.50

So, Marginal Profit is given by: MR-MC = 50-15 =Rs.35.

We can also calculate the marginal profit as the first derivative of the profit function. That is,

Profit π = TR-TC

= $(1000\sqrt{Y}) - (10Y+100\sqrt{Y}+10000)$

= $1000\sqrt{Y} - 10Y-100\sqrt{Y}-10000$

= $900\sqrt{Y}-10Y-10000$

So, marginal profit (the first derivative of the profit function) is given by

$d\pi/dY$ = $0.5*900Y^{-0.5}-10$

= $(450/\sqrt{Y})-10$

Given Y = 100. So,

= $(450/\sqrt{100})-10 = Rs.35.$

Thus, by selling an extra unit (101st) of product, the firm gets a profit of Rs.35.

Example 8.6

For the given profit function: $\pi = 2Y-0.1Y^2-3.6$, compute marginal profit function and the output level at which the firm maximizes profits.

Answer

To obtain the marginal profit function, we take the first derivative of profit (π) function with respect to output (Y):

$M\pi = d\pi/dY = 2 - 0.2Y$

To solve for the output level that maximizes profits, set $M\pi = 0$.

So, $2 - 0.2Y = 0$ Thus, $Y = 10$ units.

Example 8.7

Suppose you have a demand function $P=80-0.01Y$ and a cost function $C(Y)=25Y+5000$, where Y is the number of units demanded.

    a. Find the profit function.

    b. Find and interpret the marginal profit at 2000 units.

Solution

    a. In the given problem, we have cost function. To derive profit function, we have to work out for revenue function. So,

$$TR = Y.P_Y = Y(80-0.01Y) = 80Y-0.01Y^2$$

Now, Profit function = Revenue function − Cost function

$$= (80Y-0.01Y^2) - (25Y+5000)$$

$$= -0.01Y^2 + 55Y - 5000.$$

Considering the above profit function, now assume data for Y as discussed under Example 8.3 and compute the profit function at each level of Y and the profit function assume the same shape as given in Figure 8.17.

    b. To compute marginal profit at 2000 units of output, we need to take the derivative of the profit function $(-0.01Y^2 + 55Y - 5000)$. So,

Marginal profit $= -0.02Y+55$.

Now, substituting Y $= 2000$, we get

Marginal profit $= -0.02Y+55 = -0.02(2000)+55 = $ Rs. 15

Thus, marginal profit is simply the instantaneous rate of change of the profit. It can also be derived as the slope of a tangent line to the profit function at Y=2000. The marginal profit of Rs. 15 implies that, by increasing the production from 2000 units to 2001 units, it will lead to an increase in profit by Rs. 15.

Example 8.8

Assume the following profit function for producing and selling Y units:

$$\pi(Y) = -0.05Y^2 + 150Y - 1500$$

    a. Find the exact change in profit, if the production level increases from 100 to 101 units.

    b. Use the marginal profit function to approximate the change in profit, if Y increases from 100 to 101 units.

Solution

    a. The exact change in profit is calculated by substituting Y=100 units and Y=101 units.

$$\pi = -0.05Y^2 + 150Y - 1500 = -0.05(100)^2 + 150(100) - 1500 = \text{Rs. } 13000$$

$$\pi = -0.05Y^2 + 150Y - 1500 = -0.05(101)^2 + 150(101) - 1500 = \text{Rs. } 13140$$

Thus, by increasing the output from 100 to 101 units, profit increases by Rs. 140

b. Compute marginal profit function: $d\pi/dY = -0.1Y + 150$

Now, substituting Y $= 100$, we get

Marginal profit $= -0.1*100+150 = $ Rs. 140

Thus, marginal profit of Rs. 140 implies that, by increasing the production from 100 units to 101 units, it will lead to an increase in profit by Rs. 140.

Example 8.9

Assume the following profit function for producing and selling Y units:

$\pi(Y) = -0.02Y^2 + 20Y - 320$

a. Find the average profit per unit, if 40 units are produced.

b. Find the marginal average profit at production level 40 units.

Solution

a. Average profit per unit when 40 units are produced = $[-0.02(40)^2 + 20(40) - 320]/40 = $ Rs. 11.2

b. Marginal average profit at production level 40 units: To get this, first find the average profit function, then take its derivative and then substitute Y=40. That is,

(π/Y) $= [-0.02Y^2 + 20Y - 320]/Y = -0.02Y+20-320Y^{-1}$

$d(\pi/Y)/dY$ $= -0.02+320Y^{-2}$

Plug in Y = 40 in the above marginal average profit equation to get, $[-0.02+320Y^{-2}] = -0.02+320*(1/(40)^2) = 0.18$. This implies that, the average profit per unit will increase by approximately Rs. 0.18 per additional unit, when 40 units are produced.

Example 8.10

Compute the profit function for the given short run production function Y = f(K, L) = $\sqrt{K}\sqrt{L}$. Assume, K is a fixed input.

Solution

Given Y $= \sqrt{K}\sqrt{L} = K^{\frac{1}{2}}L^{\frac{1}{2}}$

We know, Profit function π $= P.Y-(wL+rK)$ (where, P = Price per unit of output)

$= PY - wL - rK$

Now, substituting Y $= K^{\frac{1}{2}}L^{\frac{1}{2}}$,

π $= P K^{\frac{1}{2}}L^{\frac{1}{2}} - wL - rK$

The first order condition is

$\partial\pi/\partial L$ $= 0$

So, $\partial\pi/\partial L$ $= PK^{\frac{1}{2}}0.5L^{-0.5} - w = 0$

$P K^{\frac{1}{2}}0.5L^{-0.5}$ $= w$

$L^{-0.5}$ $= w/(PK^{\frac{1}{2}}0.5) = 2w/PK^{\frac{1}{2}}$

$1/L^{0.5}$ $\qquad = 2w/PK^{\frac{1}{2}}$

Now, squaring on both the sides

$1/L$ $\qquad = 4w^2/P^2K$

$\qquad L = P^2K/4w^2$

Now, substitute L calculated above, in the given production function:

$Y = K^{\frac{1}{2}}L^{\frac{1}{2}} = K^{\frac{1}{2}}(P^2K/4w^2)^{\frac{1}{2}} = KP/2w$

Now, it is easy to write the profit function:

$\pi = PY - (wL + rK)$

$\quad = P(KP/2w) - [\{w(P^2K/4w^2)\} + (rK)]$

$\quad = P(KP/2w) - w(P^2K/4w^2) - (rK)$

The above equation represents the profit function. The same profit function can also be derived in a different way *i.e.*, SRMC = MR = P (assuming perfect market competition).

From the given production function $Y = K^{\frac{1}{2}}L^{\frac{1}{2}}$, compute 'L' *i.e.*,

$Y^2 = KL$

$L = Y^2/K$

We know, SRTC $\quad = wL + rK$

$\qquad = w(Y^2/K) + rK$

From the above SRTC equation, compute SRMC,

$SRMC = \partial SRTC/\partial Y = 2wY/K$

So, the point of profit maximization or function is given by,

SRMC $\quad = MR = P$

$(2wY/K) \quad = P$

To prove this is the point of profit maximization, let us work out SRAVC. We know in this production function, the only variable input is 'L' *and hence, SRAVC* is given by:

SRTVC = wL + rK. Since, K is a fixed input, SRTVC = wL. But, L =Y^2/K, as calculated above. So,

SRTVC $\quad = w(Y^2/K)$

So, SRAVC $\quad = SRTVC/Y = w(Y^2/K)/Y$

SRAVC $\quad = wY/K$

So, the minimum of SRAVC occurs, when Y = 0. So, the firm need not worry about shutting down the business.

Example 8.11

Assume that a firm produces a processed product with TFC=Rs. 22000, SRAVC=Rs.9/unit and price of each product is Rs. 20. Compute the break even output and indicate, whether the firm makes a profit, if it produces more than 2000 units of output?

Solution

Given cost function: C(Y)	= 22000+9Y
Given revenue function: R(Y)	= 20Y
So, at BEP, R(Y)	= C(Y)
20Y	= 22000+9Y
Y	= 2000.

Since, the BEP is 2000 units of output, the firm can make profits, if it produces more than 2000 units of output.

Example 8.12

Suppose, a firm faces a demand curve for its product $P = a - bY$, and the firm's costs of production and marketing are $C(Y) = cY + d$, where P is price, Y is quantity, and a, b, c, and d are positive constants. Find the following:

a. The formula for profit π in terms of Y.

b. The first order condition for maximum profit.

c. The second order condition for maximum profit.

Solution

a. We know, π = TR - TC

     TR $= P.Y = aY - bY^2$ (where, P = Price per unit of output)

     TC $= C(Y) = cY - d$

     So, π $= TR-TC = aY - bY^2 - (cY+d) = -bY^2 + (a-c)Y - d$

b. First order condition for maximum profit: $d\pi/dY = -2bY + (a-c) = 0$. Thus, $Y = (a-c)/2b$.

c. Second order condition for maximum profit: $d^2\pi/dY^2 = -2b < 0$. So, profit at $Y = (a-c)/2b$ is maximum.

Example 8.13

Suppose, the firm faces a demand curve for its product $P = 32 - 2Y$, and the firm's costs of production and marketing are $C(Y) = 2Y^2$. Find the following:

a. The formula for profit π in terms of Y.

b. The first order and second order conditions for maximum total revenue.

c. The price and quantity that maximize total revenue, and the corresponding value of total revenue.

d. The first order and second order conditions for maximum profit.

e. The price and quantity that maximize profit and the corresponding value of profit.

f. What would the competitive price and quantity be, assuming $C(Y) = 2Y^2$ represented the industry cost function?

Solution

a. $\pi = TR - TC = P.Y - C(Y) = 32Y - 2Y^2 - 2Y^2$

   $\pi = 32Y - 4Y^2$

b. Given $P = 32 - 2Y$. So, $TR = 32Y - 2Y^2$

   First order conditions for maximum total revenue: $d[TR]/dY = 32 - 4Y = 0$

   So, $Y = 8$ units.

   Thus, TR is maximum, when the output level is 8 units.

   Second order condition for maximum total revenue : $d^2[TR]/dY^2 = -4 < 0$.
   Thus, TR at $Y = 8$ is maximum.

c. The output quantity that maximizes TR is $Y = 8$, as proved above with reference to first and second-order conditions of TR. So, the price that maximizes TR is: $P = 32 - 2Y = 32 - 2*8 = Rs. 16$. So, TR at this level = P.Y = $16*8 = Rs. 128$. From TC function: $C(Y) = 2Y^2$, we can compute SRAVC as $SRTC/Y = 2Y^2/Y = 2Y = 2*8 = Rs.16$. Thus, price = SRAVC, the firm can continue the production programme.

d. First order condition for maximum profits: $d\pi/dY = 0$

   We know, $\pi = TR - TC = 32Y - 2Y^2 - 2Y^2 = 32Y - 4Y^2$

   So, $d\pi/dY = 32 - 8Y = 0$. Thus, $Y = 4$ units.

   Second order condition for maximum profits $(d^2\pi/dY^2) = -8 < 0$. Thus, profits at $Y = 4$ is maximum.

e. The quantity that maximizes profit is $Y = 4$, as per the above first and second-order conditions. So, the price that maximizes profit is: $P = 32 - 2Y$ $= 32 - 2(4) = Rs. 24$. So,

   Total profit at this level is: $\pi = TR - TC = 32Y - 2Y^2 - 2Y^2 = 32Y - 4Y^2$

   $= 32*4 - 4(4)^2 = Rs. 64$.

f. In perfect competition, the point of optimality is MR = P = SRMC. Given $P = 32 - 2Y$. TC $= 2Y^2$, so SRMC $= 4Y$. Thus, at the point of optimality, P = SRMC *i.e.,*

   $32 - 2Y = 4Y$.

   So, Y $= 5.33$ units.

   Similarly, competitive price at the point of optimality: $P = 32 - 2Y = 32 - 2(5.33) = Rs. 21.34$

Example 8.14

Given relationship between profit and output is: $\pi = 1,000Y - 5Y^2$. Compute the first order condition for a profit maximum. Also prove, whether that output level will lead to maximum profits.

Solution

Given profit function as, $\pi = 1,000Y - 5Y^2$

So, first order condition for profit maximum = $d\pi/dY = 0$ *i.e.,* $1,000 - 10Y = 0$

So, $Y^* = 100$

Since, second derivative $d^2\pi/dY^2$ is negative *i.e.* (-10) the above calculated $Y^* =$ 100 units of output will contribute to maximum profits.

Example 8.15

The weekly profit function for a product is given by $\pi = -0.0001 X^2 + 3X - 12,500$, where X is the number of units produced per week, and π is the profit (in Rupees). What is the maximum weekly profit? How many units should be produced for this profit?

Solution

The profit function is a quadratic function $[f(X) = aX^2 + bX + c]$ which has a maximum value. Let X is the number of units needed to maximize the weekly profit, and K is the maximum weekly profit.

X $= -(b/2a) = -(3/2*-0.0001) = 15000$ units

So, K $= 0.0001 (15000)^2 + 3(15000) - 12,500 = $ Rs. 10000

So, the firm maximize the weekly profit by producing 15,000 units and the maximum weekly profit is Rs. 10,000.

Example 8.16

A perfectly competitive firm has TR and TC curves given by:

TR = 100Y

TC = 5000 + 2Y + 0.2Y²

a. Find the profit-maximizing output for this firm.

b. What profit does the firm make?

Solution

a. The profit function is given by

π = TR – TC = 100Y – (5000 + 2Y + 0.2Y²)

= 100Y – 5000 - 2Y - 0.2Y²

= 98Y – 5000 - 0.2Y²

We get the profit maximizing output by making $\partial\pi/\partial Y = 0$

So, we differentiate to get:

$\partial\pi/\partial Y$ = 98-0.4Y = 0

So, Y = 245 units.

b. So, the maximum profit is: π = TR – TC = 100Y – (5000 + 2Y + 0.2Y²)

= 100(245) – (5000 + 2(245) + 0.2(245)²)

= Rs.7005

Since, the profit maximizing function is in quadratic form (*i.e.,* 98Y – 5000 - 0.2Y²), we get the profit function as shown through Figure 8.17.

Example 8.17

Suppose that, the SRAVC of the firm is given by SRAVC(Y) = 3 + Y. The firm's TFC are known to be Rs.3. Will the firm be earning a positive, negative, or zero profit in the short run, if it produces 3 units of output? Assume price of output is Rs.9/unit.

Solution

We know, π = TR-TC, SRTC = SRTVC+TFC, SRTVC = SRAVC * Y

SRTVC   = (3+Y)*Y = (3+3)*3 = Rs. 18

SRTC   = SRTVC+TFC = 18+3 = Rs. 21

TR   = Y.P_Y = 3*9=Rs. 27

So, π = TR-TC = 27-21 = Rs.6

Therefore, the firm earns positive economic profits.

8.6.2. Properties of the Profit Function

They include:

⭐ *Homogeneity:* The profit function is homogeneous of degree one in all prices. With pure inflation, a firm will not change its production plans and its level of profits will keep up with that inflation. Further, when there is no change in relative prices of factors and output, there will be no change in optimal solution. So, profits changes by same proportion.

⭐ *Profits are non-decreasing in output price:* This implies that, if output price rises, profits won't fall. A firm could always respond to a rise in the price of its output by not changing its input or output plans.

⭐ *Profits are non-increasing in input prices:* If the firm responded to an increase in an input price by not changing the level of that input, its costs would rise thereby, profits would fall. That is, if input prices rise, profits won't rise.

This property can be proved by Envelope theorem. Thus, we can apply the envelope theorem to see, how profits respond to changes in output and input prices. This is given by:

$\partial\pi(P_Y,r,w)/\partial P_Y = Y(P_Y,r,w)$

$\partial\pi(P_Y,r,w)/\partial r = -K(P_Y,r,w)$

$\partial\pi(P_Y,r,w)/\partial w = -L(P_Y,r,w)$

⭐ *Convex in output prices:* This implies, the profits obtainable by averaging those from two different product prices will be at least as large as those obtainable from the average of the two prices. This is given by:

$$\frac{\Pi(p_1,r,w)+\Pi(p_2,r,w)}{2} \geq \Pi\left[\frac{p_1+p_2}{2},r,w\right]$$

where, P_1 is the price of Product 1, P_2 is the price of Product 2, 'r' is the rental cost of capital and 'w' is the wage rate of labour.

As shown through Figure 8.18, profit function is a convex upward sloping function and this demonstrates that, the expected profit is higher when there is uncertainty about the output price rather than when the output price is certain. The important implication of this is that, a firm would have higher expected profits facing a low output price with probability of 0.5 and a high output price with probability of 0.5 than it would if it faced the

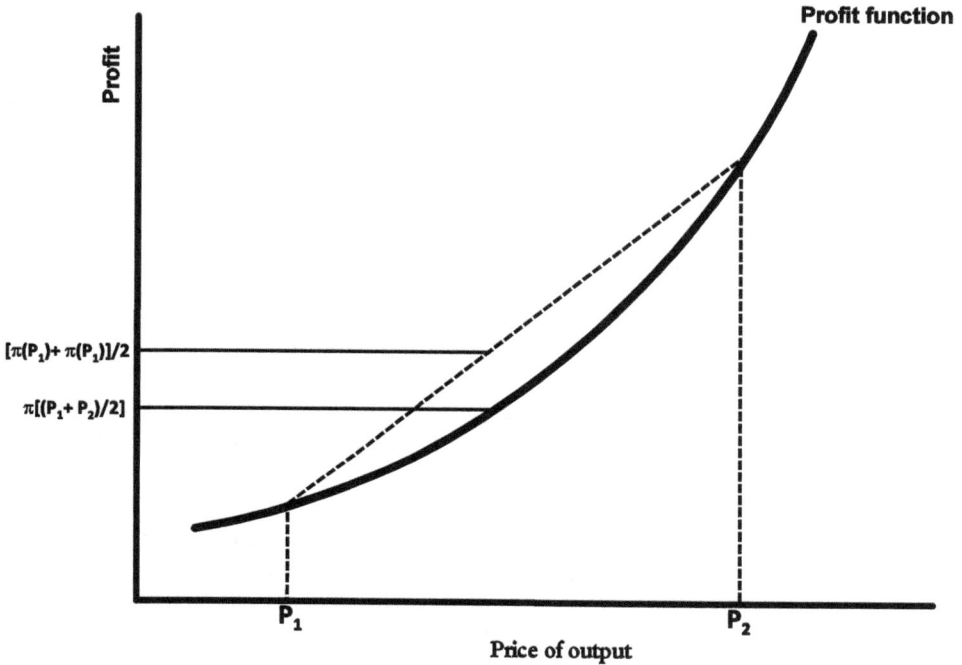

Figure 8.18: An Upward Sloping Profit Function of a Firm.

average of these two output prices with certainty. This is because, they can take advantage of high output prices by producing more and can mitigate the effects of low output prices by producing less. Note that, by recovering production function from profit function, we generate concave shaped production function.

☆ A firm's output is determined by the amount of inputs it chooses to employ and hence, profit also depends indirectly on the use of inputs.

☆ A firm's economic profit can also be expressed as a function of inputs

$$\pi(K,L) = PY - C(Y) = P\,f(K,L) - (rK + wL)$$

☆ The first-order conditions for profit maximum are:

❖ $\partial \pi / \partial K = P[\partial f / \partial K] - v = 0$

❖ $\partial \pi / \partial L = P[\partial f / \partial L] - w = 0$

☆ The second order conditions that must necessarily hold for the result to verify for profit maximization rather than minimization:

❖ $\partial^2 \pi / \partial K^2 < 0$

❖ $\partial^2 \pi / \partial L^2 < 0$

❖ $(\partial^2 \pi / \partial K^2)(\partial^2 \pi / \partial L^2) - (\partial^2 \pi / \partial K.\partial L) > 0$

☆ A profit-maximizing firm should hire any input up to the point at which its marginal contribution to revenues is equal to the marginal cost of hiring the input.

★ The derivative of the profit function with respect to factor prices gives the factor demand function. That is,

$(\partial\pi/\partial w) = -L^*(w,r,P_Y)$ and

$(\partial\pi/\partial r) = -K^*(w,r,P_Y)$

★ The derivative of the profit function with respect to output price gives the firm's supply function. This is known as Hotelling's Lemma:

$\partial\pi(w,r,P_Y)/\partial P_Y = Y^*(w,r,P_Y)$

★ *RTS and Profits function:* This relationship is given below:

❖ If a competitive firm's technology exhibits diminishing RTS, then the firm has a single long-run profit-maximizing production plan (Panel A of Figure 8.18.1).

❖ If a competitive firm's technology exhibits increasing RTS, then the firm does not have a profit-maximizing plan (Panel A of Figure 8.18.1). So, an increasing RTS technology is inconsistent with firms being perfectly competitive.

❖ If the competitive firm's technology exhibits constant RTS, then that competitive firms earn economic profits of zero (Panel C of Figure 8.18.1). That is, if the firm possesses constant RTS technology, then doubling of inputs use doubles output and doubles cost so the only possible solution is zero economic profits and there is an infinite number of input bundles that are optimal. The firm is indifferent between them, since they give

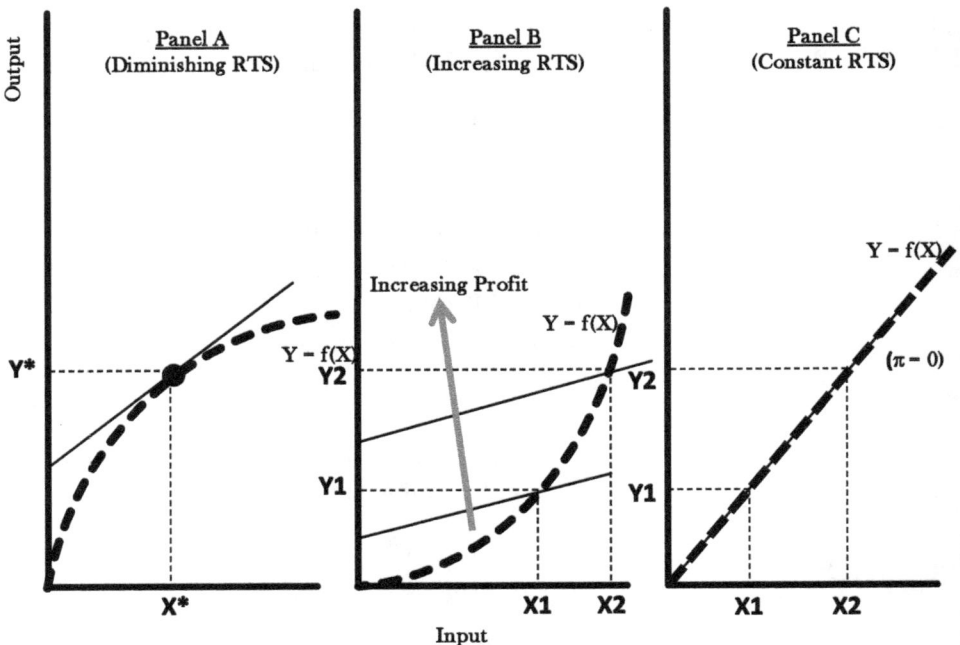

Figure 8.18.1: RTS and Profit Function of a Firm.

zero economic profits and hence, the supply function is perfectly elastic. So, when firms have constant RTS technology, the solution to profit maximization problem is not unique.

8.7. Economic Profit in Short and Long Run Production Programmes

i. Short Run Production Programme

Assume that, a firm uses inputs $j = 1, 2..., m$ to make products $i = 1,2,...n$. The output levels are $Y_1, Y_2...,Y_n$. Input levels are $X_1, X_2,...,X_m$. Product prices are $P_1, P_2...,P_n$. Input prices are $w_1, w_2...,w_m$. Also assume that, the firm is operating under perfect competition so that, all output prices and all input prices as given constants. The economic profit generated by the firm is given by:

$$\pi = P_1Y_1 + P_2Y_2 + ----- +P_nY_n - w_1X_1 - w_2X_2 ----- w_mX_m$$

Assume that, the firm's stream of periodic economic profits is $P_0, P_1, P_2, ...$ and r is the rate of interest. So, the present-value of the firm's economic profit stream is given by:

$$PV = \pi_0 + (\pi_1/(1+r)^1) + (\pi_2/(1+r)^2) + ...$$

We know, the competitive firm seeks to maximize its present value. In the short run production programme, suppose the firm is employing two inputs X_1 and X_2 and assume X_2 is a fixed input. So, the production function is represented as:

$$Y = f(X_1/X_2)$$

So, the firm's fixed cost is: $TFC = w_2*X_2$ and thereby, short run profit function is given by:

$$\pi = P_Y.Y - w_1X_1 - w_2X_2$$

An iso-profit line contains all the production plans that provide a profit level π. So, the above equation represents an iso-profit line. From the above equation, profit maximizing output (Y) can be worked out as follows:

$$P_Y.Y = \pi + w_1X_1 + w_2X_2$$
$$Y = (\pi + w_1X_1 + w_2X_2)/P_Y = ((w_1/P_Y)*X_1) + ((\pi + w_2X_2)/P_Y)$$

So, the above function is with a slope w_1/P_Y and a vertical intercept of $((\pi + w_2X_2)/P_Y)$. The same is shown below (Figure 8.19)

After drawing a number of iso-profit lines, now the firm has to locate the production plan that attains the highest possible iso-profit line, given the firm's constraint on choices of production plans. This is given by the firm's production function *i.e.,* $Y = f(X_1/X_2)$. So, now draw the production function line in the Figure 8.19 and locate the profit maximizing level of input X1 and output Y. The same is shown through Figure 8.20. So, given P_Y, X_1, w_1 and X_2, the short-run profit-maximizing plan is given in terms of X_1^*, X_2 (fixed input) and Y^* and the maximum possible profit is $\pi2$.

Thus, the above discussion (Figure 8.20) infers that, in the short-run profit-maximizing plan, the slopes of the short-run production function and the maximal

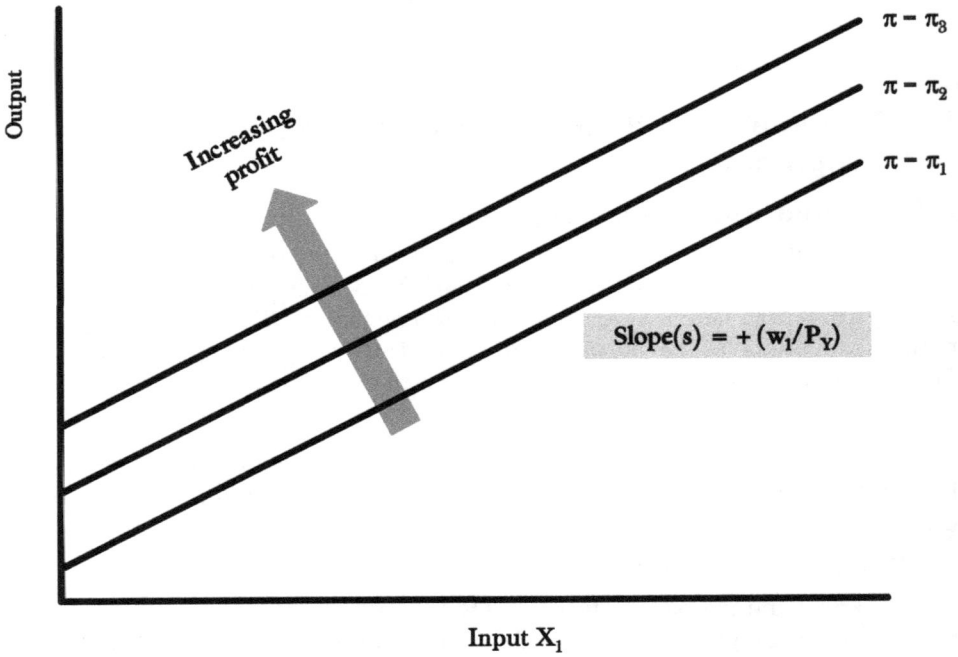

Figure 8.19: Short-Run Iso-Profit Lines.

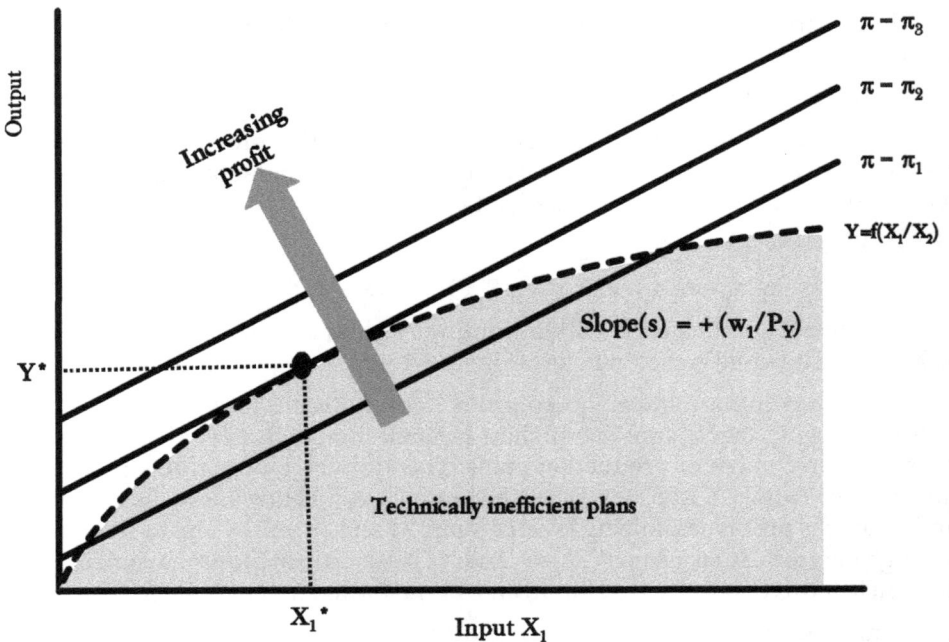

Figure 8.20: Short-Run Iso-Profit Lines.

iso-profit line are equal. We know, slope MPP_{X1} (slope of production function, $Y = f(X_1/X_2)) = w_1/P_Y$ at X_1^*, X_2 (fixed input) and Y^*. So, we can write: $MPP_{X1} * P_Y = w_1$ or VMP (or MVP)= w_1. This VMP implies, the rate at which revenue increases with the amount of input X_1 used. We can write the above equation ($MPP_{X1} * P_Y = w_1$) as ($MPP_{X1} * P_Y$) - $w_1 = 0$. So, profits will increase as X_1 increases so long as ($MPP_{X1} * P_Y$) - $w_1 > 0$ and profits will be maximum at ($MPP_{X1} * P_Y$) - $w_1 = 0$. That is, if VMP (or MVP) > w_1, then profit increases with increased application of X_1 input. Conversely, if VMP (or MVP) < w_1, then profit decreases with increased application of X_1 input.

Example for Short-Run Profit-Maximization

Assume a short-run production function: $Y = X_1^{1/3} X_2^{1/3}$ (*where,* X_2 is a fixed input). From this production function,

$$MPP_{X1} = \partial Y/\partial X_1 = (1/3) X_1^{-2/3} X_2^{1/3}$$

We know the profit-maximizing condition is: $MPP_{X1} = w_1/P_Y$ or $MPP_{X1} * P_Y = w_1$

So, VMP (= MVP or MRP, as under perfect market competition, MR=Price) = w_1

So, $(1/3) (X_1^*)^{-2/3} X_2^{1/3} * P_Y = w_1$

$(X_1^*)^{-2/3} = w_1/(1/3(X_2^{1/3})(P_Y)) = 3w_1/((X_2^{1/3})(P_Y))$

The above equation can also be written as:

$(X_1^*)^{2/3} = ((X_2^{1/3})(P_Y))/3w_1$

So, $(X_1^*) = \{((X_2^{1/3})(P_Y))/3w_1\}^{3/2} = \{(P_Y)/3w_1\}^{3/2} . X_2^{1/2}$ *Equation 8.1*

The above equation for (X_1^*) implies the firm's short-run demand for input X_1, when the level of input X_2 is kept fixed in the production programme. Now, substitute the above equation of (X_1^*) in the given production function: $Y = X_1^{1/3} X_2^{1/3}$, to get the firm's short run output level:

$Y^* = (X_1^*)^{1/3} X_2^{1/3} = [\{(P_Y)/3w_1\}^{3/2} . X_2^{1/2}]^{1/3} X_2^{1/3}$

$Y^* = \{(P_Y)/3w_1\}^{1/2} . X_2^{1/2}$ *Equation 8.2*

So, short-run profit function is given by:

$\pi = P_Y.Y^* - w_1 X_1^* - w_2 X_2$ *Equation 8.3*

ii. Long Run Production Programme

Now assume a long-run production function, where the firm can vary both the input levels. Since no input level is fixed, there are no fixed costs. Since, both X_1 and X_2 are variable, think of the firm as choosing the production plan that maximizes profits for a given value of X_2, and then varying X_2 to find the largest possible profit level. The equation of a long-run iso-profit line is:

$\pi = P_Y.Y - w_1 X_1 - w_2 X_2$

$P_Y.Y = \pi + w_1 X_1 + w_2 X_2$

$Y = (\pi + w_1 X_1 + w_2 X_2)/P_Y = ((w_1/P_Y)*X_1) + ((\pi + w_2 X_2)/P_Y)$

So, the above function is with a slope w_1/P_Y and a vertical intercept of $((\pi + w_2 X_2)/P_Y)$. Hence, an increase in X_2 causes no change to the slope, but causes an increase in the vertical intercept. The same is shown through Figure 8.21.

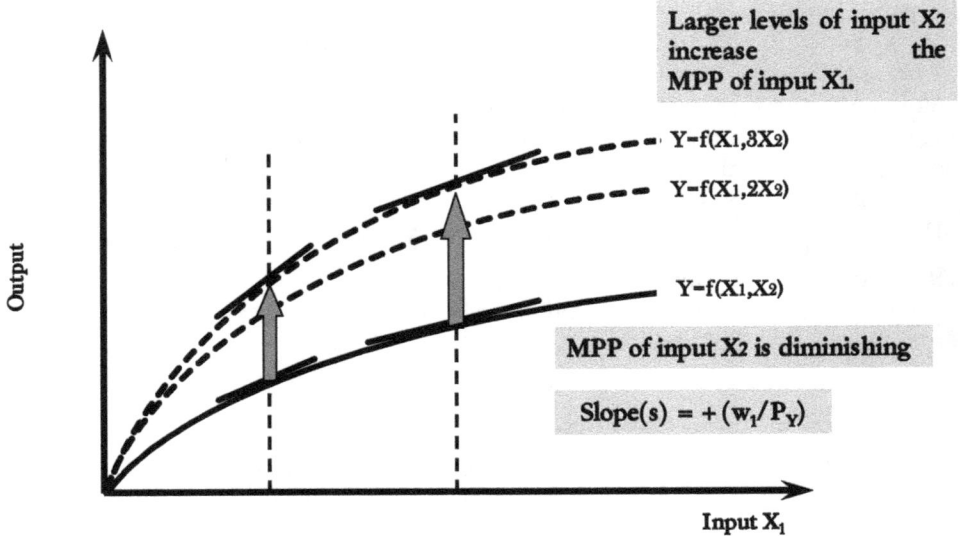

Figure 8.21: Long-Run Profit-Maximization of a Firm.

In the long-run profit-maximizing plan, the slopes of the long-run production function and the iso-profit line are equal (Figure 8.22). It is evident that, as the MPP of input X_2 is diminishing, the marginal profit of input X_2 also diminishes. This decline in marginal profit is indicated by the declining space between iso-profit lines as we move away from the origin. It is also evident that, profit will increase as X_2 increases, so long as the marginal profit of input X2 (*i.e.,* slope of iso-profit line) is equal to the slope of the long-run production function. That is, $MPP_{x2} = w_2/P_Y$ at X_1^*, each level of X_2 and Y^*. So, we can write: $MPP_{x2} * P_Y = w_2$ or VMP (or MVP)= w_2. This VMP implies, the rate at which revenue increases with the amount used of input X_2. If VMP (or MVP) > w_2, then profit increases with increased application of X_2 input. Conversely, if VMP (or MVP) < w_2, then profit decreases with increased application of X_2 input. We can write the above equation $(MPP_{x2} * P_Y = w_2)$ as $(MPP_{x2} * P_Y) - w_2 = 0$. So, profits will increase as X_2 increases so long as $(MPP_{x2} * P_Y) - w_2 > 0$ and profits will be maximum at $(MPP_{x2} * P_Y) - w_2 = 0$.

We also proved earlier in short run production programme, profits will increase as X_1 increases so long as $(MPP_{x1} * P_Y) - w_1 > 0$ and profit maximization will occur at $(MPP_{x1} * P_Y) - w_1 = 0$. So, the input levels of the long-run profit-maximizing plan must satisfy

☆ $(MPP_{x1} * P_Y) - w_1 = 0$

☆ $(MPP_{x2} * P_Y) - w_2 = 0$

That is, when VMP equals MFC (= Price) for all inputs, it is the point of profit maximization in the long run.

Example for Long-Run Profit-Maximization

In the earlier discussed short-run production function: $Y = X_1^{1/3} X_2^{1/3}$ (*where,* X_2 is a fixed input). As proved earlier,

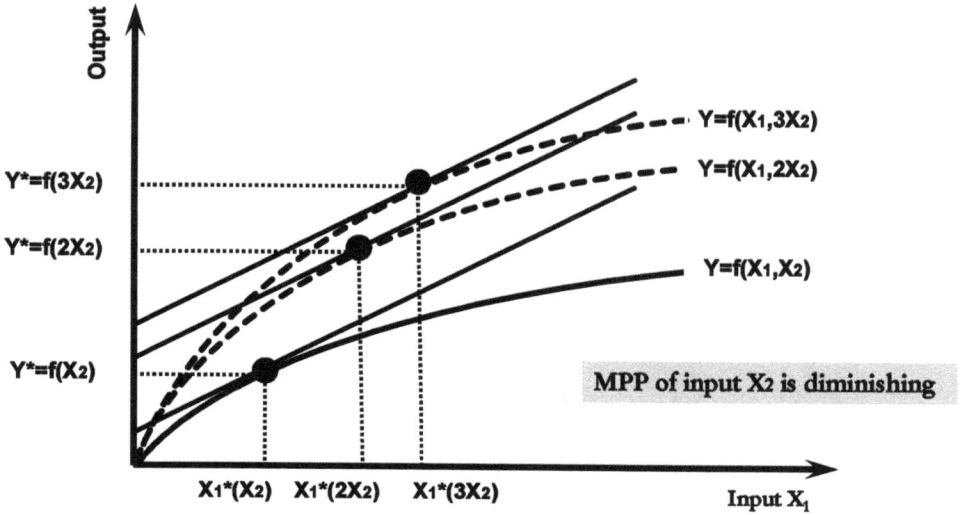

Figure 8.22: Long-Run Profit-Maximization of a Firm.

$(X_1^*) = \{(P_Y)/3w_1\}^{3/2}. X_2^{1/2}$ *As per the Equation 8.1*

$Y^* = \{(P_Y)/3w_1\}^{1/2}. X_2^{1/2}$ *As per the Equation 8.2*

$\pi = P_Y.Y^* - w_1X_1^* - w_2X_2$ *As per the Equation 8.3 (Short-run profit function)*

So, $\pi = [P_Y. [\{(P_Y)/3w_1\}^{1/2}]. X_2^{1/2}] - [w_1\{(P_Y)/3w_1\}^{3/2}. X_2^{1/2}] - w_2X_2$

$\pi = [P_Y. [\{(P_Y)/3w_1\}^{1/2}]. X_2^{1/2}] - [(w_1(P_Y)/3w_1). ((P_Y)/3w_1)^{1/2} X_2^{1/2}] - w_2X_2$

Now, taking $((P_Y)/3w_1)^{1/2}$ as common from the first two terms in the above equation,

$\pi = ((P_Y)/3w_1)^{1/2} [P_Y. X_2^{1/2}] - [((P_Y)/3).X_2^{1/2}] - w_2X_2$

$\pi = ((P_Y)/3w_1)^{1/2} [P_Y(X_2^{1/2} - (X_2^{1/2}/3))] - w_2X_2$

$\pi = ((P_Y)/3w_1)^{1/2} [P_Y(2X_2^{1/2})/3] - w_2X_2$

$\pi = ((P_Y)/3w_1)^{1/2} [(2P_Y/3)X_2^{1/2}] - w_2X_2$

Re-writing the above equation as:

$\pi = (2P_Y/3)((P_Y)/3w_1)^{1/2} (X_2^{1/2}) - w_2X_2$

In the above equation, squaring both numerator and denominator of $(2P_Y/3)$, we get,

$\pi = (4P_Y^2/9)((P_Y)/3w_1)^{1/2} (X_2^{1/2}) - w_2X_2$

$\pi = (4P_Y^3/27w_1)^{1/2}(X_2^{1/2}) - w_2X_2$

To get long run profit maximizing level of input X_2, solve for

$(\partial\pi/\partial X_2) = 0$

So, $(\partial\pi/\partial X_2) = [(4P_Y^3)/27w_1]^{1/2}. (\frac{1}{2})(X_2^{-1/2}) - w_2 = 0$

Re-writing the above equation as

$(½)[(4P_Y^3)/27w_1]^{1/2} \cdot (X_2^{-1/2}) - w_2 = 0$

$(½)[(2*2.P_Y^3)/(3*9)w_1]^{1/2} \cdot (X_2^{-1/2}) - w_2 = 0$

$(½)[(P_Y^3)/(3w_1))^{1/2}]*(2/3).(X_2^{-1/2}) - w_2 = 0$

$(1/3)[(P_Y^3)/(3w_1)]^{1/2}.(X_2^{-1/2}) - w_2 = 0$

$(1/3)[(P_Y^3)/(3w_1)]^{1/2}.(X_2^{-1/2}) = w_2$

$(X_2^{-1/2}) = w_2/(1/3)[(P_Y^3)/(3w_1)]^{1/2}$

$(1/X_2^{1/2}) = w_2/(1/3)[(P_Y^3)/(3w_1)]^{1/2}$

Squaring on both sides of the above equation, we get

$(1/X_2) = w_2^2/(1/9)[(P_Y^3)/(3w_1)]$

$(1/X_2) = w_2^2/[(P_Y^3)/(27w_1)] = 27w_1w_2^2/(P_Y^3)$

$X_2 = (P_Y^3)/(27w_1w_2^2)$

So, the long run profit maximizing level of input X_2 is given by,

$X_2 = X_2^* = (P_Y^3)/(27w_1w_2^2)$ *Equation 8.4*

Now, let us compute the long-run profit-maximizing input X_1 level. Substitute the value of X_2^* in the Equation 8.1. Let us re-write the Equation 8.1 below.

$(X_1^*) = \{(P_Y)/3w_1\}^{3/2} \cdot X_2^{1/2}$ *Equation 8.1*

So, $(X_1^*) = \{(P_Y)/3w_1\}^{3/2} \cdot [(P_Y^3)/(27w_1w_2^2)]^{1/2}$

$(X_1^*) = \{(P_Y)/3w_1\}^{3/2} \cdot (P_Y^2.P_Y)/(9*3w_1w_2^2)^{1/2}$

$(X_1^*) = \{(P_Y)/3w_1\}^{3/2} \cdot (P_Y)/(3w_1)^{1/2}(P_Y/3w_2)$

$(X_1^*) = \{(P_Y)/3w_1\}^2 \cdot (P_Y/3w_2)$

$(X_1^*) = (P_Y^3)/(27w_1^2w_2)$

Similarly, we can compute the long-run profit-maximizing output level. Substitute the value of X_2^* in the Equation 8.2. Let us re-write the Equation 8.2 below.

$Y^* = \{(P_Y)/3w_1\}^{1/2} \cdot X_2^{1/2}$ *Equation 8.2*

$Y^* = \{(P_Y)/3w_1\}^{1/2} \cdot (P_Y^2.P_Y)/(9*3w_1w_2^2)^{1/2}$

$Y^* = \{(P_Y)/3w_1\}^{1/2} \cdot (P_Y)/(3w_2^2)^{1/2}.(P_Y/3w_2)$

$Y^* = \{(P_Y)/3w_1\} \cdot (P_Y)/(3w_2)$

$(Y^*) = (P_Y^2)/(9w_1w_2)$

So, for the given prices P_Y, w_1 and w_2, and the production function, $Y=X_1^{1/3}X_2^{1/3}$, the long-run profit-maximizing production plan is given by

$X_1^*, X_2^*, Y^* = [(P_Y^3)/(27w_1^2w_2)], [(P_Y^3)/(27w_1w_2^2)], [(P_Y^2)/(9w_1w_2)]$

Exercises

1. Assume that a firm produces a processed product with TFC=Rs.650000, SRAVC=Rs. 20/unit and price of each product is Rs.70. Compute the break even output and indicate, whether the firm makes a profit, if it produces more than 13000 units of output? Also compute MC, MR and marginal profit.

2. A farmer sells 50 units of commodity X a day. The cost is Rs.0.65 a unit. The farmer estimates that, for each Rs.0.05 price increase, 2 lesser units of commodity will be sold. What cost will maximize the profit?

3. Given the following functions:

   $R(X) = 10. X$

   $C(X) = X^3 - 6.X^2 + 15.X + 5$

   X = number of items produced, in thousands of units.

   Is there a level of production for which the profit is maximum? If your answer is yes, how many items must be sold to reach that level?

4. For the given cost and demand function, find the production level that will maximize profit.

   $C(X) = 16000+500X-1.6X^2+0.004X^3$

   $P(X) = 1700 - 7X$

5. A firm's demand function for a good is given by $P = 107-2Y$ and its total cost function is given by $TC = 200+3Y$. Write the Profit function in terms of Y.

9

Linear Programming

In this chapter, let us deal with a mathematical technique called Linear Programming (LP), which can be employed to solve the farmer's problems especially, when he faces with several constraints and the objective function must be optimized. As discussed earlier in Chapter 3, when the farmer's objective is to minimize the cost in the production programme in employing two resources, he chooses the LCC of resources, where MRTS of resources is inversely equal to the price ratio of two resources. Similarly, through Chapter 4, we analyzed that, when the farmer's objective is to maximize the profits in the production programme in producing two products, he chooses the OPC, where MRPS is inversely equal to the price ratio of two products. However, in practicality, the farmer often faces several constraints in the production programme *viz.,* labour constraints, capital constraints, limited land area, procurement of raw material for processing, purchase of some advanced equipment, may enter into contractual agreements regarding supply of minimum quantity of certain products etc., towards optimizing the objective function (minimization of costs or maximization of profits). In solving such numerous constraints, so as to achieve optimal solution, traditional methods break down and LP must be used. So, LP is a mathematical technique aimed for solving constrained maximization and minimization problems, when there are many constraints and the objective function is to be optimized, as well as the constraints faced, are linear. LP was developed by the Russian Mathematician L. V. Kantorovich in 1939 for use during World War II to plan expenditures and returns in order to reduce costs to the army and increase losses to the enemy. Later, this technique was extended by the American mathematician G. B. Dantzig in 1947 and he first published the Simplex method to achieve optimal solution for the constraints the firm faces. The LP problem was first shown to be solvable in polynomial time by Leonid Khachiyan in 1979, but a larger theoretical and practical breakthrough in the field came in 1984, when Narendra Karmarkar introduced a new interior-point method for solving LP problems. The following points depict the short history of LP:

☆ In 1762, Lagrange solved tractable optimization problems with simple equality constraints.

☆ In 1820, Gauss solved linear system of equations by what is now call Causssian elimination. In 1866 Wilhelm Jordan refined the method to finding least squared errors as a measure of goodness-of-fit. Now, it is referred to as the Gauss-Jordan Method.

☆ In 1945, Digital computer emerged.

☆ In 1947, Dantzig invented the Simplex Method.

☆ In 1968, Fiacco and McCormick introduced the Interior Point Method.

☆ In 1984, Karmarkar applied the Interior Method to solve LP problems adding his innovative analysis.

Though LP technique involves laborious procedure in doing mathematical calculations, but with the advent of powerful computers, its acceptance and usefulness have been greatly enhanced in the recent period. The following are the popular definitions of LP:

LP, sometimes known as linear optimization, is the problem of maximizing or minimizing a linear function over a convex polyhedron specified by linear and non-negativity constraints. Simplistically, LP is the optimization of an outcome based on some set of constraints using a linear mathematical model.

LP is a mathematical method for determining a way to achieve the best outcome (such as maximum profit or minimum cost) in a given mathematical model for some list of requirements represented as linear relationships. More formally, LP is a technique for the optimization of a linear objective function, subject to linear equality and linear inequality constraints. LP is the process of finding the extreme values (maximum and minimum values) of a function for a region defined by inequalities.

A LP problem is an optimization problem for which:

☆ *We attempt to maximize (or minimize) a linear function of the decision variables (objective function).*

☆ *The values of the decision variables must satisfy a set of constraints, each of which must be a linear inequality or linear equality.*

☆ *A sign restriction on each variable.*

The above definitions infer that, LP = Linear Algebra + Inequalities + Optimization (minimize or maximize). Also note that, LP is not a programming language like C++, Java, or Visual Basic and is just a mathematical programming that computes how best (in an optimal way) the farmer will allocate his scarce resources among the selected enterprises or select optimum combination of enterprises for the given resources, so as to ensure cost minimization and profit maximization respectively. Thus, LP deals with a class of optimization problems, where the objective function to be optimized and all the constraints are linear in terms of the decision variables. The term 'programming' in this context indicates a schedule of actions. Considering its importance, LP is one of the most widely used Operations Research.

I. Basic Terminology Used in LP Technique

☆ *Objective function:* The LP model that expresses, what needs to be maximized or minimized, depending on the objective of the problem is called Objective function. That is, objective function implies, what to be optimized in a given LP problem.

☆ *Decision variables:* These represent the quantities of each product to be produced by the farmer in order to maximize the profits or quantities of inputs to use to minimize the costs. For example, a farmer wishes to produce paddy (X_p) and maize (X_M). Unit profit of paddy is Rs.7/unit and unit profit of maize is Rs.10/unit. Let us assume, the farmer employs only two resources *viz.,* labour (man days) and fertilizer. It is necessary to employ 60 man days/acre to produce paddy and 40 man days/acre to produce maize. Similarly, the farmer requires 30 units of fertilizer per acre to produce paddy and 25 units of fertilizer per acre to produce maize. There are 350 man days of labour and 400 units of fertilizer in total with the farmer.

In the above example:

❖ *What is the objective in words?* The farmer's wish is to maximize the profits.

❖ *What are the constraints in words?*

Labour (man days) '≤' Number of man days available

Fertilizer '≤' Quantity (units) of fertilizer available

❖ *What are the decision variables?:* The variables Paddy (X_p) and Maize (X_M) are the decision variables

❖ *Formulate the objective function:* Max Z: $7X_p + 10X_M$

❖ *Formulate the constraints:*

Subject to

$60X_p + 40X_M \leq 350$ *(Functional Constraint for Labour)*

$30X_p + 25X_M \leq 400$ *(Functional Constraint for Fertilizer)*

❖ *Write the non-negative constraints:* $X_p, X_M \geq 0$

Thus, this LP solution for the above problem helps the farmer, how to maximize the profits in the production programme with the given resource constraints in producing paddy and maize.

✭ *Constraints:* Constraints represent how the decision variables use resources, which are available in limited quantities. They refer to an upper limit on the availability of resources or a lower limit on the necessary levels to achieve. They are also called as Limitations or Restrictions. LP formulation can contain four types of mathematical constraints *viz.*, Maximum type ($\leq$), Minimum type ($\geq$), Equality type (=) and Non-constraint.

❖ *Maximum Type:* This constraint is specified as '$\leq$'. This constraint indicates that, all uses of a particular resource across the enterprises must be less than or equal to the amount of that particular total resource available. For example: $5X_1 + 7X_2 + 4X_3 \leq 45$ Man days. In this case, '$5X_1$' refers to 5 x Man days with reference to paddy enterprise. This maximum type of constraint (specified as '$\leq$' type) is generally included in maximization problems and it must be converted into equality type, so as to write the equation in standard LP form. To convert '$\leq$' type of constraint into equality constraint, we add Slack Variable or Disposal activity. This slack variable or disposal activity corresponds to the amount of unused resource. This is so because, in the production programme, the farmer need not employ the entire resource that is available with him. Note that, this slack variable is non-negative, the number of slack variables depends upon the number of constraints in LP problem and the contribution of slack variables to the objective function is zero. Say, the given objective function is:

Max Z $50X_1 + 25X_2 + 15X_3$

Subject to:

$X_1 + 2X_2 + 1X_3 \leq 10$	*(Functional Constraint for Land)*
$5X_1 + 4X_2 + 2X_3 \leq 45$	*(Functional Constraint for Labour)*
$32X_1 + 21X_2 + 15X_3 \leq 350$	*(Functional Constraint for Capital)*
$X_1, X_2, X_3 \geq 0$	*(Non-negativity constraint)*

The above form of LP model can be linearized by adding slack variables or disposal activities (X_4, X_5 and X_6) as given below.

Max Z $50X_1 + 25X_2 + 15X_3 + 0X_4 + 0X_5 + 0X_6$

Subject to

$X_1 + 2X_2 + X_3 + 1X_4 + 0X_5 + 0X_6 = 10$

$5X_1 + 4X_2 + 2X_3 + 0X_4 + 1X_5 + 0X_6 = 45$

$32X_1 + 21X_2 + 15X_3 + 0X_4 + 0X_5 + 1X_6 = 350$

X_1, X_2, X_3, X_4, X_5 and $X_6 \geq 0$

❖ *Minimum Constraint:* ($\geq$): This constraint is specified as '$\geq$'. This constraint indicates that, all uses of a particular resource must exceed minimum amount available and hence, it is called Minimum Constraint. This minimum type of constraint (specified as '$\geq$' type) must be converted into equality type, so as to write the equation in standard LP form. To convert '$\geq$' type of constraint into equality constraint, we add Surplus

Variable or Negative slack variable. This Surplus variable indicates the excess amount by which a particular requirement is met. Thus, surplus variable permits over fulfillment of a constraint. Note that, minimum constraint is generally included in minimization problems, the contribution of surplus variable to the objective function is zero and this surplus variable violates the non-negativity restriction or condition. To overcome this problem of violating non-negativity condition, we add another variable namely Artificial variable. Artificial variable is of mathematical convenience and has no physical meaning. Artificial variable should not find its place as basic variable (decision variable) in the optimal solution. A high cost or penalty is attached to the artificial variable in the objective function to ensure its elimination from optimal solution. High cost or penalty of artificial variable is indicated by 'M'. For example,

Min Z $3X_1 + 2X_2$

Subject to:

$3X_1 + 7X_2 \geq 45$ (Functional constraint for carbohydrates)

$7X_1 + 3X_2 \geq 50$ (Functional constraint for proteins)

$X_1, X_2 \geq 0$ (Non-negativity constraint)

The above standard LP model for minimization function can be linearized by adding surplus variables as given below.

Min Z $3X_1 + 2X_2 + 0X_3 + 0X_4 + MA_1 + MA_2$

Subject to

$3X_1 + 7X_2 - 1X_3 + 0X_4 + 1A_1 + 0A_2 = 45$

$7X_1 + 3X_2 + 0X_3 - 1X_4 + 0A_1 + 1A_2 = 50$

$X_1, X_2, X_3, X_4, A_1, A_2 \geq 0$

A_1 and A_2 are Artificial variables.

❖ *Equality constraint* ('=')*:* This is specified as '='. This constraint implies that, all uses of particular resource across the enterprises must be equal to the amount available. It neither permits under use nor over fulfillment. Artificial variable is added to the equality constraint and is attached with high penalty or cost. For example, if a firm decides to sell all of its goods in sets (say, one razor (X_2) and two blade packets (X_1)), the new constraint is: $2X_1 = X_2$ or $2X_1 - X_2 = 0$, then constraints can take the form of an equality. The analysis of LP problem by graphical approach involving equality constraint causes all valid points to lie exactly on the constraint line.

❖ *Non-constraint:* This is in the case of objective function, where we want to derive highest or lowest possible value depending on the problem.

☆ *Inequality Constraints:* In LP problems, constraints are given by inequalities and hence, called as Inequality constraints. They are so called because, the farmer can employ the given inputs up to, but not more than, specified quantities of the inputs. That is, the farmer has restrictions in allocating the levels of each input. In addition, there are non-negativity constraints on the solution to indicate that, the farmer neither produces a negative output nor use a negative quantity of any input.

☆ *Formulation:* It is the process of translating a real-world problem into a linear program. Once a problem has been formulated as a linear program, it can be solved by graphical method or algebraic method or Simplex method or even by a computer programme, when large scale computations are to be done. The hardest part about applying LP technique is formulating the problem followed by analysis and interpreting the findings.

☆ *Linear Equations:* All of the equations and inequalities in a linear program must, by definition, be linear. A linear function has the following form:

Max Z $a_1X_1 + a_2X_2 + a_3X_3 +.. + a_nX_n$.

In this linear equation, the a's are called the coefficients or parameters of the equation and they are fixed values. The X's are called the Decision variables of the equation and they are allowed to take on a range of values within the limits defined by the constraints. Note that, it is not necessary to always use X's to represent decision variables and descriptive labels are more preferred.

☆ *Model:* An idealized representation of something.

☆ *LP Model:* A mathematical model, where the mathematical functions appearing in both the objective function and the constraints are all linear functions.

☆ *Corner Point Property:* An optimal solution must lie at one or more corner points.

☆ *Corner-point feasible solution:* A solution that lies at the corner of the feasible region.

☆ *Feasible region:* The geometric region that consists of all the feasible solutions.

☆ *Feasible solution:* A solution for which all the constraints are satisfied.

☆ *Infeasible solution:* A solution for which at least one constraint is violated.

☆ *Optimal solution:* A best feasible solution according to the objective function. Most LPs have only one optimal solution. However, some LPs have no optimal solution, and some LPs have an infinite number of solutions.

☆ *Optimal Solution for a Maximization Problem:* A point in the feasible region with the largest objective function value is the optimal solution.

☆ *Optimal Solution for a Minimization Problem:* A point in the feasible region with the smallest objective function value is the optimal solution.

☆ *Functional constraint:* A constraint with a function of the decision variables on the left hand side. All constraints in a LP model that are not non-negativity constraints are called functional constraints. The coefficients of the constraints are often called the Technological coefficients. The number on the right-hand side of the constraint is called the constraint's right-hand side (or RHS).

✩ *Non-negativity constraint*: A constraint that expresses the restriction that a particular decision variable must be non-negative (greater than or equal to zero).

✩ *Graphical method*: A method for solving LP problems with two decision variables on a two-dimensional graph.

✩ *Sensitivity analysis:* Analysis of how sensitive the optimal solution is to the value of each parameter of the model.

✩ *Shadow price*: The values of the slack variables in the Z-C row. A shadow price is the value of one additional unit of resource that is already being fully utilized. Assuming there are no other changes to the input parameters, the change to the objective function value per unit increase to a right hand side of a constraint is called the 'Shadow Price'.

✩ *Simplex method*: An efficient solution procedure for solving LP problems.

✩ *Simplex tableau*: A table that the tabular form of the simplex method uses to compactly display the system of equations yielding the current basic feasible solution.

✩ *Additional variables used in solving LP problem:* Three types of additional variables are used in simplex method such as:

❖ *Slack variables* (S_1, S_2, S_3 etc.): These variables refer to the amount of left over or unused resources. It is a variable that is added to the left hand side of a less than or equal to type of constraint and thereby, transforms it to equality constraint. Slack variables are always represented by positive (+) sign *i.e.* non-negative. These variables will have zero coefficients in the objective function. By adding slack variables, we can convert all the inequality constraints to equalities, the right hand side of the equations being non negative.

❖ *Surplus variables* (S_1, S_2, S_3 etc.): Surplus variable is the amount of resources by which the left hand side of the equation exceeds the minimum limit. That is, it is a variable subtracted from the left hand side of a 'greater than or equal to' type of constraint, to convert it to equality constraint. It is also known as negative slack variable. In economic terms, surplus variable represent over fulfillment of the requirement. Surplus variables are always represented by negative (-) sign.

❖ *Artificial variables* (A_1, A_2, A_3 etc.): Artificial variables are temporary slack variables, which are used for purposes of calculation, and are removed later. These are non-negative variables (coefficient of +1) introduced to facilitate the computation of an initial basic feasible solution. This variable is added on the left hand side of a 'greater than or equal to' type of constraint to convert it to equality constraint. It should be noted that, artificial variables are introduced as a computational device and does not have any physical meaning. These variables (one by one) can be removed from the simplex tableau as soon as they become non-basic. These artificial variables are introduced for equality (=) and for greater than or equal to (≥) types of constraints.

Thus, the above variables are used to convert the inequalities into equality equations, as given below.

Constraint Type	Variable Added	Format
Less than or Equal to ($\leq$)	Add Slack variable	$+S$
Greater than or Equal to ($\geq$)	Subtract Surplus variable and add Artificial variable	$-S + A$
Equal to ($=$)	Add Artificial variable	$+A$

Note that, since all numbers are real values, '$\leq$' is the same as '$<$' and '$\geq$' is the same as '$>$'.

☆ *Pivot column:* The column with the largest negative (largest positive) entry in the shadow price row in the case of a profit maximization (cost minimization) problem.

☆ *Pivot number:* The number in a simplex tableau that currently is at the intersection of the pivot column and the pivot row.

☆ *Pivot row:* The row of a simplex tableau that is for the current leaving basic variable with lowest ratio value.

☆ *Dual problem:* The LP problem that has a dual relationship with the original (primal) LP problem of interest according to Duality theory.

☆ *Basic and Non-basic variables:* Basic variables are selected arbitrarily with the restriction that, there be as many basic variables as there are equations. The remaining variables are non-basic variables. For example:

$$X_1 + 2X_2 + S_1 = 32$$
$$3X_1 + 4X_2 + S_2 = 85$$

This system has two equations, we can select any two of the four variables as basic variables. The remaining two variables are then non-basic variables. A solution found by setting the two non-basic variables equal to 0 and solving for the two basic variables is a basic solution. If a basic solution has no negative values, it is a basic feasible solution.

☆ *Basic Solution:* For a set of m simultaneous equations in n variables ($n > m$), a solution obtained by setting ($n - m$) variables equal to zero and solving for remaining m variables is called a 'basic feasible solution'. The variables which are set to zero are known as non-basic variables and the remaining m variables which appear in this solution are known as basic variables.

☆ *Basic Feasible Solution:* A feasible solution to LP problem, which is also the basic solution is called the 'basic feasible solution'. Basic feasible solutions are of two types;

❖ *Degenerate:* A basic feasible solution is called degenerate, if value of at least one basic variable is zero.

❖ *Non-degenerate:* A basic feasible solution is called 'non-degenerate', if all values of m basic variables are non-zero and positive.

☆ *Optimum Basic Feasible Solution:* A basic feasible solution, which optimizes (maximizes or minimizes) the objective function value of the given LP problem is called as 'optimum basic feasible solution'.

☆ *Unbounded Solution:* A basic feasible solution, which optimizes the objective function of the LP problem indefinitely is called unbounded solution.

☆ *Transportation model:* Transportation model is primarily concerned with the optimal (best possible) way in which a product produced at different factories or plants (called sources or supply origins) can be transported to a number of places (called warehouses or demand destinations). The objective in a transportation problem is to fully satisfy the destination requirements within the operating production capacity constraints at the minimum possible cost.

II. LP Structure or Components of LP Problem in Standard Form

LP is the most commonly applied form of constrained optimization. Constrained optimization is much harder than unconstrained optimization. In the latter, the manager or decision maker aims at the highest point (or lowest point) of an objective function. For optimization to be required, there must be more than one solution available. For example, on TPP curve, any point on the function is a solution, and because the single variable is real-valued, there are an infinite number of solutions. Some kind of optimization process is then required in order to choose the very best solution from among those available. However, in case of LP technique, which falls under constrained optimization, we aim at maximizing or minimizing a linear function that is subjected to a set of linear constraints. The constraints may be equalities or inequalities. So, in case of constrained optimization, we have to find out the best point of the function, but subjected to the limits or constraints while doing so. The LP problem in a standard form comprises of the following components:

A. Objective Function

This is a mathematical expression that combines the variables to express the manager's or decision maker's goal. That is, it refers to the objective of the manager (say, farmer) in taking up the production programme in his farm. The typical plans of farmer revolve around two major objectives *viz.*, Maximization of profits and Minimization of costs. The goal of the farmer must be clearly specified before computations take place. In general, a LP model for maximization function and minimization function are of the following standard form:

i. Objective Function (Maximization Function)

$$\text{Max } Z = a_1 X_1 + a_2 X_2 + a_3 X_3 + \cdots\cdots\cdots + a_n X_n \qquad \textit{Objective function}$$

Constraints (*i.e.,* subject to):

$$b_{11}X_1 + b_{12}X_2 + b_{13}X_3 + \cdots\cdots\cdots + b_{1n}X_n \leq c_1 \qquad \textit{(Functional Constraint of Resource 1)}$$

$$b_{21}X_1 + b_{22}X_2 + b_{23}X_3 + \cdots\cdots\cdots + b_{2n}X_n \leq c_2 \qquad \textit{(Functional Constraint of Resource 2)}$$

$$b_{31}X_1 + b_{32}X_2 + b_{33}X_3 + - - - - - - - - - - + b_{3n}X_n \leq c_3 \qquad \textit{(Functional Constraint of Resource 3)}$$

$$\cdots \qquad \cdots \qquad \bullet$$
$$\cdots \qquad \cdots \qquad \bullet$$
$$\cdots \qquad \cdots \qquad \bullet$$
$$\cdots \qquad \cdots \qquad \bullet$$

$$b_{m1}X_1 + b_{m2}X_2 + b_{m3}X_3 + - - - - - - - - - - + b_{mn}X_n \leq c_m \qquad \textit{(Functional Constraint of Resource 'n')}$$

In this system of equations, 'Z' is the objective function value (Maximization of profits) that is being optimized, Xj are the decision variables whose optimal values are to be estimated, $Xj \geq 0$ (Non-negativity Constraints) and a_j, b_{ij} and c_i are the constants derived. The above form of LP model can also be expressed as:

$$Max\ Z \sum_{j=1}^{n} ajXj$$

Subject to

$$\sum_{j=1}^{n} bijXj \quad \leq ci,$$

where, i = 1 to m, j = 1 to n

Example 9.1

Suppose, a farmer has a piece of farm land, say 'L' acres to be planted with either paddy or maize or some combination of the two. The farmer has a limited amount of fertilizer, F units, and pesticide, P units. Every acre of paddy requires F_P units of fertilizer and P_P units of pesticide, while every acre of maize requires F_M units of fertilizer and P_M units of pesticide. Let S_P be the selling price of paddy per unit, and S_M be the selling price of maize per unit. If we denote the area of land planted with paddy and maize by X_P and X_M respectively, then profit can be maximized by choosing optimal values for X_P and X_M. This problem can be expressed with the following LP problem in the standard form:

Max Z: $S_P X_P + S_M X_M$ *Objective function (Maximization of profits)*

Subject to:

$X_P + X_M \leq L$ *Functional Constraint (Land)*

$F_P X_P + F_M X_M \leq F$ *Functional Constraint (Fertilizer)*

$P_P X_P + P_M X_M \leq P$ *Functional Constraint (Pesticide)*

$X_P \geq 0$, $X_M \geq 0$ (Non-negativity constraints)

which in matrix form becomes:

$$[S_P \quad S_M]\begin{bmatrix} X_P \\ X_M \end{bmatrix}$$

Subject to

$$\begin{bmatrix} 1 & 1 \\ F_P & F_M \\ P_P & P_M \end{bmatrix}\begin{bmatrix} X_P \\ X_M \end{bmatrix} \le \begin{bmatrix} L \\ F \\ P \end{bmatrix}, \begin{bmatrix} X_P \\ X_M \end{bmatrix} \ge \begin{bmatrix} 0 \\ 0 \end{bmatrix}$$

ii. Objective Function (Minimization Function)

$$\text{Min } Z = a_1X_1 + a_2X_2 + a_3X_3 + \cdots + a_nX_n \qquad \text{\textit{Objective function}}$$

Constraints (*i.e.,* subject to):

$$b_{11}X_1 + b_{12}X_2 + b_{13}X_3 + \cdots + b_{1n}X_n \ge c_1 \qquad \text{\textit{(Functional Constraint)}}$$
$$b_{21}X_1 + b_{22}X_2 + b_{23}X_3 + \cdots + b_{2n}X_n \ge c_2 \qquad \text{\textit{(Functional Constraint)}}$$
$$b_{31}X_1 + b_{32}X_2 + b_{33}X_3 + \cdots + b_{3n}X_n \ge c_3 \qquad \text{\textit{(Functional Constraint)}}$$

$$b_{m1}X_1 + b_{m2}X_2 + b_{m3}X_3 + \cdots + b_{mn}X_n \ge c_m \qquad \text{\textit{(Functional Constraint)}}$$

In this system of equations, 'Z' is the objective function value (Minimization of costs) that is being optimized, Xj are the decision variables, whose optimal values are to be estimated, $Xj \ge 0$ (Non-negativity Constraints) and a_j, b_{ij} and c_i are the constants derived. The above form of LP model can also be expressed as:

$$\text{Min } Z = \sum_{j=1}^{n} ajXj$$

Subject to

$$\sum_{j=1}^{n} bijXj \ge ci,$$

where, i = 1 to *m, j* = 1 to *n*

Example 9.2

A fertilizer firm wishes to prepare special fertilizer mixture at a minimal cost by mixing two fertilizers, F_A and F_B. The mixture is to contain at least 45 units of phosphate, at least 36 units of nitrogen and at least 40 units of potassium. Fertilizer A costs the firm Rs. 1.00 per unit. Fertilizer B costs the firm Rs. 1.75 per unit. Fertilizer A contains

5 units of phosphate, 2 units of nitrogen and 2 units of potassium. Fertilizer B contains 3 units of phosphate, 3 units of nitrogen and 5 units of potassium. How many units of each fertilizer should the firm use in order to minimize the cost.

Min Z: $1F_A + 1.75F_B$ *Objective function (Minimization of cost)*

Subject to:

$5F_A + 3F_B \geq 45$ *Functional Constraint (Phosphate)*

$2F_A + 3F_B \geq 36$ *Functional Constraint (Nitrogen)*

$2F_A + 5F_B \geq 40$ *Functional Constraint (Potassium)*

$F_A \geq 0, F_B \geq 0$ (Non-negativity constraints)

$$\begin{bmatrix} 1 & 1.75 \end{bmatrix} \begin{bmatrix} F_A \\ F_B \end{bmatrix}$$

$$\begin{bmatrix} 5 & 3 \\ 2 & 3 \\ 2 & 5 \end{bmatrix} \begin{bmatrix} F_A \\ F_B \end{bmatrix} \geq \begin{bmatrix} 45 \\ 36 \\ 40 \end{bmatrix}, \begin{bmatrix} F_A \\ F_B \end{bmatrix} \geq \begin{bmatrix} 0 \\ 0 \end{bmatrix}$$

Thus, the objective function in the above two examples indicates, how each variable contributes to the value to be optimized in solving the problem. Thus, the objective function takes the following general form:

$$Maximize \text{ or } Minimize\ Z = \sum_{j=1}^{n} ajXj$$

Here, 'aj' is the objective function coefficient corresponding to the jth variable and Xj is the jth decision variable. The objective function coefficients indicate the contribution to the value of the objective function of one unit of the corresponding variable. For example, if the objective function is to maximize the profits, and 'Xj' is the jth activity in the model, then 'aj' (the objective function coefficient corresponding to Xj) gives the profits generated by one unit of activity 'j'. In case of cost minimization example, 'Xj' might be the amount of resource 'j' (say, fertilizer) used in achieving the goal. In this case, 'aj' would be the cost of using one unit of resource 'j'. Note that, the way the general objective function was written as above implies that, there is a coefficient in the objective function corresponding to each variable. Of course, some variables may not contribute to the objective function. In such case, the variable will have a coefficient of zero or the variable need not be included in the objective function at all.

The above examples also indicate that, an LP model (maximization or minimization function) comprises of the following components:

    ☆ *Decision variables:* They are the variables that appear in the objective function of the LP model and they indicate levels of activity of a firm.

☆ *Objective function:* A linear mathematical relationship describing an objective of the firm, in terms of decision variables - this function is to be maximized or minimized.

☆ *Constraints:* They are the requirements or restrictions placed on the firm by the operating environment, stated in linear relationships of the decision variables.

☆ *Parameters:* They refer to the numerical coefficients and constants used in the objective function and constraints.

Considering the above components, the following are the characteristics of LP problems:

☆ A decision amongst alternative courses of action is required.

☆ The decision is represented in the LP model by decision variables.

☆ The LP problem encompasses a goal, expressed as an objective function that the Manager or Decision maker wants to achieve.

☆ Restrictions (represented by constraints) refer to the maximum or minimum level of resources to be employed to achieve the objective function *i.e.* they limit the extent of achievement of the objective.

☆ The objective and constraints must be definable by linear mathematical functional relationships.

B. Alternative Courses of Action

The limited resources available on the farm may be used in several alternative ways for producing different types of enterprises. That is, there must be alternative courses of action to choose from. For example, if a farmer wishes to produce three different enterprises, the farmer may use LP to decide how to allocate the limited resources among the three enterprises. If there were no alternatives to select from, we would not need LP.

C. Resource Restrictions or Constraints

These are mathematical expressions that combine the variables to express limits on the possible solutions. For example, a constraint may express the idea that the number of labour available in a processing factory is limited to operate a particular machine or that only a certain amount of fertilizer is available with the farmer for kharif season. LP problem does exist only, when the resources available with the farmer are limited. If all the resources are available in plenty on the farm, the farmer will plan the production activity that contributes to maximum profits. But, in general, the resources with the farmer are limited and hence, he has to plan the enterprises within these limits. Thus, the presence of restrictions or constraints limits the degree to which the farmer can pursue the objective function. For example, deciding how many units of each product the farmer should produce is restricted by the availability of scarce resources. So, the objective function can be maximized (or minimized) subject to limited resources (the constraints). These constraints define the possible values that the variables of a LP problem may take. They typically represent resource constraints, or the minimum or maximum level of some activity or condition. They take the following general form:

(Profit maximization objective function) subject to constraints

$$\sum_{j=1}^{n} b_{ij} X_j \leq c_i,$$

where, $i = 1$ to m, $j = 1$ to n

(Cost minimization objective function) subject to constraints

$$\sum_{j=1}^{n} b_{ij} X_j \geq c_i,$$

where, $i = 1$ to m, $j = 1$ to n

where X_j = the jth decision variable,

b_{ij} = the coefficient on X_j in constraint 'i', and

c_i = the right-hand-side coefficient on constraint 'i'.

Note that 'i' is an index that runs from 1 to m and each value of 'i' corresponds to a constraint and 'j' is an index that runs from 1 to n.

Thus, the above expression represents 'm' constraints (equations or more precisely inequalities) with this form. Resource constraints are a common type of constraint. In a resource constraint, the coefficient 'bij' indicates the amount of resource 'i' used for each unit of activity 'j', as represented by the value of the variable X_j. The right-hand side of the constraint (ci) indicates the total amount of resource 'i' available in the production programme. Note that, in the earlier examples, the constraint is written as a less than or equal to constraint and greater than or equal to constraint. A greater than or equal to constraint can always be converted to a less than or equal to constraint by multiplying it by -1. Similarly, equality constraint can be written as two inequalities: a less than or equal to constraint and a greater than or equal to constraint. Besides the above two, there are also non-negativity constraints and this implies that, the variables of LP problem must always take non-negative values (*i.e.*, they must be greater than or equal to zero) and the technical reasons about the non-negativity constraints are beyond the scope of this book.

D. Linear Equations

The objective function and functional constraints in LP problems must be expressed in terms of linear equations or inequalities.

E. Variables or Decision Variables

The variables in a LP problem are a set of quantities that need to be determined in order to solve the problem; *i.e.*, the problem is solved when the best values of the variables have been identified. The variables are also called Decision variables because, the problem is to decide what value each variable should take and based on these values, the optimal solution is determined. Typically, the variables represent the amount of a resource to use or the level of some activity. In Example 9.2, Min Z: $1F_A$ + $1.75F_B$ is the objective function for minimization of cost and F_A and F_B are the decision variables. Note that, the values of the variables are not known when you start the problem. The goal is to find values of the variables that provide the best value of the objective function.

Thus, LP problem is an optimization problem for which we do the following:

☆ Identify the decision variables.

☆ Formulate the objective function (Maximization or Minimization function) based on the selected decision variables.

☆ The values of the decision variables must satisfy a set of constraints.

☆ Each constraint must be a linear equation or inequality.

☆ A sign restriction is associated with each variable. For each variable Xj, the sign restriction specifies either that Xj must be non-negative ($Xj \geq 0$) or that Xj may be unrestricted in sign.

Example 9.2.1: The above discussed components of LP model are shown through the following example: Assume a biscuit manufacturing company plans to produce two types of biscuits, one with a round shape and another with a square shape. The following resources are used in manufacturing the biscuits:

❖ Raw material, of which daily availability is 150 kg.

❖ Machinery, of which daily availability is 15 machine hours.

❖ Labor, of which daily availability is 40 man-hours.

The resources used are shown in the following table. If the unit profit of round and square biscuits is Rs 3.00 and Rs 2.00 respectively, how many round and square biscuits should be produced to maximize total profit?

Resources Used

Resources	Requirement/Unit		Daily Availability
	Round Biscuits	Square Biscuits	
Raw material	100	115	150 kgs
Machine	10	12	15 machine hours
Labour	3	2	40 man hours

Components of LP Problem

☆ *Key Decision:* To determine the number of round and square biscuits to be produced.

☆ *Decision Variables:* Let X_1 be the number of round biscuits to be produced daily, and X_2 be the number of square biscuits to be produced daily

☆ *Objective function:* It is given that the profit on each unit of round biscuits is Rs 3.00 and of square biscuits is Rs. 2.00. The objective is to maximize profits, therefore, the total profit will be given by the equation, Max Z= $3X_1+2X_2$

☆ *Constraints:* Now, the manufacturing process is imposed by a constraint with the limited availability of raw material. For the production of round biscuits, $100X_1$ of raw material is used daily and for the production of square biscuits, $115X_2$ of raw material is used daily.

It is given that the total availability of raw material per day is 150 kgs. Therefore, the constraint for raw material is, $100X_1 + 115X_2 \leq 150$

Similarly, the constraint for machine hours is, $10X_1+12X_2 \leq 15$ and

The constraint for the manpower is, $3X_1+2X_2 \leq 40$

Since the resources are to be used within or below the daily availability level, inequality sign of less than or equal sign ($\leq$) is used. Further, we cannot produce negative number of units of biscuits which is a non-negative constraint expressed as, $X_1 \geq 0, X_2 \geq 0$

Thus, the LP model for the given problem is,

Maximize $Z = 3X_1 + 2X_2$

Subject to constraints,

$100X_1+115X_2 \leq 150$

$10X_1+12X_2 \leq 15$

$3X_1+2X_2 \leq 40$

where $X_1 \geq 0, X_2 \geq 0$

III. Assumptions in LP Technique

Since, the objective function (maximization of profits or minimization of costs) that the farmers seek to optimize as well as the constraints that they face are often linear over the relevant range of operation, LP technique is very useful. However, this technique is based on the certain assumptions. We know, an assumption is a simplifying condition taken to hold true in the system being analyzed in order to render the model mathematically tractable (solvable). The following are the important assumptions of LP technique:

☆ *Linearity:* As mentioned earlier, the objective function that the farmer seeks to optimize (*i.e.*, maximize or minimize) is linear and can be represented graphically by straight lines. This linearity applies to constraint inequalities as well, since the addition of slack and surplus variables convert all inequalities into linear equations. So, linearity implies, the objective function (*i.e.*, maximization or minimization) can be described by a linear function of the decision variables. That is, the mathematical function involves only the first powers of the variables ($3X_1, 5X_1$) and with no cross products (say, $3X_1*5X_1$).

☆ *Constraints set or Functional constraints:* The constraints set can be expressed as a set of linear equations. In addition to the linear requirements, non-negativity condition state that, the variables cannot assume negative values, as negative quantity of resources and output does not have a meaning.

☆ *Proportionality:* The contribution of any decision variable to the objective function is proportional to its value. That is, the contribution to the objective function from each decision variable is proportional to the value of the decision variable. This contribution is assumed constant and independent of the variable level. Similarly, the use of each resource per unit of each decision variable is assumed constant and independent of variable level. Thus, there are no economies of scale. For example, in the profit maximization problem, the contribution from one unit of paddy area towards profit maximization is Rs. 60, from two units of paddy area towards profit maximization is Rs. 120, from three units of paddy area towards profit maximization is Rs. 180 and so on. Similarly, in diet problem, the contribution to the cost of the diet from one kilogram of apples is Rs. 30, from two kilograms of apples is Rs. 60 and from three kilograms of apples is Rs. 90 and so on. Similarly, if the net returns per unit of paddy produced is Rs. 40, then if 100 units are produced, then net returns are Rs. 4000. So, under this proportionality assumption, the total contribution of paddy enterprise to the objective function is always proportional to its level. This assumption also applies to resource usage within the constraints. For example, a farmer's labour requirement for one acre of paddy is 125 man days. If the farmer cultivates paddy in 4 acres of land, his total labour requirement will be 500 man days. Thus, the total labour man days employed in paddy cultivation is always strictly proportional to the acreage under the crop. That means, each decision variable in every equation must

ss

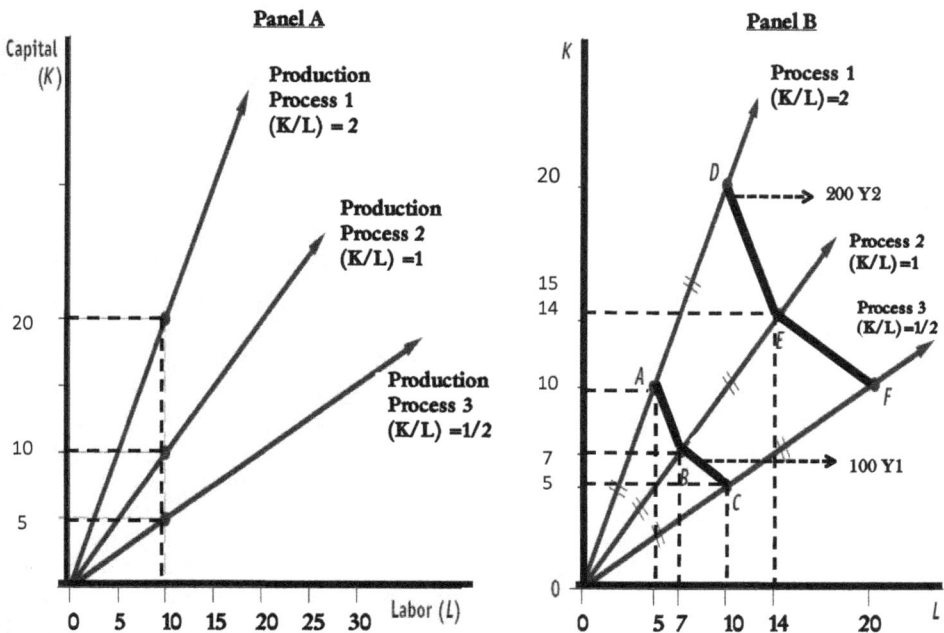

Figure 9.1: Linear Programming (Kinked) isoquants Showing Different Production Process.

appear with a constant coefficient (*i.e.*, the variable is multiplied by a number and nothing else). So, in objective function, proportionality implies that, the marginal rate of contribution to the objective (maximization and minimization) of each variable is assumed to remain constant throughout the entire range of activity levels in the problem. In particular, variables cannot be multiplied or divided by other variables, cannot be raised to an exponent other than 1, or be arguments of other functional relationships (say, sin X or log X). In the functional constraints, proportionality implies that, resource usage per variable is assumed constant throughout the entire operational range of the problem.

☆ *Additivity:* The contribution to the objective function for any decision variable is independent of the values of the other decision variables. That is, this assumption deals with the relationships among the decision variables. Simply put, their contributions to an equation in objective function must be additive. So, the total value of the objective function equals the sum of the contributions of all decision variables in the objective function. Similarly, total resource use in the objective function is the sum of the resource use of each variable. This requirement rules out the possibility of interaction or multiplicative terms appear in the objective function or the functional constraints. For example, the total labour man days for paddy are the sum of number of man days of labour across different farm operations on paddy. In the general LP formulation, considering variables X_1 and X_2, the value of the objective function must always equal a_1 times X_1 plus a_2 times X_2. Using X_1 does not affect the per unit net return of X_2 and *vice versa*. Similarly using X_1 does not alter the resource requirement of X_2. Thus, this assumption of additivity implies that, the combined effect of the decision variables in any one equation is the algebraic sum of their individual weighted effects. The weighting, of course, is due to the proportionality constants. That means, the variables can be added or subtracted together, but never multiplied or divided by each other. For example, total profit (or total cost) is the sum of the individual product's profits (or resources costs). In the functional constraints, additivity implies that, total resource usage is likewise the sum of individual resource usage per variable (say, product produced).

Proportionality and additivity amount to linearity. The broader implication of linearity is that, the variables are assumed to be mutually independent. In other words, the products are assumed to be neither complements nor substitutes of each other and there is no interaction between the variables. If proportionality and additivity cannot be assumed to hold, the problem would call for a non-linear programming solution approach. Thus, the objective function for an LP problem must be a linear function of the decision variables and it has two implications:

❖ The contribution of the objective function from each decision variable is proportional to the value of the decision variable.

❖ The contribution to the objective function from any decision variable is independent of the other decision variables.

✰ *Divisibility* (*Continuity*): Each decision variable is allowed to assume fractional (non-integer) values. That is, the decision variables can take on any value within a given feasible range. To make the model workable (computationally tractable), we must be prepared to accept non-integer solutions. Sometimes, the values of decision variables only make sense, if they are integers; then we need an extension of LP called Integer programming. Since we are using continuous variables, the LP model assumes that the decision variables can take on fractional variables. In many situations, the LP is being used on a large enough scale that one can round the optimal decision variables up or down to the nearest integer and get an answer that is reasonably close to the optimal integer solution. For example, if a LP model for a farmer production plan said to produce 39.992 units of paddy, we can probably produce 40 units of paddy and be close to an optimal solution. This rounding or truncating of the optimal LP decision variables will not greatly affect the solution.

✰ *Certainty:* Each linear coefficient of the objective function and functional constraints is known with certainity and is not based on probabilistic approach. That is, the coefficients in the objective function 'aj', the coefficients in the functional constraints 'bij' and the right hand side of the functional constraints in the LP model are known as constants and they have no probabilistic elements whatsoever. So, the parameter values are known with certainty. This is technically never true in the real world; some

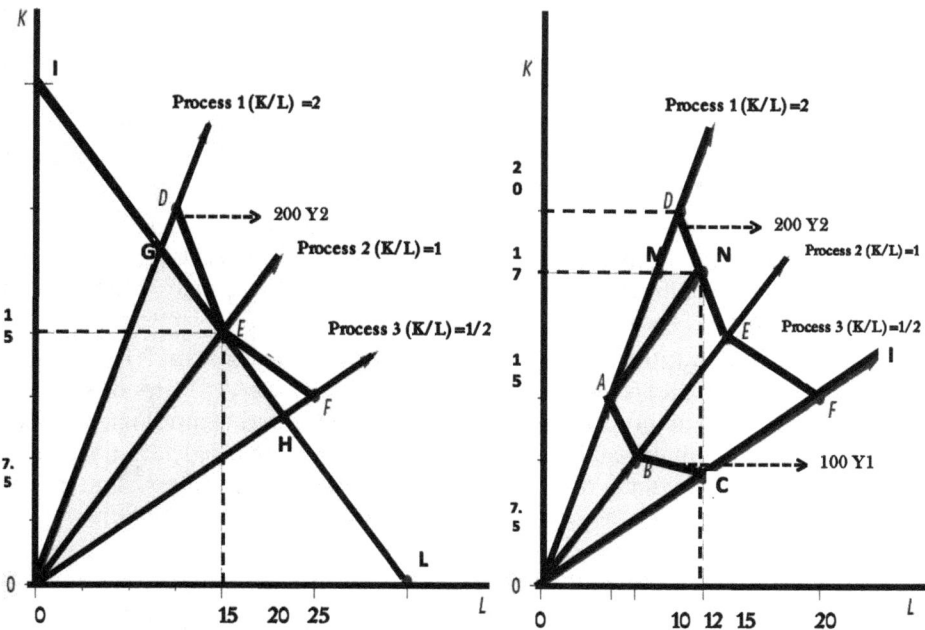

Figure 9.2: Feasible Solutions and Optimal Solution in Linear Programming (Kinked) Isoquants.

degree of uncertainty is always present especially in long-term period. However, for short-term problems, the level of uncertainty tends to be minimal and one can often work under the assumption of complete certainty and then take small parameter variations into account with sensitivity analysis. In case of long-term problems, the aspects involve pronounced uncertainty and this call for decision making using stochastic programming (probabilistic method) instead of standard LP. So, considering certainty assumption in this model, the values of the variables are exactly equal to the responses represented by the coefficients. As per this assumption in the given LP model (for maximization of profits), the parameters aj, bij and ci are known constants. The optimum solution derived is predicated on perfect knowledge of all the parameter values. Since all exogenous factors are assumed to be known and fixed, LP models are sometimes called non-stochastic models as contrasted with models explicitly dealing with stochastic factors. This assumption gives rise to the term 'deterministic' analysis. Thus, after developing a LP model, it is often useful to conduct sensitivity analysis by varying one of the exogenous parameters and observing the sensitivity of the optimal solution to that variation. For example, in the LP model regarding profit maximization, the profits derived from a product depends upon the quantity of resources employed, prices of resources, output, prices of products etc., and all of these could be random variables.

☆ *Data:* In employing the LP technique to solve a problem, it is assumed that data are available to formulate the problem.

☆ Objective function is the sole criterion for choosing among the decision variables.

☆ The decision variables are fully manipulatable within the feasible region and are under the control of the decision maker. Further, all appropriate decision variables have to be included in the model.

☆ The constraints fully identify the bounds placed on the decision variables by resource availability, technology, the external environment etc. Thus, any choice of the decision variables, which simultaneously satisfies all the constraints, is admissible.

☆ Input and output prices are constant and we have constant RTS. Constant input prices and constant RTS mean that, MCs and ATCs are constant and are linear. The production takes place with limited technologically fixed input combinations. Because of this limited technologically fixed input combinations that a farmer can use to produce output, the isoquants are not smooth and bear kinks as shown through Panel B of the Figure 9.1.

IV. Production Processes in LP

Though LP technique enjoys wider applications, it is more frequently applied in taking production decisions with the objective functions *i.e.*, maximization of profits and minimization of costs. As discussed earlier through Panel E of the Figure 3.6 on

LP isoquants, output can be produced with only a limited number of combinations *i.e.*, at kinks on the isoquants. The ratio of the inputs at each possible (limited) combination on an isoquant represent production process or activity and the same can be shown as a straight line ray from the origin. In Panel A of the Figure 9.1, an output of Y_1 (100 units) can be produced at three possible input ratios or production process *viz.*, $K/L = 2$, $K/L = 1$ and $K/L = \frac{1}{2}$. These production processes are indicated by a ray from the origin with the slope of K/L for each respective production process. In production process of $K/L = 2$, it implies, for every two units of capital (K), one unit of labour (L) will be used to produce Y_1 output (100 units). In production process of $K/L = 1$, it implies, for every one unit of K, one unit of L will be used to produce the same Y_1 output (100 units). In production process of $K/L = \frac{1}{2}$, it implies, for every one unit of K, two units of L will be used to produce the same Y_1 output (100 units). Thus, to produce the same level of output Y_1, the inputs are combined in different proportions across different production processes. This also implies that, to produce output Y_1, there are three processes, each using a particular combination of K and L. By joining these input combinations or ratios of K/L across different production process, we get an isoquant representing output Y_1 (Panel B of the Figure 9.1). Since limited production possibilities (processes) are there to produce output Y_1, the derived isoquant is not smoothly curved as in case of good substitutes (Figure 3.5), but it will have kinks indicating the points of limited production processes available to produce the same level of output. In Panel B, it is clear that, output Y_1 can be produced at three kinks or production processes (A, B and C) of different K/L ratios *viz.*, 2, 1 and ½ respectively. That is, at kink A, the farmer employs 10 units of K and 5 units of L, at kink B, the farmer employs 7 units of K and 7 units of L and at kink C, the farmer employs 5 units of K and 10 units of L and by joining these three kinks A, B and C, we get an isoquant of output Y_1 (100 units). As mentioned earlier, the isoquant so derived is not a smooth convex curve, but bear kinks indicating the three production processes that are possible to produce output Y_1. Since, the production programme experiences constant RTS, doubling both L and K exactly doubles the output ($Y_2 = 200$ units). Thus, isoquant Y_2 = 200 units will be produced at three kinks D, E and F with input combinations (20K + 10L), (14K + 14L) and (10K + 20L) respectively. Thus, the two isoquants Y_1 and Y_2 lie parallel to each other. Note that, greater the number of processes available to produce a particular commodity, the less pronounced are these kinks and thereby, the isoquants approach the smooth curves as discussed in Figure 3.5.

As discussed in Chapter 3, to achieve LCC of resources, the iso-cost line should be tangent to the isoquant from below or when the slope of iso-cost line equals the slope of isoquant. The same is true for the LP analysis. In Panel A of the Figure 9.2, the iso-cost line (IL) is tangent to the kinked isoquant at point 'E' thereby, indicating the feasible region OGH for producing the output $Y_2 = 200$ units. The feasible region implies that, it is the area of attainable input combinations, so as to produce the given level of output and beyond that region, the combination of inputs is not possible to produce a given level of output. The same can be shown through Panel A of the Figure 9.2, as both capital intensive (which involve K/L ratio more than 2) and labour intensive (which involve K/L ratio less than ½) production programmes beyond OGH region are not possible to attain LCC of resources or optimal combination (optimal solution) of resources. Among the feasible points showing different input combinations in the feasible region OGH, the only one optimal solution is at point E, where iso-cost line lie tangent to the isoquant from below or the slope of iso-cost line equals the slope of isoquant. So, at this optimal solution (point), the farmer employs 15 units each of L and K, so as to produce the given level of output $Y_2 = 200$ units. However, when the farmer faces no cost-constraint, but faces a possibility of allocating only 12L and 17K inputs combination (*i.e.*, two constraints regarding allocation of two inputs), then the feasible region is given by OMNC (Panel B of Figure 9.2). That is, in this region OMNC, the feasible combinations of two inputs exist to produce a given level of output ($Y_2 = 200$ units). However, the optimal solution (point) is at 'N', as the farmer can employ only 12L and 17K inputs combination. To reach this point 'N', the farmer employs Production process 1 up to point A (*i.e.*, on isoquant $Y_1 = 100$ units) and remaining 100 units of output through Production process 2 (OB=AN). This implies that, given two constraints regarding the allocation levels of two inputs, the farmer can reach the maximum output of $Y_2 = 200$ units by employing two production processes. In Panel B, OA and OB are called 'vectors'. Thus, ON is equal to the sum of vectors OA and OB.

It is clear from the above discussion that, when the farmer faces cost constraint (*i.e.*, employing iso-cost line in the analysis in Panel A of Figure 9.2), he employs only one process (production process 2 *i.e.*, (K/L) =1) to achieve optimal solution (LCC) in the production programme. However, when the farmer faces two constraints (Panel B of Figure 9.2 regarding allocation levels of two inputs), the farmer required two processes to reach the optimum solution. From this, we can generalize that, to reach the optimal solution, a farmer will require no more processes than the number of constraints that he faces in producing the output. Sometimes, even fewer processes will do. For example, if the farmer faces the constraints regarding allocation of only 10L and 20K (Panel B of Figure 9.2 regarding allocation levels of two inputs), the feasible region changes and now the optimum solution would be at point D, and the output $Y_2 = 100$ units can be produced by employing only production process 1. Note that, to reach any point on an isoquant between two adjacent production processes, we use the process to which the point is closer, in proportion to 1 minus the distance of the point from the process (ray). For example, if point 'N' was one-quarter of the distance DE from point D along the isoquant Y_2, the farmer would produce $1 – ¼ = ¾$ of the output of 200 units *i.e.*, 150 units with production process 1 and the remaining $1/4^{th}$ output (50 units) with production process 2 (Panel B of Figure 9.2). The amount of each input that is used in each process is then proportional to the output produced by each process.

Assume that, in Panel A of the Figure 9.2, if the ratio of wage rate of labour (w) to the rental price of capital (r) is increased, then the iso-cost line IL become steeper and now, the optimal solution would remain at point E as long as the new IL iso-cost (constraint) line remained flatter than the segment DE on the isoquant for $Y_2 = 200$ units. If w/r still rises, the iso-cost line IL becomes still steeper and gets coincided with segment DE on the isoquant thereby, the farmer can produce 200 units of output with production process 1 or production process 2 or any combination of production process 1 and production process 2. If w/r rose still further, the iso-cost line still becomes more steeper and the farmer would reach the optimal solution at point D on the isoquant.

V. Formulation of LP Model

As discussed earlier, LP is a widely used mathematical modeling technique to determine the optimal solution for the maximizing or minimizing a linear function subject to linear constraints. The constraints may be equalities or inequalities. Before going into the analytical framework for addressing an optimization problem, let us look at the basic format for formulating the LP problem for profit maximization (Table 9.1) and cost minimization (Table 9.2).

Table 9.1: Formulation of LP Model Involving the Allocation of Resources to Activities (Objective function is to maximize profits with reference to Table 9.3)

Restrictions (Resources)	Resource Usage per Unit of Activity (Product)				Quantities of Resources Available (Total)
	Product 1	Product 2	....	Product N	
1	b_{11}	b_{12}	....	b_{1n}	c_1
2	b_{21}	b_{22}	....	b_{2n}	c_2
3	b_{31}	b_{32}	....	b_{3n}	c_3
.	.	.	.	.	.
.	.	.	.	.	.
J	b_{m1}	b_{m2}	....	b_{mn}	c_m
Contribution to Max Z per unit of activity	a_1	a_2	....	a_n	

Table 9.2: Formulation of LP Model Involving the Allocation of Resources to Activities (Objective function is to minimize costs with reference to Table 9.4)

Ingredients	Contribution by Each Unit of Activity (Product)				Max Limit of Ingredients (units)
	Product 1	Product 2	....	Product N	
1	b_{11}	b_{12}	....	b_{1n}	c_1
2	b_{21}	b_{22}	....	b_{2n}	c_2
3	b_{31}	b_{32}	....	b_{3n}	c_3
.	.	.	.	.	.
.	.	.	.	.	.
J	b_{m1}	b_{m2}	....	b_{mn}	c_m
Contribution to Min Z per unit of activity (product)	a_1	a_2	....	a_n	

Many variants can be posed in the formulation of LP problem and this makes the LP technique to apply to a wide variety of settings. For example, the optimization problem could aim at:

⭐ Minimizing the costs in the production programme in purchasing three inputs from different sources so that, how much of each input to buy subject to constraints on minimum and maximum levels of inputs.

⭐ Maximizing the profits in the production programme subject to resource (labor and raw materials) constraints.

⭐ Formulation of a minimum cost transportation plan determining the amount of goods to transport across each available route subject to constraints on supply availability and demand.

⭐ Scheduling school buses to minimize the total distance travelled when carrying students.

⭐ Selecting the product mix in a food processing firm to make best use of machine and labor-hours available, while maximizing the firm's profit.

⭐ Selecting the blends of raw materials in feed mills to produce finished feed combinations at minimum cost.

⭐ Designing the distribution system that will minimize total shipping cost from several warehouses to various market locations.

Note that, in solving a constrained optimization problem by LP technique, the most difficult aspect is formulation of the problem in a LP format or framework. After formulating the problem, the actual solution to the problem is then straightforward. Simple LP problems with only a few variables can be easily solved graphically or algebraically. However, for the complex problems involving more number of variables, the use of computer software programmes is inevitable. Now, let us proceed to solve LP problems based on Graphical and Simplex methods.

VI. Solutions to LP Problems

LP is an efficient way of determining optimum plan, only if there are numerous (but finite) enterprises or processes and a numerous restrictions in attaining a specific objective (maximization function or minimization function). For achieving this optimal plan out of the feasible solutions, we can employ several methods like:

⭐ Graphical method

⭐ Analytical method or Trial and error method

⭐ Simplex method

⭐ Big-M method

⭐ Two phase simplex method

⭐ Dual simplex method

⭐ Revised simplex method

Among the above methods, let us discuss two popular methods *viz.*, Graphical method and Simplex method.

A. Graphical Method

We already know that, LP problem is a linear function of objective function and decision variables are subjected to a number of linear inequalities. Fortunately problems of this type with just two decision variables can be easily solved by using graphical approach. So, the easiest way to solve small LP problems, when there are only two decision variables (say, units of paddy to produce and units of maize to produce) is by employing graphical solution approach. However, this method is not suitable, if the LP problem addresses more than two variables, as it is not possible to plot the solution on a two dimensional graph. Let us employ this approach to address LP problems of maximization function and minimization function.

i. Profit Maximization Objective Function
Step 1
The first basic step involved is formulation of LP problem. This refers to translating the real-world problem in the form of mathematical equations that represent the objective function, functional constraints and non-negativity constraints. This formulation of LP problem forms the crux in the research study, as it guides the researcher in collecting requisite data and subsequent steps in finding the optimal solution. This also makes the researcher to transform all the collected data into tabular form for mathematical computations.

Example 9.3
Assume a profit maximization problem, where a farmer employs two resources *viz.*, fertilizer and labour to produce two commodities *viz.*, paddy and maize. The unit profit or net income per unit for paddy is Rs.6 and for maize is Rs.8. The total quantity of fertilizer available is 300 units and total number of man days available are 110 days. To produce paddy and maize, it requires 30 and 20 units of fertilizer respectively and 5 and 10 labour man days respectively.

The above given problem contains the information for the LP problem and it can be formulated as given below.

Table 9.3: Input-Output Data in Producing Paddy and Maize by the Farmer

Resources	Amounts of Inputs Required to Produce One Unit of Output		
	Paddy (X_1)	Maize (X_2)	Total Resources Available
Fertilizer (units)	30	20	300
Labour (man days)	5	10	110
Net income	6	8	

The above tabular form of LP problem can be conveniently expressed as mathematical equations as given below.

Max Z $6X_1+8X_2$

Subject to:

$30X_1 + 20X_2 \leq 300$ (Functional Constraint for fertilizer)

$5X_1 + 10X_2 \leq 110$ (Functional Constraint for labour man days)

$X_1, X_2 \geq 0$ (Non-negativity constraints)

Step 2

Now, the above constraint inequalities will be converted into equalities as given below.

$30X_1 + 20X_2 = 300$ (Functional Constraint for fertilizer)

$5X_1 + 10X_2 = 110$ (Functional Constraint for labour man days)

Step 3

Compute horizontal and vertical intercepts from each functional constraint equation.

$30X_1 + 20X_2 = 300$ (Functional Constraint for fertilizer)

Assume $X_1 = 0$. So, $30(0) + 20X_2 = 300$

So, $X_2 = 15$ units. This 15 units of X_2 represents X_2 intercept on the graph when $X_1 = 0$. This implies, all the fertilizer is used to produce maize. Similarly, assume $X_2 = 0$. Then,

$30(X_1) + 20(0) = 300$

So, $X_1 = 10$ units. This 10 units of X_1 represents X_1 intercept on the graph when $X_2 = 0$. This implies, all the fertilizer is used to produce paddy. When these two intercepts were joined on the graph, we get a straight line (Panel A of the Figure 9.3). Similar procedure is followed to compute X_1 intercept and X_2 intercept from functional constraint for labour man days. So, from the equation: $5X_1 + 10X_2 = 110$, $X_2 = 11$ units when $X_1 = 0$ (this implies, all the labour are used to produce maize) and $X_1 = 22$ when $X_2 = 0$ units (this implies, all the labour are used to produce paddy). When these two intercepts were joined on the graph, we get a straight line (Panel B of the Figure 9.3).

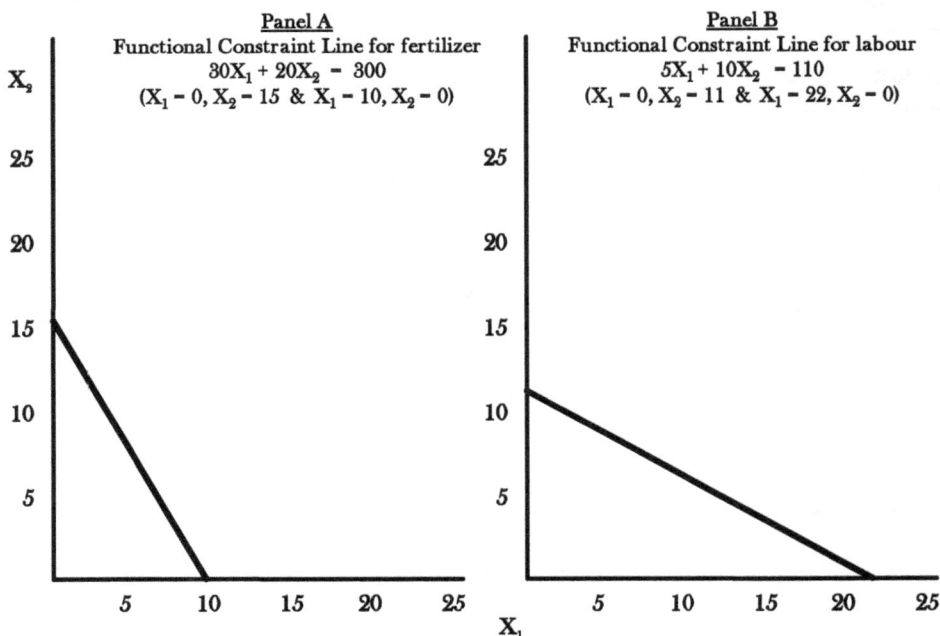

Figure 9.3: Functional Constraint Lines for Fertilizer and Labour Man Days.

Step 4

These two straight lines are now placed on the same graph (Figure 9.4). The simplest way to locate the feasible region is to plug in the coordinates of the origin (0,0) and see whether this point satisfies the constraint. If it does, then all points on the origin side of the line are feasible (valid), and all points on the other side of the line are infeasible or invalid. (If (0,0) does not satisfy the constraint, then all points on the other side and away from the origin are feasible (valid), and all points on the origin side of the constraint line are infeasible or invalid). Now feasible solution region or solution space is represented by the area on the graph that is valid for all constraints. Choosing any point in this area will result in a valid solution. *In case of maximization function, the optimal value corresponds to the greatest value of the coordinates (in case of minimization function, the optimal value corresponds to the lowest value of the coordinates).*

We will use the origin (0,0) to check the valid side (feasible region) for both constraint lines. For fertilizer constraint line, $30(0) + 20(0)$ is < 300 and thereby, this coordinate (0,0) is valid. For labour man days constraint line, the coordinate (0,0) is also valid, as $5(0) + 10(0)$ is < 110. Likewise, we can estimate the valid coordinates for the above two constraint lines and the coordinates that satisfies these two constraint lines are up to the points A, B, C and D and thereby, ABCD shaded area (Figure 9.4) is the feasible region or solution space. Let us examine now the coordinates beyond this shaded region ABCD with reference to the two constraint lines. Assume $X_1 = 10$ and $X_2 = 15$ and with reference to fertilizer constraint line: $30(X_1) + 20(X_2)$ is < 300, then: $30(10) + 20(15)$ is >300 and thereby, this coordinate (10,15) is not valid. Similarly, assume $X_1 = 15$ and $X_2 = 15$ and with reference to labour man days constraint line: $5(X_1) + 10(X_2)$ is < 110, then: $5(15) + 10(15)$ is >110 and thereby, this coordinate (15,15)

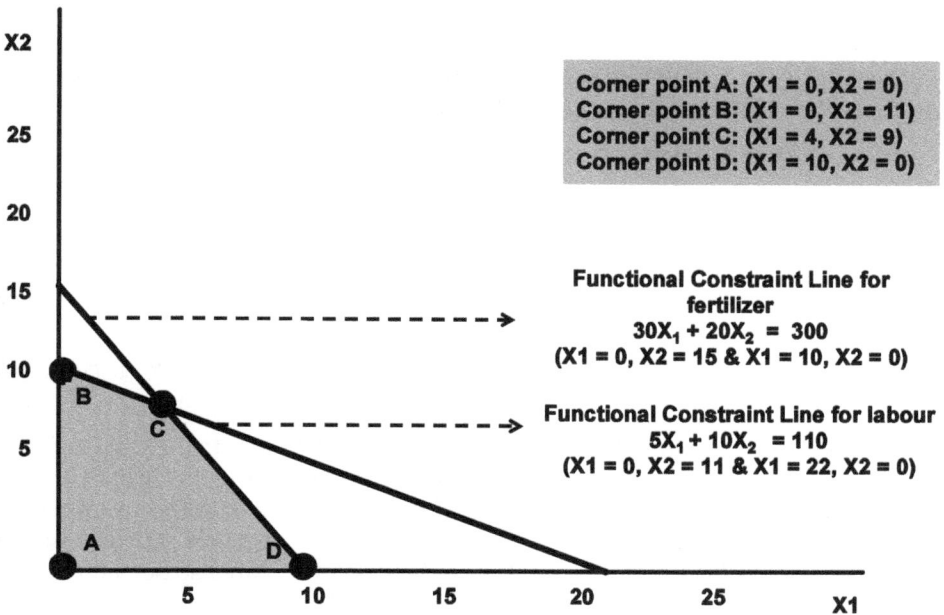

Corner point A: $(X1 = 0, X2 = 0)$
Corner point B: $(X1 = 0, X2 = 11)$
Corner point C: $(X1 = 4, X2 = 9)$
Corner point D: $(X1 = 10, X2 = 0)$

Functional Constraint Line for fertilizer
$30X_1 + 20X_2 = 300$
$(X1 = 0, X2 = 15 \ \& \ X1 = 10, X2 = 0)$

Functional Constraint Line for labour
$5X_1 + 10X_2 = 110$
$(X1 = 0, X2 = 11 \ \& \ X1 = 22, X2 = 0)$

Figure 9.4: Finding Optimal Solution Based on Corner Point Approach.

is not valid. So, any coordinate outside the region ABCD is not valid to meet the functional constraints and hence, the region ABCD constitute the feasible region. There are several approaches to locate the optimal solution from the feasible region, but the two important approaches include: Corner point approach and Iso-profit line approach. Let us discuss their methodologies here under for this example.

a. Corner Point Approach

This is the simplest approach to estimate optimal solution from the feasible region ABCD shown in the Figure 9.4. In the figure, both the constraint lines for fertilizer and labour are drawn and this gives the shaded region ABCD that satisfies both the constraints. In the shaded area ABCD, 'A', 'B', 'C' and 'D' are the corner points. This approach states that, *'the optimal solution to any LP problem is at the corner point or extreme point of the feasible region that contribute to maximum profit (Maximization function) or minimum cost (Minimization function)'*. In this example, the optimal solution in the feasible (shaded) region ABCD will lie at one of the corner points *i.e.*, 'A' or 'B' or 'C' or 'D' that contribute to maximum profits. Thus, optimal solution always occurs at corners. When more than one corner corresponds to an optimal solution, each corner and all points along the line connecting the corners correspond to optimal solutions. Let us find out the values at the corner points 'A', 'B', 'C' and 'D' with reference to the objective function and the highest value at one of these four points corresponds to optimal solution in the feasible region ABCD.

Optimal Solution or Profit at Corner Point A: $(X_1 = 0, X_2 = 0)$: $6X_1 + 8X_2 = 6(0) + 8(0) = 0$

Optimal Solution or Profit at Corner Point B: $(X_1 = 0, X_2 = 11)$: $6X_1 + 8X_2 = 6(0) + 8(11) = 88$

Optimal solution or Profit at Corner point C: To fix the coordinates at point C, where the two constraints lines intersect each other, we follow simultaneous equations approach. We know the two functional constraints:

$30X_1 + 20X_2 = 300$ (Functional Constraint for fertilizer)

$5X_1 + 10X_2 = 110$ (Functional Constraint for labour man days)

Multiply the second equation with -2 and by adding these two equations, we get $X_1 = 4$. By substituting X_1 in any of the above two equations, we get $X_2 = 9$. So, Optimal solution or Profit at Corner point C is given by: $(X_1 = 4, X_2 = 9)$: $6X_1 + 8X_2 = 6(4) + 8(9) = 96$.

Optimal solution or Profit at Corner point D: $(X_1 = 10, X_2 = 0)$: $6X_1 + 8X_2 = 6(10) + 8(0) = 60$

Among the above four corner points, point 'C' contributes to highest profits *i.e.* Rs. 96 and thereby, this is the optimal solution in the feasible region for this problem of producing 4 units of paddy and 9 units of maize. Note that, in this example, the optimal solution is at corner point 'C' *i.e.* at the point of intersection of two constraint lines, but this is not the case always. The optimal solution can also be at the corner points bordering on the X_1 and X_2 axes *i.e.* at point 'B' or at point 'D'. It all depends upon the values of the objective function coefficients and the angle of the iso-profit line that is discussed in the ensuing pages.

Proving the optimal solution: For the optimal solution to be correct, the total outputs must be equal to the total inputs available on the farm. In the above example, we obtained optimal solution at point C, where the farmer maximizes his total profits by producing 4 units of paddy and 9 units of maize. In order to determine the total amount of each input used by the farmer to produce 4 units of paddy and 9 units of maize, please refer to the columns (2) and (3) of the Table 9.3. It is shown that, to produce one unit of paddy, the farmer employs 30 units of fertilizer (F) and 5 labour man days (L) *i.e.*, 30F + 5L and to produce one unit of maize, the farmer employs 20 units of fertilizer (F) and 10 labour man days (L) *i.e.*, 20F + 10L. Since the farmer produces 4 units of paddy and 9 units of maize, the total inputs used to produce these two enterprises is shown here under.

Paddy	Maize
Total output x Inputs = Total inputs used	Total output x Inputs = Total inputs used
4 x 30F = 120F	9 x 20 F = 180F
4 x 5L = 20L	9 x 10L = 90L

So, the total amount of inputs used among the enterprises is given by,

Total amount of fertilizer used : 120F + 180F   = 300F

Total number of labour man days employed : 20L + 90L   = 110L

The last column of Table 9.3 shows the maximum amount of fertilizer available to the farmer is 300 and maximum number of labour man days available are 110. From this, we can infer that, the total amount of fertilizer available to the farmer (300 units) is equal to the total amount of fertilizer employed (300 units) and total number of labour man days available (110) are equal to the total number of labour man days employed. This infers that point 'C' in the Figure 9.4 represents the optimal solution and not at A, B or D.

b. Iso-Profit Line Approach

Another approach of solving the LP problem graphically is by computing the iso-profit line in taking up two enterprises paddy and maize. This approach is comparatively quicker in estimating the optimal solution compared to the earlier approach, as it is not required to calculate profit at each and every corner point in the feasible (shaded) region. An iso-profit line is a line that indicates same level of total profit of the given objective function. So, any point on the iso-profit line indicates same profits for a given objective function. *As per this approach, the criterion for maximization of profits (minimization of costs) is when the highest iso-profit line (lowest iso-cost line) touches the highest or extreme point of the feasible region (lowest point of the feasible region).*

Assume a profit level of Rs.48 and compute X_1 and X_2 with reference to the objective function *i.e.,* : Max Z $6X_1+8X_2 = 48$. Set, $X_1 = 0$ and then $X_2 = 6$. Now set $X_2=0$ and then $X_1=8$. Now the line connecting 8 units of X_1 and 6 units of X_2 is called iso-profit line (dotted line in Figure 9.5). As per the criterion of this approach, this iso-profit line does not touch the extreme point of the shaded region ABCD. So, again arbitrarily set another profit level say Rs. 72. Again follow the same procedure to

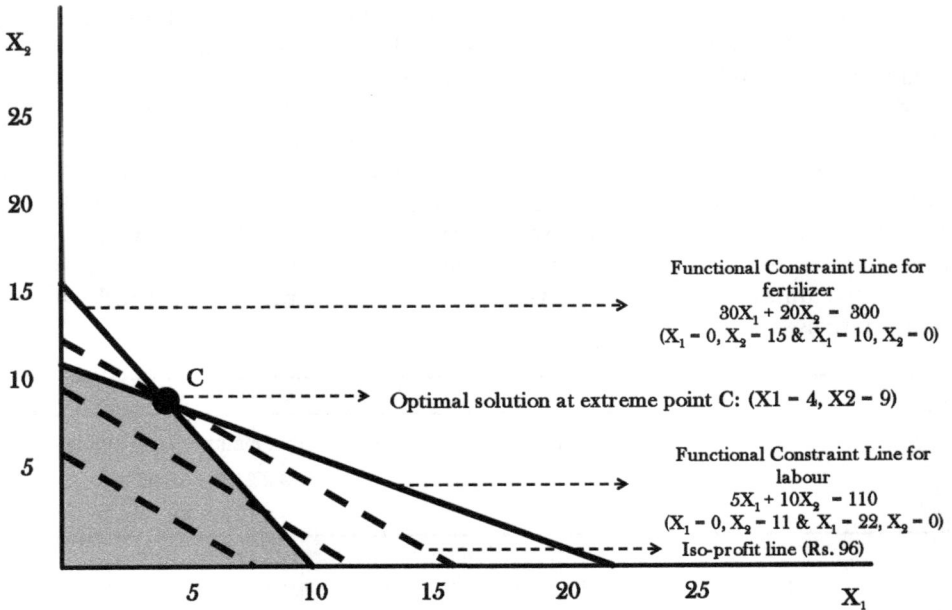

Figure 9.5: Finding Optimal Solution Based on Iso-Profit Line Approach.

compute X_1 and X_2 with reference to the objective function *i.e.,* Max Z $6X_1 + 8X_2 = 72$ and therefore, $X_1 = 12$ and $X_2 = 9$. Since this iso-profit line connecting 12 units of X_1 and 9 units of X_2 does not touch the extreme point of the shaded region ABCD, the optimal solution is not attained. Continuing this procedure is often laborious and time consuming and hence, draw a line that lies parallel to the previous iso-profit lines that connects the extreme point of the shaded area ABCD. This line passes through the point 'C' and (as computed in earlier approach), the coordinates at corner point C is ($X_1 = 4, X_2 = 9$). So, now with reference to the objective function (profit maximization): Max Z $6X_1 + 8X_2 = 6(4) + 8(9) =$ Rs.96 *i.e.,* by producing 4 units of paddy and 9 units of maize. This iso-profit line (Z=96) is drawn considering the objective function, Max Z: $6X_1 + 8X_2$ with $X_1 = 16$ and $X_2 = 0$; $X_2 = 12$ and $X_1 = 0$, as discussed above with reference to profit level of Rs.48.

Range of Optimality

Note that, the optimal solution will remain unchanged as long as

☆ An objective function coefficient lies within its range of optimality

☆ There are no changes in any other input parameters.

The value of the objective function will change if the coefficient multiplies a variable, whose value is non-zero.

ii. Dual of the Problem

With every LP problem, another LP problem is associated, which is called the dual of the original (or the primal) problem. In the above case for maximization problem, there is a dual of minimization of cost. To formulate the dual problem for primal problem, the following points are to be noted:

☆ The rows and columns are inter-changed.

☆ The direction of inequalities in the constraints is reversed. In the above case, the primal is maximization of profits and hence, the functional constraints have '≤' sign. So, in its dual (minimization of cost), the functional constraints have '≥' sign.

☆ The number of variables is reversed.

The following is the general relationship between primal and its dual LP problem:

Primal Problem	Dual Problem
Maximization function	Minimization function
Max $Z = a_1X_1 + a_2X_2$	Min $Z = c_1Y_1 + c_2Y_2 + c_3Y_3$
Subject to	Subject to
$b_{11}X_1 + b_{12}X_2 \leq c_1$	$b_{11}Y_1 + b_{21}Y_2 + b_{31}Y_3 \geq a_1$
$b_{21}X_1 + b_{22}X_2 \leq c_2$	$b_{12}Y_1 + b_{22}Y_2 + b_{32}Y_3 \geq a_2$
$b_{31}X_1 + b_{32}X_2 \leq c_3$	$Y_i \geq 0$
$X_i \geq 0$	

Let us write the dual problem now for the above studied (primal) example as follows:

Primal Problem

Max $Z : 6X_1 + 8X_2$

Subject to : $30X_1 + 20X_2 \leq 300$

$5X_1 + 10X_2 \leq 110$

$X_1, X_2 \geq 0$

Dual Problem

Min $Z : 300A + 110B$

Subject to : $30A + 5B \geq 6$ (Functional Constraint for Paddy X_1)

$20A + 10B \geq 8$ (Functional Constraint for Maize X_2)

$A, B \geq 0$

Step 1

Now, the above constraint inequalities will be converted into equalities as given below.

$30A + 5B = 6$ (Functional Constraint for Paddy X_1)

$20A + 10B = 8$ (Functional Constraint for Maize X_2)

Step 2

Compute horizontal and vertical intercepts from each functional constraint equation.

30A + 5B $\quad$ = 6 (Functional Constraint for Paddy X_1)

Assume A $\quad$ = 0. So,

30(0)+5B $\quad$ = 6

So, B=1.2 units. This 1.2 units of B represents B–intercept on the graph when A=0. This implies, only labour input is employed in producing paddy X_1 and no fertilizer is employed. Similarly, assume B=0. Then,

30(A) + 5(0) = 6

So, A=0.2 units. This 0.2 units of A represents A-intercept on the graph when B=0. This implies, only fertilizer input is employed in producing paddy X_1 and no labour are employed. When these two intercepts were joined on the graph, we get a straight line (Panel A of Figure 9.6). Similar procedure is followed to compute A intercept and B intercept from functional constraint for maize X_2. So, from the equation: 20A + 10B = 8, B = 0.8 units when A=0 (this implies, only labour input is employed in producing maize X_2 and no fertilizer is employed) and A = 0.4 units when B=0 (this implies, only fertilizer input is employed in producing maize X_2 and no labour is employed). When these two intercepts were joined on the graph, we get a straight line (Panel B of Figure 9.6).

Step 3

These two straight lines are now placed on the same graph (Figure 9.7). As mentioned earlier, in case of minimization function, the optimal value corresponds to the lowest value of the coordinates. We can estimate the valid coordinates for the above two constraint lines and the coordinates that satisfies these two constraint

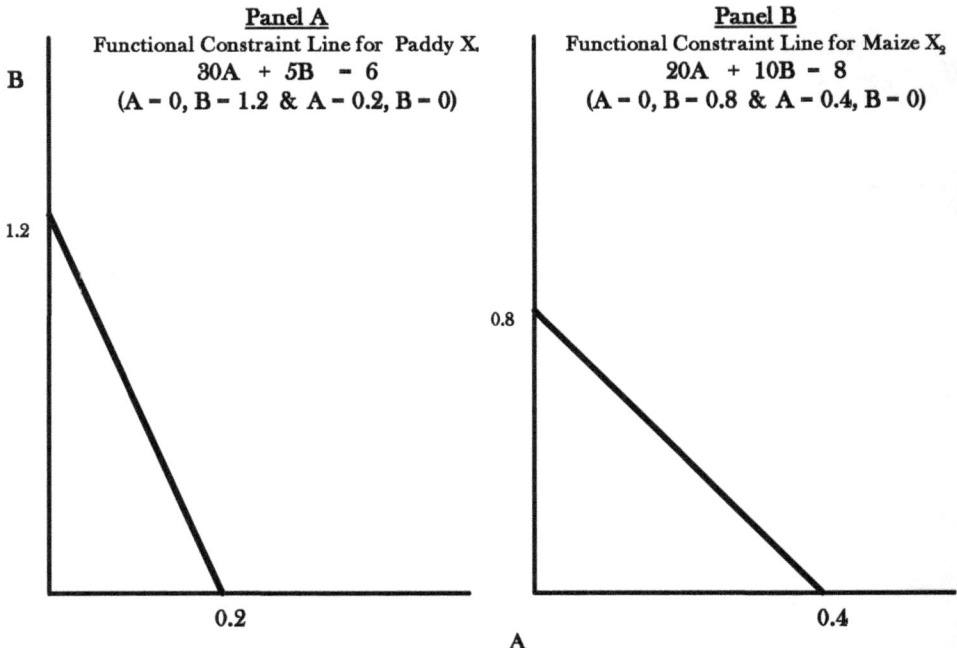

Panel A
Functional Constraint Line for Paddy X.
30A + 5B = 6
(A - 0, B - 1.2 & A - 0.2, B - 0)

Panel B
Functional Constraint Line for Maize X_2
20A + 10B - 8
(A - 0, B - 0.8 & A - 0.4, B - 0)

Figure 9.6: Functional Constraint Lines for Paddy X_1 and Maize X_2.

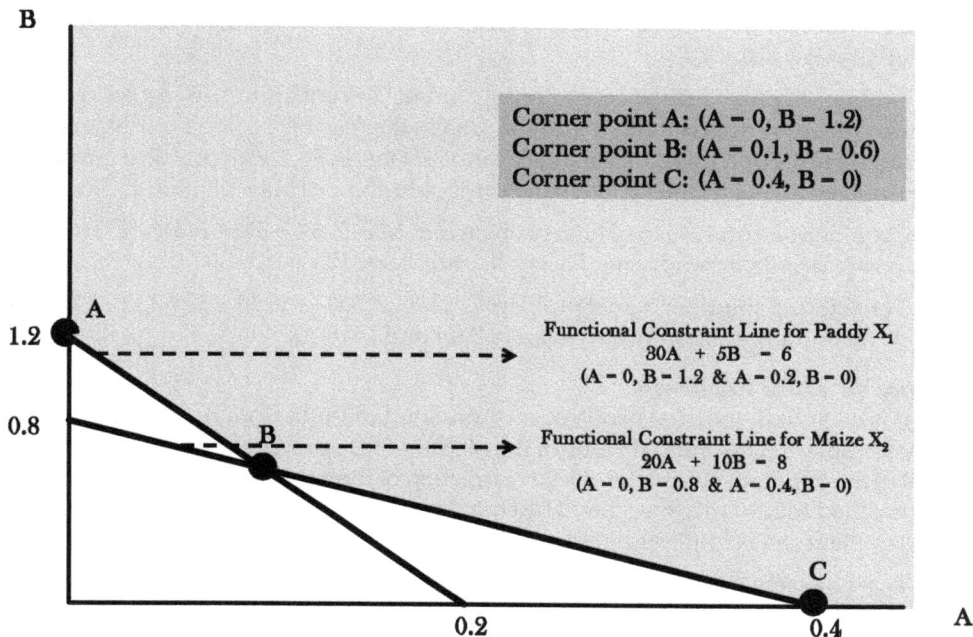

Figure 9.7: Finding Optimal Solution Based on Corner Point Approach.

lines are beyond the points A, B and C and thereby, ABC shaded area is the feasible region. That is, any coordinate outside the region ABC is valid to meet the functional constraints and hence, the region outside ABC constitutes the feasible region. Let us follow Corner point approach to derive optimal solution for this dual problem. This approach states that, *'the optimal solution to any LP problem is at the corner point or extreme point of the feasible region that contribute to minimum cost (Minimization function)'.*

In this example, the optimal solution in the feasible (shaded) region beyond ABC will lie at one of the corner points *i.e.*, 'A' or 'B' or 'C' that contribute to minimum cost. Let us find out the values at the corner points 'A', 'B' and 'C' with reference to the objective function and the lowest value at one of these three points corresponds to optimal solution in the feasible region beyond ABC.

Optimal solution or Cost at Corner point A: ($A = 0, B = 1.2$): $300A + 110B = 300(0) + 110(1.2) = $ Rs. 132

Optimal solution or Cost at Corner point B: To fix the coordinates at point B, where the two constraints lines intersect each other, we follow simultaneous equations approach. We know the two functional constraints:

$30A + 5B = 6$ (Functional Constraint for Paddy X_1)

$20A + 10B = 8$ (Functional Constraint for Maize X_2)

Multiply the first equation with -2 and by adding these two equations, we get A = 0.1. By substituting A in any of the above two equations, we get B = 0.6. So, Optimal solution or Cost at Corner point B is given by: ($A = 0.1, B = 0.6$): $300A + 110B = 300(0.1) + 110(0.6) = $ Rs.96.

Optimal solution or Cost at Corner point C: $(A = 0.4, B = 0.0)$: $300A+110B = 300(0.4)$ + $110(0.0)$ = Rs. 120.

Among the above three corner points, point 'B' contributes to lowest cost *i.e.*, Rs.96 and thereby, this is the optimal solution in the feasible region for this problem by employing 0.1 units of fertilizer and 0.6 units of labour. So, for all practical purposes, the primal and dual problems have the same solution *i.e.*, Max Z = Min Z. That is,

Considering solution to primal problem *i.e.*, Max Z $6X_1+8X_2 = 6(4) + 8(9)$ = Rs.96 (Maximum profits in producing Paddy X_1 and Maize X_2)

Considering solution to dual problem *i.e.*, Min Z $300A+110B = 300(0.1) + 110(0.6)$ = Rs.96 (Minimum cost in employing fertilizer and labour).

Primal vs. Dual Problems

It is clear that, the dual problem is formulated directly from the corresponding primal problem. The optimal value of the objective function of the primal problem is equal to the optimal value of the objective function of the corresponding dual problem. This is called the Duality theorem. The characteristics of the primal problem and the dual problem can be differentiated as follows:

The characteristics of the primal problem and the dual problem can be differentiated as follows:

☆ If the primal problem involves maximization problem, the dual problem is minimization and *vice versa.*

☆ The profit constant 'aj' in the primal problem replaces the capacity constants 'cj', while writing the dual problem.

☆ If the primal problem involves '≤' signs (Maximization function), the dual problem involves '≥' signs (Minimization function) and *vice versa.*

☆ The RHS constraint inequalities of the functional constraints in the primal problem are shown as constants in the objective function of the dual problem.

☆ A new set of variables appear in the dual problem.

☆ If there are 'n' decision variables and 'm' inequalities or constraints in the primal problem, then in the dual problem there will be 'm' decision variables and 'n' inequalities or constraints.

☆ The 'dual of the dual' problem is the original primal problem itself.

☆ If the primal problem has a solution, then its dual will also have the same solution.

☆ If the primal problem has multiple solutions, then the dual has degenerate solution.

☆ If the primal problem has infeasible solution, then the dual has infeasible or unbounded solution.

☆ If the primal problem has unbounded solution, then the dual has infeasible or unbounded solution.

Note that, the concept of duality can be used in a wide variety of applications including:

☆ It may be more efficient to solve the dual than the primal.

☆ The dual solution provides important economical interpretation such as shadow prices, *i.e.*, the marginal values of the RHS elements

iii. Cost Minimization Objective Function

Step 1

The first basic step involved is formulation of LP problem.

Example 9.4

Assume a cost minimization problem that, where a consumer prefers two foods Meat X_1 and Fish X_2 to derive two nutrients *viz.*, carbohydrates and proteins. The cost per unit of food X_1 is Rs. 2 and for food X_2 is Rs.6. The minimum requirement of carbohydrates is 3 units and minimum requirement of proteins is 8 units. The other requisite data are shown through Table 9.4.

The above given problem contains the information for the LP problem and it can be formulated as given below.

Table 9.4: Dietary Requirements of a Consumer from Two Foods

Nutritional Elements	Foods		
	Meat (X₁)	Fish (X₂)	Minimum Daily Requirement
Carbohydrates (units)	1	2	3
Protein (units)	2	8	8
Unit cost	2	6	

The above tabular form of LP problem can be conveniently expressed as mathematical equations as given below.

Min Z $2X_1+6X_2$

Subject to:

$1X_1 + 2X_2 \geq 3$ (Functional Constraint for carbohydrates)

$2X_1 + 8X_2 \geq 8$ (Functional Constraint for proteins)

$X_1, X_2 \geq 0$ (Non-negativity constraint)

Step 2

Now, the above constraint inequalities will be converted into equalities as given below.

$1X_1 + 2X_2 = 3$ (Functional Constraint for carbohydrates)

$2X_1 + 8X_2 = 8$ (Functional Constraint for proteins)

Step 3

Compute horizontal and vertical intercepts from each functional constraint equation.

$1X_1 + 2X_2 = 3$ (Functional Constraint for carbohydrates)

Assume $X_1 = 0$. So, $1(0)+2X_2=3$

So, X_2=1.5 units. These 1.5 units of X_2 represent X_2–intercept on the graph when $X_1 = 0$. This implies, all the carbohydrates are derived from food X_2 and nothing from food X_1. Similarly, assume X_2=0. Then,

$$1(X_1) + 2(0) = 3$$

So, X_1=3 units. These 3 units of X_1 represent X_1-intercept on the graph when X_2=0. This implies, all the carbohydrates are derived from food X_1 and nothing from food X_2. When these two intercepts were joined on the graph, we get a straight line (Panel A of Figure 9.8). Similar procedure is followed to compute X_1 intercept and X_2 intercept from functional constraint for proteins. So, from the equation: $2X_1 + 8X_2 = 8$, $X_2 = 1$ units when X_1=0 (this implies, all the proteins are derived from food X_2 and nothing from food X_1) and $X_1 = 4$ units when X_2=0 (this implies, all the proteins are derived from food X_1 and nothing from food X_2). When these two intercepts were joined on the graph, we get a straight line (Panel B of Figure 9.8).

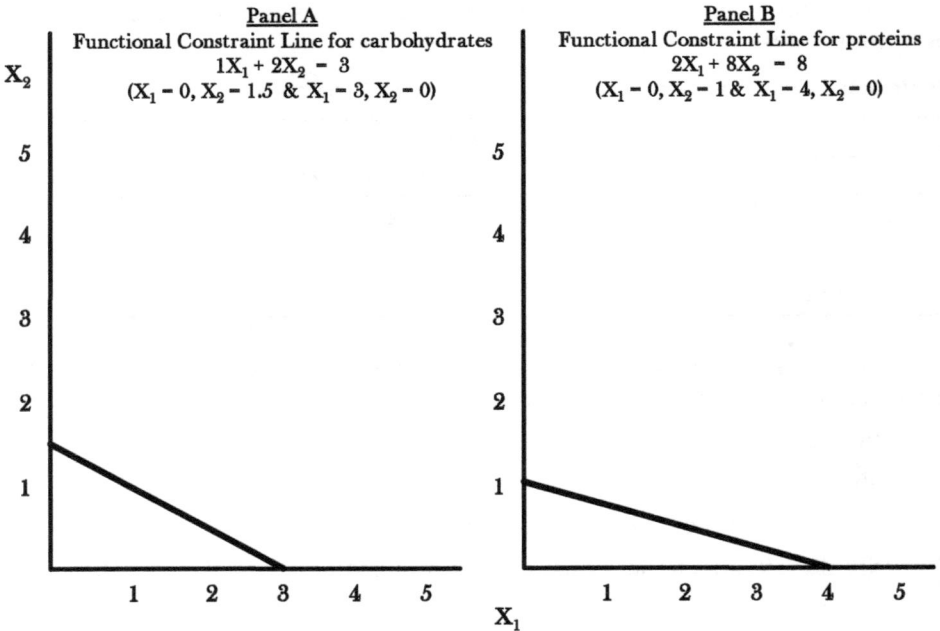

Figure 9.8: Functional Constraint Lines for Carbohydrates and Proteins.

Step 4

These two straight lines are now placed on the same graph (Figure 9.9). Feasible solution region is represented by the area on the graph that is valid for all constraints. Choosing any point in this area will result in a valid solution. In case of minimization function, the optimal value corresponds to the lowest value of the coordinates. We will use the origin (0,0) to check the valid side (feasible region) for both constraint lines. For carbohydrates constraint line, $1(0) + 2(0)$ is < 3 and thereby, this coordinate (0,0) is not valid. For proteins constraint line, the coordinate (0,0) is also not valid, as $2(0) + 8(0)$ is < 8. Likewise, we can estimate the valid coordinates for the above two constraint lines and the coordinates that satisfies these two constraint lines are beyond

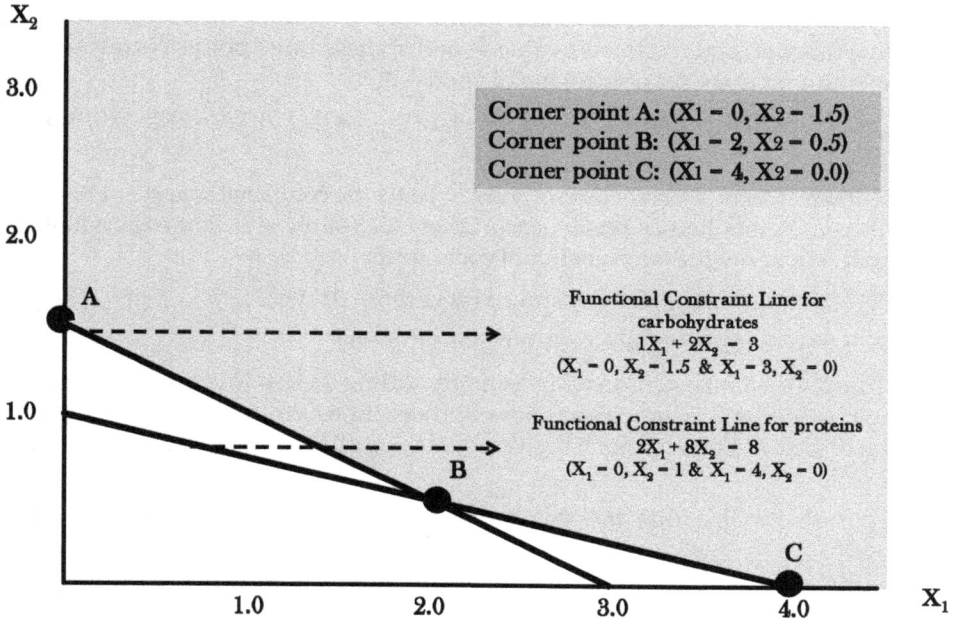

Figure 9.9: Finding Optimal Solution Based on Corner Point Approach.

the points A, B and C and thereby, ABC shaded area is the feasible region. Let us examine now the coordinates in this shaded region ABC with reference to the two constraint lines. Assume $X_1 = 4.5$ and $X_2 = 0.5$ and with reference to carbohydrates constraint line: $1X_1 + 2X_2$ is ≥ 3, then: $1(4.5) + 2(0.5)$ is >3 and thereby, this coordinate $(4.5, 0.5)$ is valid. Assume $X_1 = 2.5$ and $X_2 = 3$ and with reference to proteins constraint line: $2X_1 + 8X_2 \geq 8$, then: $2(2.5) + 8(3)$ is >8 and thereby, this coordinate $(2.5, 3.0)$ is valid. So, any coordinate outside the region ABC is valid to meet the functional constraints and hence, the region outside ABC constitutes the feasible region. There are several approaches to locate the optimal solution from the feasible region, but the two important approaches include: Corner point approach and Iso-cost line approach. Let us discuss their methodologies here under for this example.

a. Corner Point Approach

This is the simplest approach to estimate optimal solution from the feasible region *i.e.*, outside ABC region shown in the Figure 9.9. In the figure, both the constraint lines for carbohydrates and proteins are drawn and this gives the shaded region beyond ABC that satisfies both the constraints. In the shaded area beyond ABC, 'A', 'B' and 'C' are the corner points. This approach states that, *'the optimal solution to any LP problem is at the corner point or extreme point of the feasible region that contribute to minimum cost (Minimization function)'*. In this example, the optimal solution in the feasible (shaded) region beyond ABC will lie at one of the corner points *i.e.*, 'A' or 'B' or 'C' that contribute to minimum costs. Thus, optimal solution always occurs at corners. When more than one corner corresponds to an optimal solution, each corner and all points along the line connecting the corners correspond to optimal solutions.

Let us find out the values at the corner points 'A', 'B' and 'C' with reference to the objective function and the lowest value at one of these three points corresponds to optimal solution in the feasible region beyond ABC.

Optimal solution or Cost at Corner point A: $(X_1 = 0, X_2 = 1.5)$: $2X_1 + 6X_2 = 2(0) + 6(1.5)$ = Rs.9

Optimal solution or Cost at Corner point B: To fix the coordinates at point B, where the two constraints lines intersect each other, we follow simultaneous equations approach. We know the two functional constraints:

$1X_1 + 2X_2 = 3$ (Functional Constraint for carbohydrates)

$2X_1 + 8X_2 = 8$ (Functional Constraint for proteins)

Multiply the first equation with -2 and by adding these two equations, we get X_1 = 2. By substituting X_1 in any of the above two equations, we get $X_2 = 0.5$. So, Optimal solution or Cost at Corner point B is given by: $(X_1 = 2, X_2 = 0.5)$: $2X_1 + 6X_2 = 2(2) + 6(0.5)$ = Rs.7.

Optimal solution or Cost at Corner point C: $(X_1 = 4, X_2 = 0)$: $2X_1 + 6X_2 = 2(4) + 6(0)$ = Rs.8

Among the above three corner points, point 'B' contributes to lowest cost *i.e.*, Rs.7 and thereby, this is the optimal solution in the feasible region for this problem by consuming 2 units of food X_1 and 0.5 units of food X_2. Note that, in this example, the optimal solution is at corner point 'B' *i.e.*, at the point of intersection of two constraint lines, but this is not the case always. The optimal solution can also be at the corner points bordering on the X_1 and X_2 axes *i.e.*, at point 'A' or at point 'C'. It all depends upon the values of the objective function coefficients and the angle of the iso-cost line that is discussed here under.

b. Iso-cost Line Approach

Another approach of solving the LP problem graphically is by computing the iso-cost line in having two foods X_1 and X_2. This approach is comparatively quicker in estimating the optimal solution compared to the earlier approach, as it is not required to calculate cost at each and every corner point in the feasible (shaded) region. An iso-cost line is a line that indicates same level of total cost of the given objective function. So, any point on the iso-cost line indicates same cost for a given objective function. *As per this approach, the criterion for minimization of costs is when the lowest iso-cost line touches the lowest point of the feasible region.*

Assume a cost level of Rs.7 and compute X_1 and X_2 with reference to the objective function *i.e.*, Min Z $2X_1 + 6X_2 = 7$. Set $X_1 = 0$ and then $X_2 = 1.1$. Now, set $X_2 = 0$ and then $X_1 = 3.5$. Now the line connecting 3.5 units of X_1 and 1.1 units of X_2 is called iso-cost line (Figure 9.10). As per the criterion of this approach, this iso-cost line passes through the extreme point B of the shaded region ABC. Any cost level beyond Rs.7 will not pass through the lowest point of the shaded region. For example, at cost level Rs. 14, considering the objective function: Min Z $2X_1 + 6X_2 = 14$. Set $X_1 = 0$ and then X_2 = 2.3. Now, set $X_2 = 0$ and then $X_1 = 7.0$. Now the points connecting 7.0 units of X_1 and 2.3 units of X_2 is called iso-cost line and this not pass through lowest point of the shaded region. So, the iso-cost line of Rs.7 passes through the lowest point 'B' of the

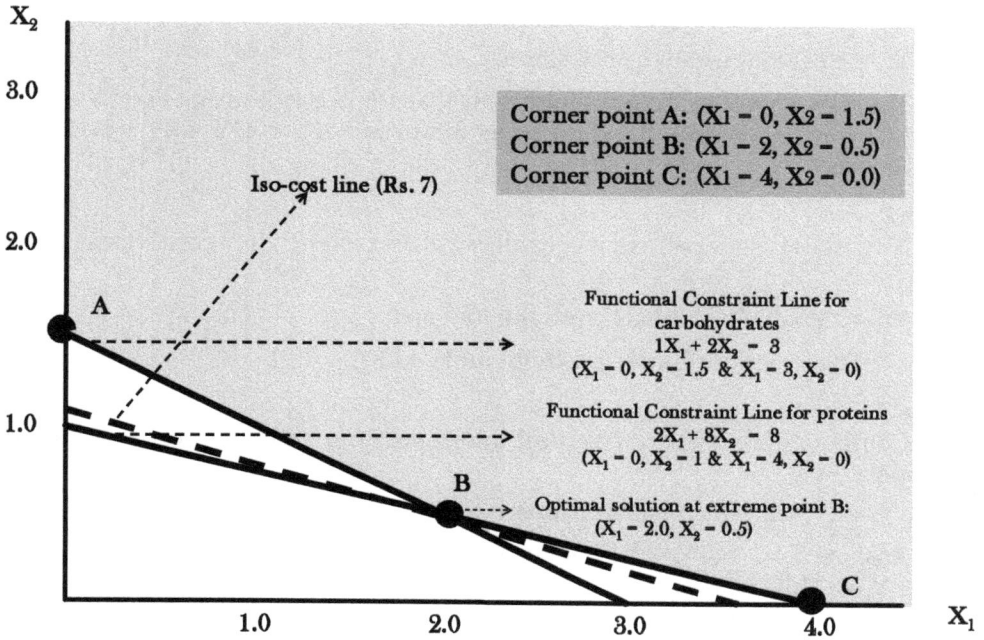

Figure 9.10: Finding Optimal Solution Based on Iso-Cost Line Approach.

shaded region and as computed in earlier approach, the coordinates at corner point B is $(X_1 = 2, X_2 = 0.5)$. So, now with reference to the objective function, cost minimization can be achieved as: Min Z $2X_1 + 6X_2 = 2(2) + 6(0.5) = $ Rs.7 *i.e.*, by consuming 2 units of food X_1 and 0.5 units of food X_2.

iv. Dual Problem

Every minimization problem has its corresponding maximization problem known as the dual. The primal of the above discussed problem is:

Min Z $2X_1 + 6X_2$

Subject to:

$1X_1 + 2X_2 \geq 3$ (Functional Constraint for carbohydrates)

$2X_1 + 8X_2 \geq 8$ (Functional Constraint for proteins)

$X_1, X_2 \geq 0$ (Non-negativity constraints)

Step 1

Let Y_1 and Y_2 be the prices of two foods X_1 and X_2 respectively. So, the objective function for the dual (maximization of value of diet) is:

Max Z $3Y_1 + 8Y_2$

Subject to:

$1Y_1 + 2Y_2 \leq 2$ (Functional Constraint for Food X_1)

$2Y_1 + 8Y_2 \leq 6$ (Functional Constraint for Food X_2)

$Y_1, Y_2 \geq 0$ (Non-negativity condition)

The above functional constraints imply that, the expenditure on Food X_1 ($1Y_1 + 2Y_2 \leq 2$) cannot exceed Rs. 2 and the expenditure on Food X_2 ($2Y_1 + 8Y_2 \leq 6$) cannot exceed Rs.6.

Step 2

Now, the above constraint inequalities will be converted into equalities as given below.

$1Y_1 + 2Y_2 = 2$ (Functional Constraint for Food X_1)

$2Y_1 + 8Y_2 = 6$ (Functional Constraint for Food X_2)

Step 3

Compute horizontal and vertical intercepts from each functional constraint equation.

$1Y_1 + 2Y_2 = 2$ (Functional Constraint for Food X_1)

Assume $Y_1 = 0$. So, $Y_2 = 1$. This 1 unit of Y_2 represents Y_2–intercept on the graph when $Y_1 = 0$. This implies, all the nutrients are derived from proteins of Food X_1 and nothing from carbohydrates. Similarly, assume $Y_2 = 0$. Then, $Y_1 = 2$ units. This 2 units of Y_1 represents Y_1–intercept on the graph when $Y_2 = 0$. This implies, all the nutrients are derived from carbohydrates of Food X_1 and nothing from proteins. When these two intercepts are joined on the graph, we get a straight line (Panel A of Figure 9.11). Similar procedure is followed to compute Y_1 intercept and Y_2 intercept from functional constraint of Food X_2. So, from the equation: $2Y_1 + 8Y_2 = 6$, $Y_2 = 0.75$ units when $Y_1 = 0$ (this implies, all the nutrients are derived from proteins of Food X_2 and nothing from carbohydrates) and $Y_1 = 3$ units when $Y_2 = 0$ (this implies, all the nutrients are derived from carbohydrates of Food X_2 and nothing from proteins). When these two intercepts are joined on the graph, we get a straight line (Panel B of Figure 9.11).

Step 4

These two straight lines are now placed on the same graph. In the Figure 9.12, A, B and C are the corner points of the feasible (shaded) region. That is, both the constraint lines for Food X_1 and Food X_2 gives the shaded region below ABC that satisfies both the constraints. Let us find out the values at the corner points 'A', 'B' and 'C' with reference to the objective function and the highest value at one of these three points corresponds to optimal solution in the feasible region below ABC.

Optimal solution or Value at Corner point A: ($Y_1 = 0$, $Y_2 = 0.75$): Max Z $3Y_1 + 8Y_2 = 3(0) + 8(0.75)$ = Rs.6

Optimal solution or Cost at Corner point B: To fix the coordinates at point B, where the two constraints lines intersect each other, we follow simultaneous equations approach. We know the two functional constraints:

$1Y_1 + 2Y_2 = 2$ (Functional Constraint for Food X_1)

$2Y_1 + 8Y_2 = 6$ (Functional Constraint for Food X_s)

Proteins Y$_2$

Panel A
Functional Constraint Line for Food X.
$1Y_1 + 2Y_2 - 2$
$(Y_1 - 0, Y_2 - 1 \ \& \ Y_1 - 2, Y_2 - 0)$

Panel B
Functional Constraint Line for Food X$_2$
$2Y_1 + 8Y_2 - 6$
$(Y_1 - 0, Y_2 - 0.75 \ \& \ Y_1 - 3, Y_2 - 0)$

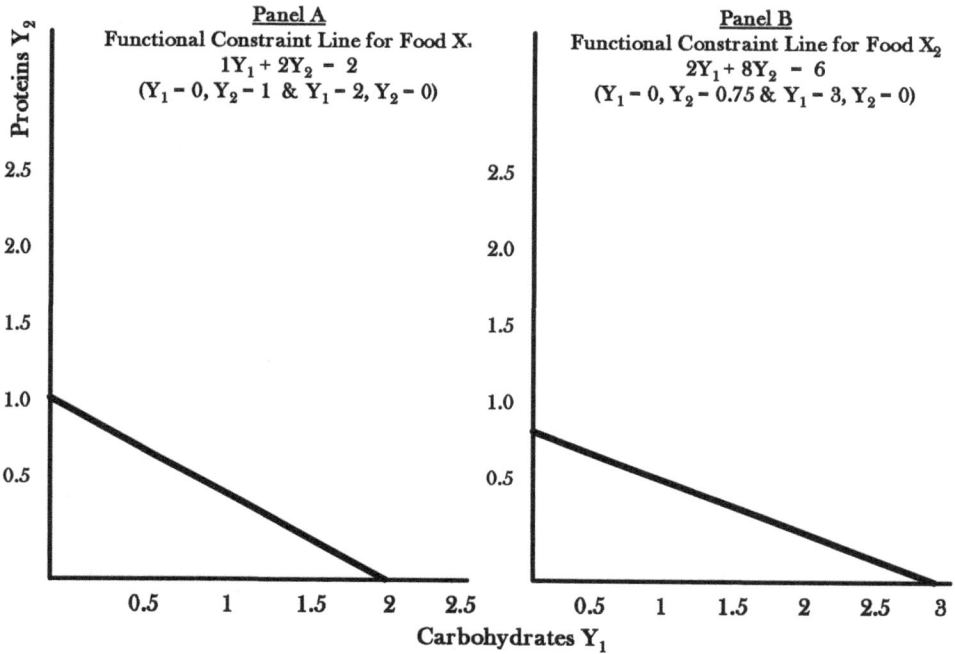

Carbohydrates Y$_1$

Figure 9.11: Functional Constraint Lines for Food X1 and Food X2.

Multiply the first equation with -2 and by adding these two equations, we get Y_2 = 0.5. By substituting Y_1 in any of the above two equations, we get $Y_1 = 1$. So, Optimal solution or Value at Corner point B is given by: $(Y_1 = 1, Y_2 = 0.5)$: Max Z $3Y_1+8Y_2 =$ 3(1)+8(0.5) = Rs.7

Optimal solution or Value at Corner point C: $(Y_1 = 2, Y_2 = 0)$: Max Z $3Y_1+8Y_2 =$ 3(2)+8(0) = Rs.6

Among the above three corner points, point 'B' contributes to highest value *i.e.* Rs.7 and thereby, this is the optimal solution in the feasible region for this problem. So, for all practical purposes, the primal and dual problems have the same solution *i.e.* Min Z = Max Z. That is,

Considering solution to primal problem *i.e.* Min Z $2X_1 + 6X_2 = 2(2) + 6(0.5) =$ Rs.7 (Minimum cost of diet).

Considering solution to dual problem *i.e.* Max Z $3Y_1+8Y_2 = 3(1)+8(0.5) =$ Rs.7 (Maximum value of diet).

So, both in primal problem and in dual problem, the consumer incurs Rs. 7 expenditure to attain optimal solution, so as to attain minimization of cost and maximum value of diet respectively.

As discussed above, in the context of LP, we call the solution region of the system of constraints as the feasible region and the points within this region as feasible points. So, the question now arises, which of all the feasible points will optimize the

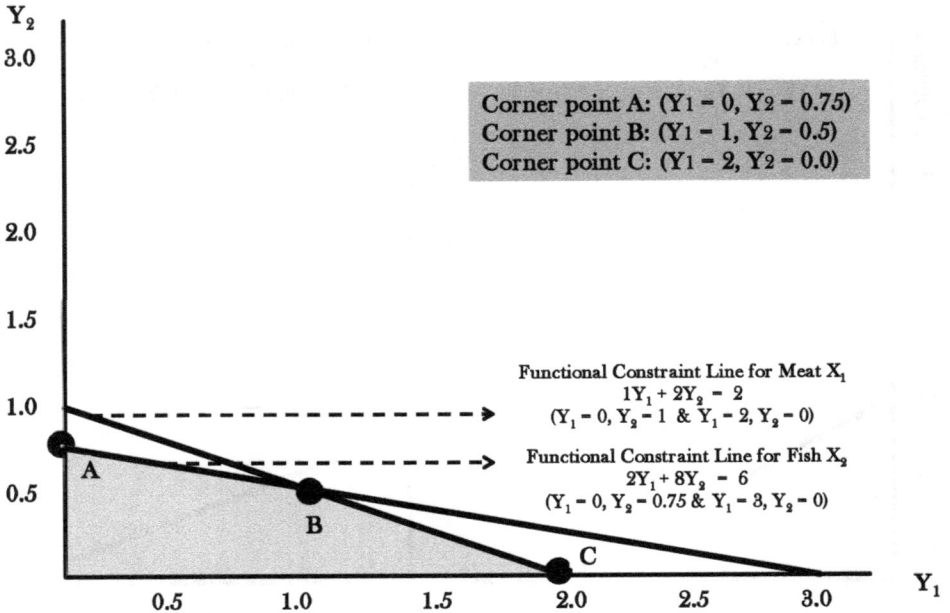

Figure 9.12: Finding Optimal Solution Based on Corner Point Approach.

objective function? Testing all of the points in the feasible region would be an impossible task. So, the Fundamental Theorem of LP limits the number of points we have to test and it is given below.

 ☆ If the solution to a LP problem exists, it will occur at a corner point.

 ☆ If two adjacent corner points are optimal solutions, then all points on the line segment between them are also optimal solutions.

 ☆ LP problems with bounded feasible regions will always have optimal solutions.

 ☆ LP problems with unbounded feasible regions may or may not have optimal solutions.

v. General Procedure of Graphical Approach

The steps followed in solving LP problem based on graphical approach are listed here under.

 ☆ Express the objective function of the problem as an equation and the constraints as inequalities.

 ☆ Convert the functional inequalities into linear equalities.

 ☆ Compute X-axis and Y-axis intercepts for both the functional constraints.

 ☆ Plot the two functional constraints on the graph and define the feasible region. The feasible solution region or solution space is represented by the area on the graph that is valid for all constraints. In case of maximization function, the optimal value corresponds to the greatest value of the coordinates. In case of minimization function, the optimal value corresponds to the lowest value of the coordinates.

☆ Shade the common portion of the graph that satisfies all the constraints simultaneously. This shaded area is called the 'feasible region' (or solution space) of the given LP problem (Figure 9.13). Any point in this shaded region is called feasible solution and provides values that satisfy all constraints.

☆ There are several approaches to locate the optimal solution from the feasible region, but the two important approaches include: Corner point approach and Iso-profit line approach (Maximization function) or Iso-cost line approach (Minimization function). *In corner points approach, 'the optimal solution to any LP problem is at the corner point or extreme point of the feasible region that contribute to maximum profit (Maximization function) or minimum cost (Minimization function)'. In case of Iso-profit line (Iso-cost line) approach, the criterion for maximization of profits (minimization of costs) is when the highest iso-profit line (lowest iso-cost line) touches the highest or extreme point of the feasible region (lowest point of the feasible region). This represents the optimal solution to the problem subject to the constraints faced.* Note that,

❖ The optimal solution cannot fall in the interior of the feasible region

❖ The optimal solution must occur at a 'corner point' of the feasible region.

❖ In searching for the optimal solution, we only have to examine the corner points.

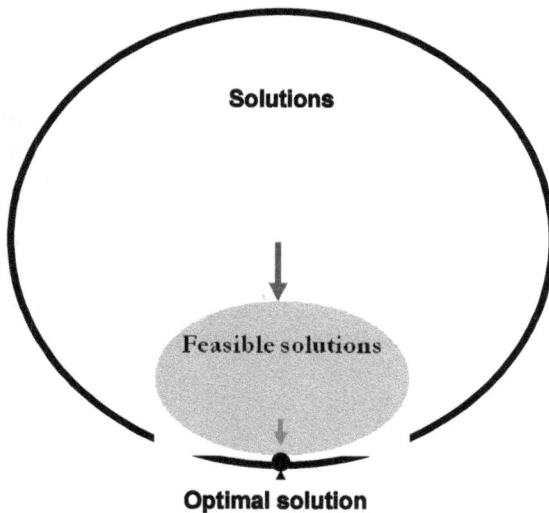

Solutions

Feasible solutions

Optimal solution

Optimal solution is the feasible solution that achieves the maximal (or minimal) objective value

Solution

• **Determine feasible region by drawing constraint lines**

• **Locate Feasible region that satisfy all coordinates of constraints**

• **Construct iso-profit lines (Maximization function) or iso-cost lines (Minimization function)**

• **Locate the optimal solution**

Figure 9.13: Generalized Graphical Approach in Solving LP Problem.

vi. Sensitivity Analysis

Farm managers are usually interested in more than the optimal solution to a LP problem. In addition to knowing the value of each decision variable and the value of the objective function, they want to know, how sensitive these answers are when parameters changes. For example, what happens, if the coefficients of the objective function and functional constraints are not exact or if they change by 10 or 15 percent? What happens if right-hand-side values of the constraints change? So, sensitivity analysis helps to test the sensitivity of the optimum solution with respect to changes of the coefficients in the objective function, coefficients in the functional constraints or the constant terms in the constraints. Because solution for a LP problem is based on the constancy of parameters or coefficients of the decision variables in objective function and the variables in functional constraints, the subject of sensitivity analysis comes into play. Hence, sensitivity analysis is also called as Post-optimality analysis. There are two approaches to perform sensitivity analysis to analyze, how sensitive an optimal solution is to changes made with respect to objective function and functional constraints. The first is simply a trial-and-error approach. This approach usually involves resolving the entire problem, preferably by computer, each time one input data item or parameter is changed. This approach however takes a long time to test a series of possible changes. The second approach popularly called as Analytic post-optimality method, wherein after an LP problem has been solved, we determine a range of changes in the coefficients of objective function and functional constraints to analyze the optimal solution or change the variables in the solution. This is done without resolving the whole problem. LP software, such as Excel's Solver or POM for Windows will be used for this analysis. The analysis based on these two approaches is beyond the scope of this book.

vii. Special Cases in Graphical Method

a. Alternate (or Multiple) Optimal Solutions

In the above examples, for each graphical solution, there was one optimal solution (unique solution). However, in certain cases, a given LP problem may have more than one (multiple) optimal solutions. Each of such optimal solutions is termed as alternative optimal solution. This occurs, when the objective function (Z) line say, the highest iso-profit line (or lowest iso-cost line) coincides with the farthest boundary (or nearest boundary) of the solution space or feasible region, and then the problem is said to possess multiple optimal solutions. In other words, the slope of the objective function is same as that of the constraint forming the boundary of the feasible region. Consider the following examples:

Example 9.5

Max $Z = 10X_1 + 6X_2$

Subject to

$5X_1 + 3X_2 \leq 30$ *Functional constraint for fertilizer*

$X_1 + 2X_2 \leq 18$ *Functional constraint for pesticides*

$X_1, X_2 \geq 0$

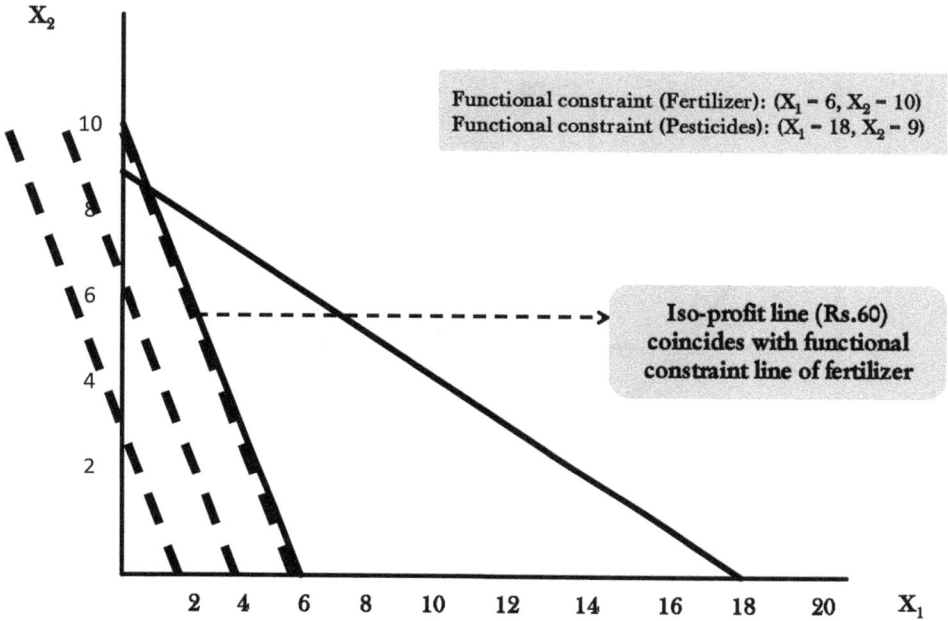

Figure 9.14: Alternate (Multiple) Optimal Solutions in LP Problem.

Solving the above problem by graphical method (say, by iso-profit line approach), the highest iso-profit line (Rs.60) coincides with the slope of one of the functional constraint line $5X_1 + 3X_2 \leq 30$ thereby, there are alternate (or multiple) optimal solutions (Figure 9.14).

Example 9.6

Max $Z = X_1 + 2X_2$

Subject to

$X_1 \leq 80$

$X_2 \leq 60$

$5X_1 + 6X_2 \leq 600$

$X_1 + 2X_2 \leq 160$

$X_1, X_2 \geq 0$

In the Figure 9.15, there is no unique outer most corners cut by the objective function line (Iso-profit line approach). For example, all points that lie between B to C lying on line BC represent optimal solutions and all these will give the same optimal value (maximum profit) of Rs.160. This is given below:

☆ At point B, the coordinates are (40, 60) and thereby, profit is given by: Max $Z = X_1 + 2X_2 = 40 + 2(60) = $ Rs. 160.

☆ At point C, the coordinates are (60, 50) and thereby, profit is given by: Max $Z = X_1 + 2X_2 = 60 + 2(50) = $ Rs. 160.

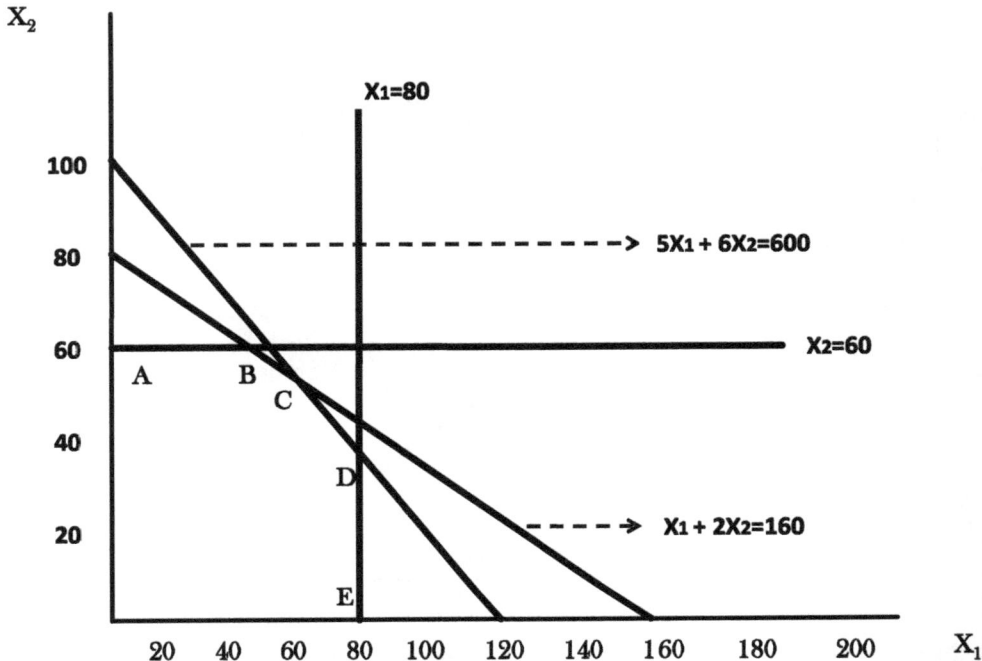

Figure 9.15: Alternate (Multiple) Optimal Solutions in LP Problem.

So, every point on the line BC maximizes the value of the objective function and the given problem has multiple solutions. Thus, it is clear that,

☆ When more than one corner corresponds to an optimal solution, each corner and all points along the connecting line segment will correspond to optimal solutions.

☆ Whenever all coefficients of one equation are the same multiples of another equation's coefficients, the lines are parallel. When the objective function line is parallel to a constraint line, there are multiple optimal solutions. In the above Example 9.5,

Max $Z = 10X_1 + 6X_2$ (Objective function)

$5X_1 + 3X_2 \leq 30$ (Functional constraint)

The ratio of X1 terms (10 and 5) is 10/5 or 2. The ratio of X_2 terms (6 and 3) is 6/3, also 2. Thus, the two lines are parallel and multiple optimal solutions exist.

Other Examples

Multiple optimal solutions can also be derived from the following cases:

Case 1

Max $Z = 10X_1 + 12X_2$

Subject to

$5X_1 + 6X_2 < 60$ (resource one)

$8X_1 + 4X_2 < 72$ (resource two)

$3X_1 + 5X_2 < 45$ (resource three)

$X_1, X_2 > 0$

Case 2

Maximize $Z = 40X_1 + 30X_2$

Subject to:

$1X_1 + 2X_2 \leq 40$

$4X_1 + 3X_2 \leq 120$

$X_1, X_2 \geq 0$

Case 3

Max $Z = 3X_1 + 2X_2$

Subject to:

$X_1 \leq 4$

$2X_2 \leq 12$

$3X_1 + 2X_2 \leq 18$

$X_1, X_2 \geq 0$

b. Unbounded Solution

Some of the LP problems may not have a finite solution. When the values of one or more decision variables and the value of the objective function are permitted to increase infinitely without violating the feasibility condition, then the solution is said to be unbounded. So, unbounded solution is a solution, whose objective function is infinite. It is to be noted that, the solution may be unbounded for maximization type of objective function with at least one of the functional constraint equations having no $\leq$ sign. This is because, in minimization type of objective function, the lower boundary is formed by non-negative condition for decision variables. Consider the following examples:

Example 9.7

Max $Z = 3X_1 + 5X_2$

Subject to

$2X_1 + X_2 \geq 7$

$X_1 + X_2 \geq 6$

$X_1 + 3X_2 \geq 9$

$X_1, X_2 \geq 0$

As shown through Figure 9.16, the corner points of feasible region are A, B, C and D. The coordinates for the corner points are: A (0, 7), B (1, 5), C (4.5, 1.5) and D (9, 0). So, the objective function at A, B, C and D corner points is given by,

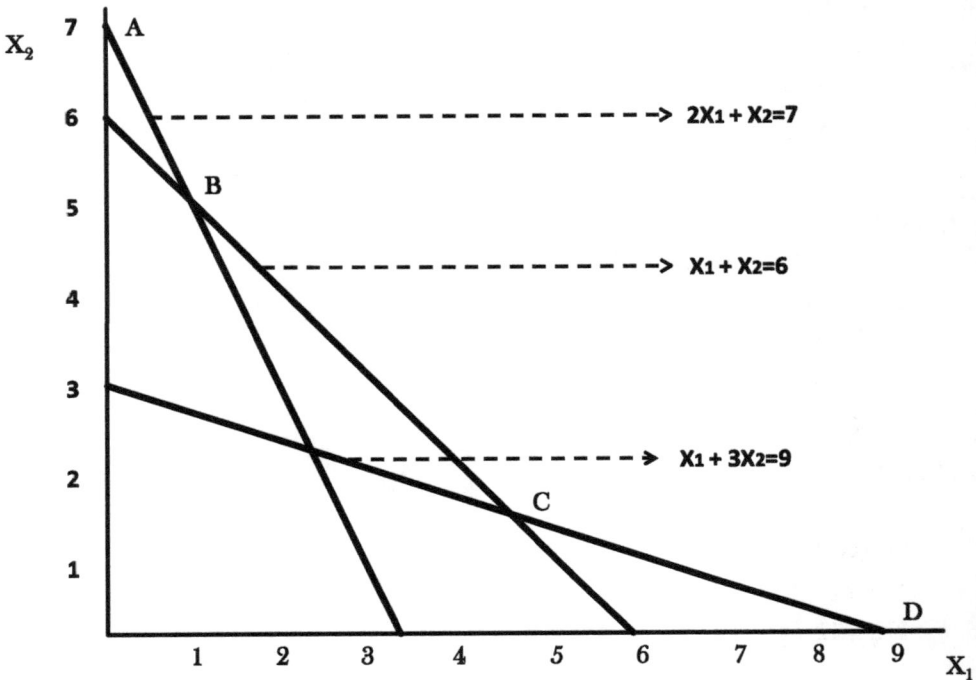

Figure 9.16: Unbounded Solution in LP Problem.

At corner point A: Max Z = 3X1 + 5X2 = 3(0) + 5(7)   = Rs.35

At corner point B: Max Z = 3X1 + 5X2 = 3(1) + 5(5)   = Rs. 28

At corner point C: Max Z = 3X1 + 5X2 = 3(4.5) + 5(1.5) = Rs. 21

At corner point D: Max Z = 3X1 + 5X2 = 3(9) + 5(0)   = Rs. 27

So, the values of objective function at corner points A, B, C and D are 35, 28, 21 and 27 respectively. But, there exists infinite number of points in the feasible region, which is unbounded. The value of objective function will be more than the value of these four corner points *i.e.* the maximum value of the objective function occurs at ∞. Hence, the given problem has unbounded solution.

Example 9.8

Max $Z = 3X_1 + 5X_2$

Subject to

$X_1 \le 4$

$X_1, X_2 \ge 0$

The graphical solution of the above problem (Figure 9.17) reveals that, there is no closing boundary for the solution space and hence, Z will be maximum at infinite value of X_2. Hence, the solution is unbounded. So, unbounded solution occurs, when the LP problem has no feasible solution.

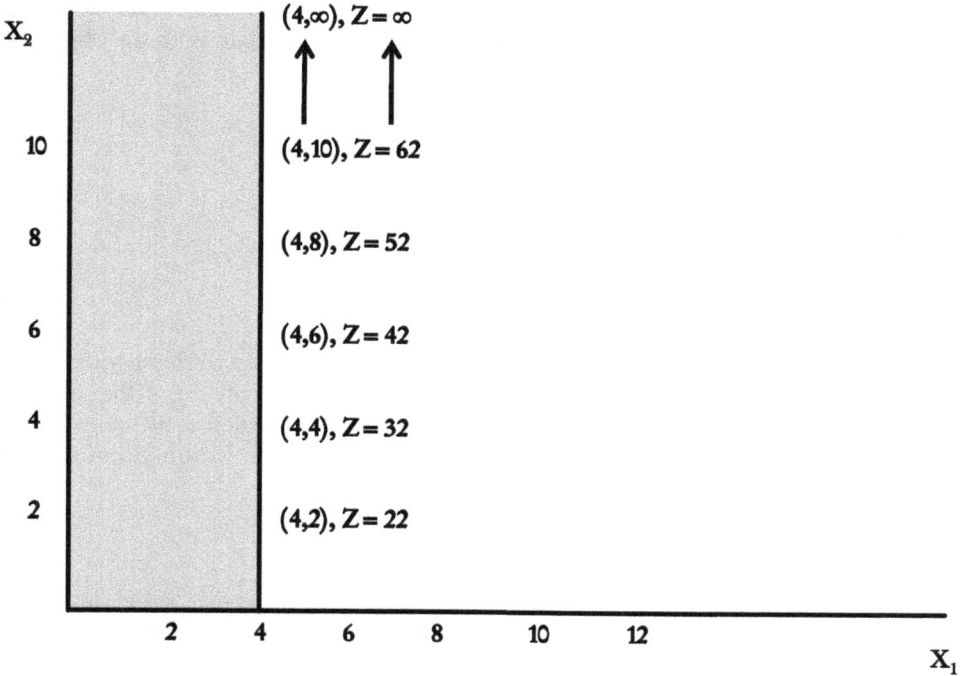

$(4,\infty),\ Z=\infty$

$(4,10),\ Z=62$

$(4,8),\ Z=52$

$(4,6),\ Z=42$

$(4,4),\ Z=32$

$(4,2),\ Z=22$

Figure 9.17: Unbounded Solution in LP Problem.

Other Examples

Unbounded solutions can also be derived from the following cases:

Case 1

Max $Z = 3X_1 + 2X_2$

Subject to

$X_1 - X_2 \geq 1$

$X_1 + X_2 \geq 3$

$4.5X_1 + 3X_2 \geq 9$

$X_1, X_2 \geq 0$

Case 2

Max $Z = 4X_1 + 2X_2$

Subject to

$X_1 \geq 4$

$X_2 \leq 2$

$X_1, X_2 \geq 0$

c. Infeasible Solution

Infeasibility is a condition, when constraints are inconsistent (mutually exclusive) *i.e.*, there are no points that satisfy all of the constraints of the problem simultaneously. So, there is no unique (single) feasible region. It should be noted that, infeasibility depends solely on constraints and has nothing to do with the objective function. Consider the following examples:

Example 9.9

$$\text{Max } Z = 3X_1 - 2X_2$$

Subject to

$$X_1 + X_2 \leq 1$$
$$2X_1 + 2X_2 \geq 4$$
$$X_1, X_2 \geq 0$$

The graphical solution (Figure 9.18) reveals that, to satisfy the first constraint, the solution must lie to the left of line AB. To satisfy the second constraint, the solution must lie to the right of line CD. There is no point (X_1, X_2), which satisfies both the constraints simultaneously. Hence, this problem has no solution because, the constraints are inconsistent.

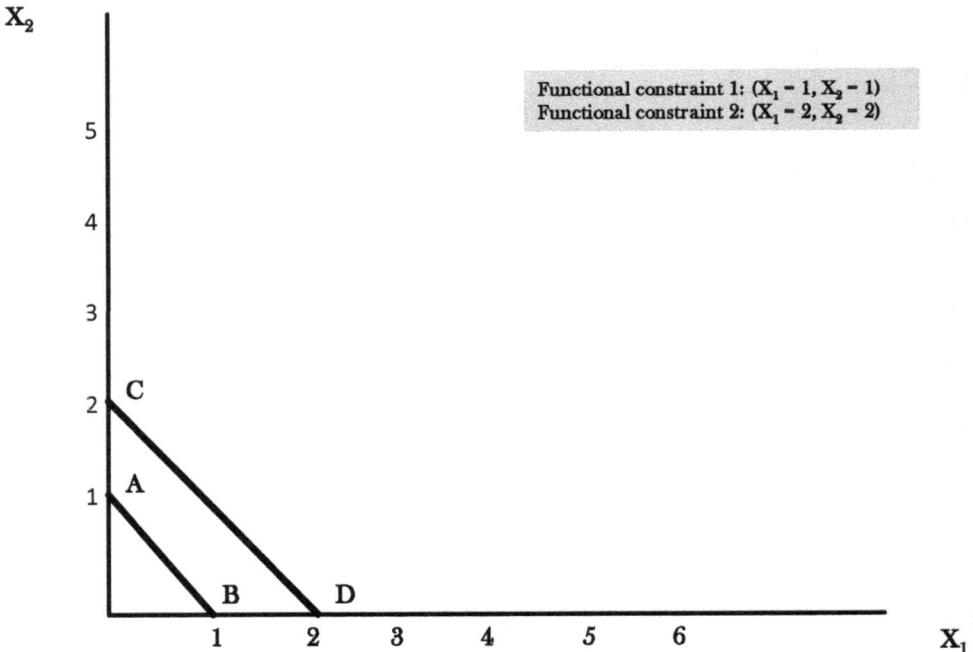

Functional constraint 1: $(X_1 - 1, X_2 - 1)$
Functional constraint 2: $(X_1 - 2, X_2 - 2)$

Figure 9.18: Infeasible Solution in LP Problem.

Example 9.10

$$\text{Min } Z = 200X_1 + 300X_2$$

subject to

$$2X_1 + 3X_2 \geq 1200$$
$$X_1 + X_2 \leq 400$$

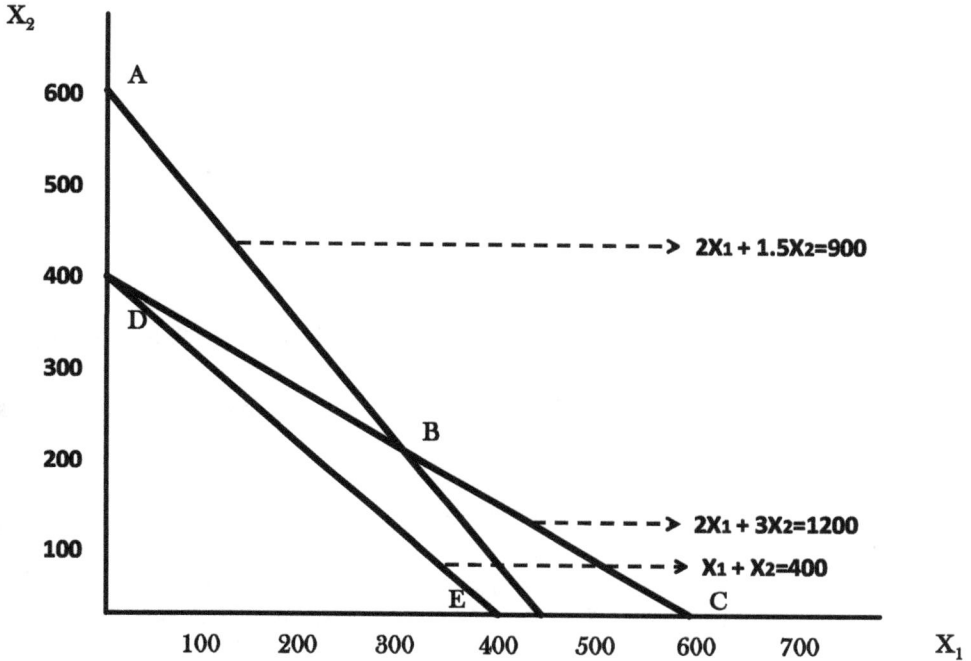

Figure 9.19: Infeasible Solution in LP Problem.

$$2X_1 + 1.5X_2 \geq 900$$
$$X_1, X_2 \geq 0$$

In the Figure 9.19, the region located on the right of ABC includes all solutions, which satisfies the first and the third constraints. The region located on the left of DE includes all solutions, which satisfies the second constraint. Thus, the problem is infeasible because, there is no set of points that satisfy all the three constraints.

Other Examples
Infeasible solutions can also be derived from the following cases:

Case 1
Max $Z = 5X_1 + 3X_2$

Subject to

$4X_1 + 2X_2 \leq 8$

$X_1 \geq 4$

$X_2 \geq 6$

$X_1, X_2 \geq 0$

Case 2

$$\text{Max } Z = 3X_1 + 5X_2$$

Subject to

$$X_1 \leq 4$$

$$2X_2 \leq 12$$

$$3X_1 + 2X_2 \leq 18$$

$$3X_1 + 5X_2 \geq 50$$

$$X_1, X_2 \geq 0$$

From the above discussion pertaining to the graphical approach for solving LP problem, we can conclude that,

☆ Alternate optimal solutions occur, when more than one point optimizes the objective function.

☆ Unboundness occurs, when the objective function can become infinitely large (maximum) or infinitely small (minimum).

☆ Infeasibility in solution occurs, when a model has no feasible point.

☆ A Corner-Point Feasible (CPF) solution is a solution that lies at a corner of the feasible region. The LP problem must possess CPF solutions and at least one optimal solution. Furthermore, the best CPF solution must be an optimal solution. Thus, if a LP problem has exactly one optimal solution, it must be a CPF solution. If the problem has multiple optimal solutions, at least two must be CPF solutions.

B. Simplex Method

For LP problems involving only two variables, the graphical solution method discussed earlier is convenient. However, in practice, most LP problems contain more than two variables and a large number of constraints and hence, it is better to use an algebraic technique of Simplex method. In 1947, George B. Dantzig, then part of a research group of the U.S. Air Force known as Project SCOOP (Scientiûc Computation of Optimum Programs), developed the simplex method for solving the general LP problem. Hence, this method is also called as Dantzig's simplex method in honour of the mathematician, who devised this approach. The simplex method ensures two advantages in terms of feasibility and optimality. The search for the optimality starts from a basic feasible solution. The solution is tested for optimality and if it is optimal, then the search is stopped. The search for optimal solution is continued by designing a new and better basic feasible solution *i.e.* if the solution is found not optimal, a new feasible solution is designed and this is continued till the optimal solution is attained. Thus, the simplex method comprises of several iterations or plans till the optimal solution (*i.e.* maximum or minimum values of the objective function) is attained. The extraordinary computational efficiency and robustness of the simplex method, together with the availability of high-speed digital computers, have made LP the most powerful optimization method ever designed and the most widely applied in the business environment. This method is applicable to any type of problem that can be formulated in terms of linear constraints. Now, let us study addressing the LP problems through employing simplex method with reference to both profit maximization and cost minimization objective functions.

i. Profit Maximization Objective Function

Example 9.11

Assume a farmer has 12 units of land, 48 man days of labour and Rs.360 of capital. He wishes to cultivate paddy, groundnut and red gram in his farm. One unit of paddy production requires 6 man days of labour and Rs.36 of capital. One unit of groundnut production requires 6 man days of labour and Rs. 24 of capital. One unit of red gram production requires 2 man days of labour and Rs.18 of capital. The net income from the production of paddy, groundnut and red gram are Rs.40, Rs.30 and Rs. 20 per unit respectively. Suggest optimum production programme to the farmer considering the resource constraints.

Answer

Step 1

The above information can be conveniently presented in the form of table:

	Amounts of Inputs Required to Produce One Unit of Output			
Resources	Paddy (X_1)	Groundnut (X_2)	Redgram (X_3)	Total Resources Available
Land (units)	1	1	1	12
Labour (man days)	6	6	2	48
Capital (Rs.)	36	24	18	360
Net income	40	30	20	

Step 2

The above tabular form of LP problem can be conveniently expressed as mathematical equations. That is, translate the given data in the table into inequalities as given below.

Max Z $40X_1+30X_2+20X_3$

Subject to:

$1X_1+1X_2+1X_3 \leq 12$ units (Land)

$6X_1+6X_2+2X_3 \leq 48$ man days (Labour)

$36X_1+24X_2+18X_3 \leq$ Rs.360 (Capital)

The above expression of LP problem is said to be in 'Original form' or 'General form'. The desired largest (or smallest) value of the objective function is called the Optimal value, and a collection of values of X_1, X_2, X_3. that gives the optimal value constitutes an optimal solution. The variables X_1, X_2, X_3. are called the decision variables.

Step 3

Then, all these inequalities are to be converted into equalities by adding slack variables or disposal activities. This form of expression of LP problem represent LP problem in Standard form. So, a LP problem is in standard form, if it seeks to maximize the objective function subject to the given constraints and representing in terms of slack variables. That is, since the left-hand side of each inequality is less than or equal to the right-hand side, there must exist non-negative numbers and that can be added to the left side of each equation to produce the following system of linear equations:

$$1X_1+1X_2+1X_3 +X_4 \leq 12 \text{ units (Land)}$$
$$6X_1+6X_2+2X_3 \qquad +X_5 \leq 48 \text{ man days (Labour)}$$
$$36X_1+24X_2+18X_3 \qquad +X_6 \leq \text{Rs.360 (Capital)}$$

The variables X_4, X_5 and X_6 are called slack variables with respect to land, labour and capital resources because, they take up the 'slack' in each inequality. Now, the above unequal mathematical equations turn into equalities with the addition of slack variables as given below.

Max Z $40X_1+30X_2+20X_3+0X_4+0X_5+0X_6$

Subject to:

$$1X_1+1X_2+1X_3+1X_4+0X_5+0X_6 \qquad = 12$$
$$6X_1+6X_2+2X_3 +0X_4+1X_5+0X_6 \qquad = 48$$
$$36X_1+24X_2+18X_3 +0X_4+0X_5+1X_6 \quad = 360$$
$$X_1, X_2, X_3, X_4, X_5 \text{ and } X_6 \geq 0$$

This LP problem is called 'linear' because, the objective function to be maximized and the functional constraints (inequalities) involve the terms which are of the first degree. There is no interaction term in terms of two or more variables *i.e.*, there is no second degree (power) or more in the above equations. A linear program is said to be in Standard form or Augmented form, in which all the constraints are written as equalities. The above format can also be written as:

Max Z $40X_1+30X_2+20X_3+0X_4+0X_5+0X_6$

Subject to:

$$X_4 = 12 - 1X_1-1X_2-1X_3$$
$$X_5 = 48 - 6X_1-6X_2-2X_3$$
$$X_6 = 360 - 36X_1-24X_2-18X_3$$
$$X_1, X_2, X_3, X_4, X_5 \text{ and } X_6 \geq 0$$

This layout is called a dictionary. Thus, setting X_1, X_2 and X_3 to zero, we can read off the values for the other variables: X_4, X_5 and X_6 as $X_4 = 12$, $X_5 = 48$ and $X_6 = 360$. This specific solution is called a dictionary solution. So, dependent variables, on the left, are called basic variables and independent variables, on the right, are called non-basic variables. Note that, all the variables in the current dictionary solution are non-negative. Such a solution is called feasible solution. But, the initial dictionary solution need not be always feasible.

Initial Basic Feasible Solution

Now we assume that, nothing can be produced. Therefore, the values of the decision variables are zero *i.e.*, $X_1=0$, $X_2=0$ and $X_3=0$. When we are not producing anything, obviously we left with unused capacity *i.e.*, represented by slack variables. That means, $X_4=12$, $X_5=48$ and $X_6=360$. Thus, the current solution has three slack variables *i.e.*, X_4, X_5 and X_6 with non-zero solution values and three decision variables *i.e.*, X_1, X_2 and X_3 with zero values. Variables with non-zero values are called basic variables and variables with zero values are called non-basic variables. So, when we are not producing anything, in the above given equations, X_4, X_5 and X_6 are basic variables and X_1, X_2 and X_3 are non-basic variables. So, the basic feasible solution at the initial tableau is (0, 0, 0, 12, 48, 360) where, $X_1 = 0$, $X_2 = 0$ and $X_3 = 0$, $X_4 = 12$, $X_5 = 48$, $X_6 = 360$ and $Z = 0$. The solution at the initial tableau is associated to the origin point at which all the decision variables are zero. If all the variables in basic solution are *more than or equal* to zero, then it is called Basic Feasible Solution (BFS). Thus, an initial basic feasible solution is obtained by setting $X_1=0, X_2=0, X_3=0$ such that, $X_4=12$, $X_5=48$, $X_6=360$. Note that, if there are 'm' constraints in the given problem, the number of slack variables or disposal activities added will be 'm'.* In this example, there are three constraints with respect to land, labour and capital and hence, three disposal activities X_4, X_5 and X_6 are added. It is at this point, we begin applying the simplex method to solve the formulated LP problem.

Thus, a basic solution is an augmented corner point solution and it has the following properties:

☆ Each variable is designated as either a non-basic variable or a basic variable.

☆ The number of basic variables equals the number of functional constraints. Therefore, the number of non-basic variables equals the total number of variables minus the number of functional constraints.

☆ The non-basic variables are set equal to zero.

Note *: *Objective function (Maximization function):*

$$\text{Max } Z = a_1X_1 + a_2X_2 + a_3X_3 + \text{---------} + a_nX_n \qquad \textit{Objective function}$$

Constraints (*i.e.*, subject to):

$$b_{11}X_1 + b_{12}X_2 + b_{13}X_3 + \text{----------} + b_{1n}X_n \le c_1 \qquad \textit{(Functional Constraint of Resource 1)}$$

$$b_{21}X_1 + b_{22}X_2 + b_{23}X_3 + \text{----------} + b_{2n}X_n \le c_2 \qquad \textit{(Functional Constraint of Resource 2)}$$

$$\begin{matrix} \cdot & \cdot & & \cdot & & \cdot \\ \cdot & \cdot & & \cdot & & \cdot \end{matrix}$$

$$b_{m1}X_1 + b_{m2}X_2 + b_{m3}X_3 + \text{-----------} + b_{mn}X_n \le c_m \qquad \textit{(Functional Constraint of Resource 'n')}$$

After adding slack variables, the corresponding system of constraint equations is:

$$b_{11}X_1 + b_{12}X_2 + b_{13}X_3 + \text{----------} + b_{1n}X_n + S_1 = c_1$$
$$b_{21}X_1 + b_{22}X_2 + b_{23}X_3 + \text{----------} + b_{2n}X_n + S_2 = c_2$$

$$\begin{matrix} \cdot & \cdot & & \cdot & & \cdot \\ \cdot & \cdot & & \cdot & & \cdot \end{matrix}$$

$$b_{m1}X_1 + b_{m2}X_2 + b_{m3}X_3 + \text{-----------} + b_{mn}X_n + Sm = c_m$$

where, S_1, S_2 and S_3 are the slack variables or disposal activities

☆ The values of the basic variables are obtained as simultaneous solution of the system of equations (functional constraints in augmented form). The set of basic variables are called 'basis'.

☆ If the basic variables satisfy the non-negativity constraints, the basic solution is a BFS.

Step 4

In order to simplify handling the above mathematical equations in the problem, they are placed in the tabular form called Simplex tableau. The initial simplex tableau is given below (Table 9.5):

Table 9.5: Simplex tableau

Contri-bution	Restri-ctions (Resources)	Restriction Levels	Real (Production) Activities			Slack Variables/Disposal Activities		
			Paddy X_1/unit	Groundnut X_2/unit	Red Gram X_3/unit	Land X_4	Labour X_5	Capital X_6
0	Land (units)	12	1	1	1	1	0	0
0	Labour (man days)	48	6	6	2	0	1	0
0	Capital (Rs.)	360	36	24	18	0	0	1
	Net Income (C) (Rs.)		40	30	20	0	0	0
	Opportunity Cost (Z)		0	0	0	0	0	0
	Shadow price (Z-C)		−40	−30	−20	0	0	0

Explanation of the notations of the Simplex tableau:

1. In the second column, all the resources or restrictions *viz.*, land, labour and capital are given and they are known as basic variables. Note that, any variables that are not listed under the second column are not basic variables.

2. In the third column, the maximum levels of the three resources *viz.*, land, labour and capital are given and it is called as Restriction levels. So, this column indicates the values of basic variables.

3. The numbers in the 'Z' row under each variable is the opportunity cost. This indicates the value of other activity that must be sacrificed to produce one more unit of output. All values of 'Z' row in Table 9.5 are zero because, all resources are unused.

4. The difference between opportunity cost (Z) and net income (C) gives the shadow price. This row is also called as Evaluation row or Criterion row. It is the row, the Marginal Value Productivities (MVPs) are the same as those

in the objective function, but with negative signs indicating the sacrifice of not including a particular activity. However, it is to be kept in mind that, it amounts to a positive gain by picking up the particular activity.

5. In all the disposal activities columns, enter the coefficients of slack variables as indicated in the mathematical equations.

Now, transfer the data from the above matrix of Step 5 to the Plan I as given below.

Step 5: The above data are presented through matrices as shown below:

$$[40\ 30\ 20\ 0\ 0\ 0]\begin{bmatrix}X_1\\X_2\\X_3\\X_4\\X_5\\X_6\end{bmatrix} - \text{Max Z}$$

Subjected to:-

$$\begin{bmatrix}1&1&1&1&0&0\\6&6&2&0&1&0\\36&24&18&0&0&1\end{bmatrix}\begin{bmatrix}X_1\\X_2\\X_3\\X_4\\X_5\\X_6\end{bmatrix}\begin{bmatrix}-12\\-48\\-360\end{bmatrix}$$

$$\begin{bmatrix}X_1\\X_2\\X_3\\X_4\\X_5\\X_6\end{bmatrix} \geq 0$$

Plan I

Contri-bution (Net Income)	Restric-tion	Resource Activity Level	Real Activities			Disposable Activities			Ratio
			Paddy	Groundnut	Red Gram	Land	Labour	Capital	
			X_1	X_2	X_3	X_4	X_5	X_6	
0	Land X_4	12	1	1	1	1	0	0	12/1 = 12
0	Labour X_5	48	6	6	2	0	1	0	48/6 = 8
0	Capital X_6	360	36	24	18	0	0	1	360/36 = 10
	Net income (C)		40	30	20	0	0	0	
	Opportunity cost (Z)		0	0	0	0	0	0	
	Shadow price (Z-C)		-40	-30	-20	0	0	0	
Value of programme	0								

Computation Procedure

The following computational procedure is followed to derive optimal plan from the basic solution:

Opportunity Cost (Z)

In the above table (Plan I), Opportunity cost (Z) is calculated by the formula:

Σ(Contribution x Corresponding real activities of Paddy X_1, Groundnut X_2 and Red gram X_3)

$(0 \times 1 + 0 \times 6 + 0 \times 36) = 0$ (For column 4)

$(0 \times 6 + 0 \times 6 + 0 \times 2) = 0$ (For column 5)

$(0 \times 36 + 0x24 + 0x18) = 0$ (For column 6)

Σ(Contribution x Corresponding disposal activity values of Land X_4, Labour X_5 and Capital X_6)

$(0 \times 1 + 0 \times 0 + 0 \times 0) = 0$ (For column 7)

$(0 \times 0 + 0 \times 1 + 0 \times 0) = 0$ (For column 8)

$(0 \times 0 + 0 \times 0 + 0 \times 1) = 0$ (For column 9)

Ratio

To calculate Ratio, consider lowest or highest negative shadow price (*i.e.*, -40) and consider that column real activities of Paddy X_1. Divide resource activity level values of Land X_4, Labour X_5 and Capital X_6 (*i.e.*, column 3) with corresponding real activities of Paddy X_1 of lowest shadow price column (*i.e.*, column 4) *i.e.*, 1, 6 and 36 to get Ratios: *i.e.*, 12/1 =12; 48/6 =8; 360/36=10.

Value of the Programme

It is given by Σ(Contribution x Corresponding resource activity level) for each row of Land X_4, Labour X_5 and Capital X_6 restrictions *i.e.*, [(0x12)+(0x48)+(0x360)] =0.

Among the computed ratio values in I Plan, consider lowest ratio (i.e, 8) and eliminate that row (*i.e.*, Labour X_5 row) in the next plan (*i.e.*, Plan II). Now, replace that row (*i.e.*, Labour X_5 row) by employing the pivot value of the column with respect to lowest shadow price column in Plan I (*i.e.*, -40 shadow price column). So, considering the Labour X_5 row and column of the lowest shadow price (-40), the pivot value is 6 *i.e.*, the intersection value of the selected row and selected column. Now, divide the entire eliminated Labour X_5 row values with the pivot value (6) and include them as Paddy X_1 row, as shown through Plan II. This is given by:

=48/6 = 8

=6/6   = 1

=6/6   = 1

=2/6   = 1/3

=0/6   = 0

=1/6   = (1/6)

=0/6   = 0

Now, transfer the above calculated values as Paddy X_1 row values in Plan II. Thus, it is clear that, after computing Plan I, the row corresponding to lowest Ratio (8) is the outgoing row (Labour X_5) and it is replaced by the real activity (Paddy X_1) that corresponds to lowest shadow price or highest negative shadow price (-40) by dividing all the values of outgoing row (Labour X_5) with the pivot element of outgoing row and incoming real activity. The pivot element (or pivot number or pivot value or key number) is the common element that lies at the intersection of outgoing row and real activity column with lowest shadow price or highest negative shadow price. The row (Labour X_5) with pivot number is called Key row and other rows (Land X_4 and Capital X_6) are called non-key rows. Thus, the departing row corresponds to the smallest non-negative ratio. The entering activity or variable corresponds to the smallest (the most negative) entry in the shadow price column of the tableau. The entry or the number in the departing row and the entering activity column of the lowest shadow price or highest negative shadow price is called the pivot.

Plan II

Contri-bution (Net Income)	Restric-tion	Resource Activity Level	Real Activities			Disposable Activities			Ratio
			Paddy X_1	Groundnut X_2	Red Gram X_3	Land X_4	Labour X_5	Capital X_6	
0	Land X_4	4	0	0	2/3	1	-1/6	0	6
40	Paddy X_1	8	1	1	1/3	0	1/6	0	24
(Paddy net income)									
0	Capital X_6	72	0	-12	6	0	-6	1	12
	Net income (C)		40	30	20	0	0	0	
	Opportunity cost (Z)		40	40	40/3	0	20/3	0	
	Shadow price (Z-C)		0	10	-20/3	0	20/3	0	
Value of programme	320								

Note: To calculate non-key row values in Plan II for Land X_4 and Capital X_6, the following formula is used:

N=O-(I x P), where O=Previous row value of the restriction (Land X_4 and Capital X_6) in previous Plan I, I= Incoming row value in Plan II (*i.e.*, Paddy X_1 values of row 2 in this current Plan II), P=Pivot value for Land X_4 and Capital X_6 corresponding to the lowest shadow price value (-40) column in the previous I Plan (*i.e.*, 1 and 36 respectively).

So, for Land X_4 in II Plan:

N = 12-(8x1) = 4

= 1-(1x1) = 0

= 1-(1x1) = 0

$$= 1-(1/3 \times 1)=2/3$$
$$= 1-(0 \times 1) = 1$$
$$= 0-(1/6 \times 1)=-1/6$$
$$= 0-(0 \times 1) = 0$$

Transfer the above values for land X_4 in Plan II

Similarly, for Capital X_6 in II Plan:

$$N= 360-(8 \times 36) = 72$$
$$= 36-(1 \times 36) = 0$$
$$= 24-(1 \times 36) = -12$$
$$= 18 -(1/3 \times 36) = 6$$
$$= 0-(0 \times 36) = 0$$
$$= 0-(1/6 \times 36) = -6$$
$$= 1-(0 \times 36) = 1$$

Transfer the above values for Capital X_6 in Plan II.

So, the rule for transformation of non-key rows is given by the formula: N=O-(I x P). That is, subtract from the old row number in the previous plan, the product of the incoming row number (in the current plan) and pivot value for that activity in the previous plan.

After computing resource activity levels, real activities and disposal activities for Land X_4 and Capital X_6 rows, follow the same procedure as in I Plan, to compute opportunity cost values, shadow prices and ratios. That is,

Opportunity Cost (Z)

It is calculated by the formula:

Σ(Contribution x Corresponding real activities of Paddy X_1, Groundnut X_2 and Red gram X_3)

$(0 \times 0 + 40 \times 1 + 0 \times 0)$	$= 40$ (For column 4)
$(0 \times 0 + 40 \times 1 + 0 \times -12)$	$= 40$ (For column 5)
$(0 \times (2/3) + 40 \times (1/3) + 0 \times 6)$	$= 40/3$ (For column 6)

Σ(Contribution x Corresponding disposal activity values of Land X_4, Labour X_5 and Capital X_6)

$(0 \times 1 + 0 \times 0 + 0 \times 0)$	$= 0$ (For column 7)
$(0 \times (-1/6) + 40 \times (1/6) + 0 \times -6)$	$= 20/3$ (For column 8)
$(0 \times 0 + 40 \times 0 + 0 \times 1)$	$= 0$ (For column 9)

Ratio

To calculate Ratio, consider lowest shadow price (*i.e.*,-20/3) and consider that column real activities of Red gram X_3. Divide resource activity level values of Land X_4,

Paddy X_1 and Capital X_6 (*i.e.*, column 3) with corresponding real activities of Red gram X_3 of lowest shadow price column (*i.e.*, column 6) *i.e.* (2/3), (1/3) and 6 to get Ratios *i.e.,*: 4/(2/3)=6, 8/(1/3)=24 and 72/6=12.

Among the computed ratio values in Plan II, consider lowest ratio (i.e, 6) and eliminate that row (*i.e.* Land X_4 row) in the next plan (*i.e.* Plan III). Now, replace that row (*i.e.* Land X_4 row) by employing the pivot value of the column with respect to lowest shadow price (*i.e.,*-20/3). So, considering the Land X_4 row and column of the lowest shadow price (-20/3), the pivot value is (2/3) *i.e.*, the intersection value of the selected row and selected column. Now, divide the entire eliminated Land X_4 row values with the pivot value (2/3) and include them as Red gram X_3 row, as shown through Plan III. This is given by:

$$=4/(2/3) = 6$$
$$=0/(2/3) = 0$$
$$=(0)/(2/3) = 0$$
$$=(2/3)/(2/3) = 1$$
$$=1/(2/3) = 3/2$$
$$= (-1/6)/(2/3) = -1/4$$
$$= (0)/(2/3) = 0$$

Transfer the above calculated values as row values for Red gram X_3 in Plan III.

Value of the Programme

It is given by Σ(Contribution x Corresponding resource activity level) for each row of Land X_4, Paddy X_1 and Capital X_6 restrictions *i.e.*, [(0x4)+(40x8)+(0x72)] =320

Plan III

Contri-bution (Net Income)	Restric-tion	Resource Activity Level	Real Activities			Disposable Activities		
			Paddy	Groundnut	Red Gram	Land	Labour	Capital
			X_1	X_2	X_3	X_4	X_5	X_6
20 Redgram X_3 (Redgram net income)		6	0	0	1	3/2	-1/4	0
40 Paddy X_1 (Paddy net income)		6	1	1	0	-1/2	1/4	0
0 Capital X_6		36	0	-12	0	-9	-9/2	1
Net income (C)			40	30	20	0	0	0
Opportunity cost (Z)			40	40	20	10	5	0
Shadow price (Z-C)			0	10	0	10	5	0
Value of programme			360					

Note: To calculate non-key row values in Plan III of Paddy X_1 and Capital X_6, the following formula will be used:

N=O-(I x P), where O=Previous row value of the restriction (Paddy X_1 and Capital X_6) in previous Plan II, I= Incoming row value in this plan (*i.e.*, Red gram X_3 values of row 1 in this current plan (III Plan), P= Pivot value for Paddy X_1 and Capital X_6 corresponding to the lowest shadow price value (-20/3) column in the previous plan *i.e.*, II Plan (*i.e.*, 1/3 with reference to Paddy X_1 and 6 with reference to Capital X_6).

So, for Paddy X_1 in Plan III:

$$N = O - (I \times P) = 8 - (6 \times 1/3) \qquad = 6$$
$$= 1 - (0 \times 1/3) \qquad = 1$$
$$= 1 - (0 \times 1/3) \qquad = 1$$
$$= 1/3 - (1 \times 1/3) \qquad = 0$$
$$= 0 - (3/2 \times 1/3) \qquad = -1/2$$
$$= 1/6 - (-1/4 \times 1/3) \qquad = 1/4$$
$$= 0 - (0 \times 1/3) \qquad = 0$$

Transfer the above calculated values as row values for Paddy X_1 in Plan III

Similarly, for Capital X_6 in Plan III:

$$N = O - (I \times P) = 72 - (6 \times 6) \qquad = 36$$
$$= 0 - (0 \times 6) \qquad = 0$$
$$= -12 - (0 \times 6) \qquad = -12$$
$$= 6 - (1 \times 6) \qquad = 0$$
$$= 0 - (3/2 \times 6) \qquad = -9$$
$$= -6 - (-1/4 \times 6) \qquad = -9/2$$
$$= 1 - (0 \times 6) \qquad = 1$$

Transfer the above calculated values as row values for Capital X_6 in Plan III.

Value of the Programme

It is given by Σ(Contribution x Corresponding resource activity level) for each row of Red gram X_3, Paddy X_1 and Capital X_6 restrictions *i.e.*, [(20x6)+(40x6)+(0x360)] =360

Criteria for Stopping Computation of Plans

To arrive at the optimal solution, the criterion is that, when all the Z-C values (*i.e.*, Shadow price values) are either zero or positive. In the above Plan III, all Z-C values are either zero or positive and hence, this Plan III gives the optimal solution. Hence,

Max Z $40X_1+30X_2+20X_3$

$40(6)+30(X_2)+20(6)$

=Rs. 360

Thus, considering Plan III, select Paddy X_1 and Red gram X_3 enterprises in 6 units each and by doing so, we get a maximum profit of Rs. 360/- (also indicated by Valuation of programme). Remaining Capital X_6 *i.e.*, '36' represents disposal activity and this infer the amount left over after investing on paddy and red gram. The same can be checked from the functional constraint equation of Capital X_6, as given below:

$$36X_1 + 24X_2 + 18X_3 \le 360$$

$$36 \times (6) + (24X_2) + 18(6) \le 360$$

So, by investing on Paddy X_1 and Red gram X_3 enterprises, the maximum revenue possible is Rs. 324/- (*i.e.*, <360/-) and Rs. 36/- is left over with farmer. So, the farmer's maximizing plan includes cultivating paddy (X_1) and Red gram (X_3) in 6 units each and employing 36 man days under Paddy (X_1) and 12 man days in Red gram (X_3) as given below. The farmer is left over with Rs.36 of unused capital. Thus, the farmer's plan includes:

☆ All the 12 units of land should be utilized (6 units each under Paddy X_1 and Red gram X_3). That is,

$1X_1+1X_2+1X_3 \le 12$ units (Land)

$1(6)+1X_2+1(6) = 12$.

☆ All the labour will be utilized on the farm. That is,

$6X_1+6X_2+2X_3 \le 48$ man days

$6(6)+6X_2+2(6) = 48$ man days (Labour).

☆ As calculated above, the farmer is able to use only Rs.324 of capital and remaining Rs.36 capital is unused in this plan.

Marginal Value Productivity (MVP)

It is interesting that, Z-C values under the slack variables or disposal activities of resources under optimal plan (*i.e.*, Plan III) can be interpreted as the MVP of resources under given set of conditions. So, in Plan III, under X_4, X_5 and X_6 disposal activities:

☆ MVP_{Land} : Rs. 10

☆ MVP_{Labour} : Rs.5

☆ $MVP_{Capital}$: Rs.0

This implies that, the farmer can pay at most Rs. 10 for renting additional unit of land and Rs.5 for hiring additional labour, but nothing for rental use of additional unit of capital borrowed by him. It is evident from the values of shadow price (Z-C) that,

☆ The value of shadow price: 10 under X_4 (land disposal activity) in the optimal plan (Plan III) implies that, MVP_{land} = Rs. 10/-. That is, if the farmer could increase one more unit of land, his net income would increase by Rs 10/- *i.e.*, from Rs 360 to 370. This can be easily verified with the help of marginal rates of substitution values under X_4 (disposal activity for land) in the optimal plan. The values are 3/2 for red gram X_3, -1/2 for paddy X_1 and -9 for capital X_6 indicating that, an increase in one unit of land will increase X_3 (*i.e.*, area under red gram) by 3/2 units (1.5 units), decrease paddy area (X_1) by ½ units (*i.e.*, 0.5 units) and also decrease X_6 (*i.e.*, capital) by Rs 9. From the above information, the optimal plan for 13 units of land can be written as follows (*i.e.*, if the land area in the farm is increased from 12 units to 13 units).

❖ (6) +1.5   = 7.5 units of land under red gram, X_3

❖ (6) – 0.5   = 5.5 units of land under paddy X_1

❖ (36) – 9   = 27 *i.e.*, capital use decreased by Rs. 9/-

The reader can check the above information, as the farmer now uses 7.5 units of land under red gram X_3, 5.5 units of land under paddy X_1 *i.e.*, 13 units of land in total and total capital use decreases by Rs 9 *i.e.*, from Rs. 360 to Rs. 351. So, the net farm income of the new plan is:

Max Z : $40X_1$ +$30X_2$ + $20X_3$

(40*5.5) + $30X_2$ + 20(7.5)

220 + $30X_2$ + 150

= Rs 370/-

Thus, it is proved that, the MVP of land is Rs. 10, as the net income from land was increased to Rs. 370 from Rs. 360 by increasing one unit of land in the farm cultivation.

☆ The value of 5 under labour X_5 disposal activity in the optimal plan (Plan III) implies that, MVP_{labour} = Rs. 5. That is, if the farmer could increase one more labour, his net income would increase by Rs. 5 *i.e.*, from Rs. 360 to Rs. 365.

☆ The $MVP_{capital}$ is equal to zero, as the farmer already has Rs. 36 in excess in implementing the optimal plan (Plan III).

Sensitivity Analysis - Shadow Prices

The above discussion also infers that, the MVP of resources is known as Shadow prices or Accounting prices or Imputed values or Implicit values. They represent the true or intrinsic value of resources and hence, the farmer cannot pay more than these amounts for each additional units of resources. The quantities or values of these resources multiplied by their respective MVP (*i.e.*, shadow price) of each resource and their sum will indicate the TVP of resources and it will be equal to the value of the objective function of the optimal plan. In this example, TVP is given by:

(12x10)+ (48x5)+(360x0)   = 40(6)+30(X_2)+20(6)

Rs.360   =   Rs.360

(TVP from resources side) = (Value of the objective function of the optimal plan)

So, the TVP of farm resources is Rs.360.

The shadow price represents the change in optimal value of the objective function per unit increase in the right hand side of a constraint. This concept can also be better explained with reference to the Figure 9.5 through changing the right hand side of the fertilizer constraint by one unit and the same was shown through Figure 9.19.1. In the Figure 9.19.1, with increase in the right hand side of the fertilizer constraint from 300 to 301, the new X1 and X2 units are 10.03 and 15.05 respectively. So, the new functional constraint line of fertilizer does not pass through the original optimal point (corner point) 'C', but away (right side) from it. So, the new higher iso-profit line of Rs.98.6 (*i.e.,* Max Z: (6 (5.1) + 8(8.5)) = Rs. 98.6) will pass through the new optimal point (corner point) 'D' with reference to 5.1 units of X1 and 8.5 units of X2. Thus, the shadow price of fertilizer is given by: 98.6 – 96 = Rs. 2.6. Thus, shadow price of fertilizer implies the change in optimal value of the objective function due to per unit increase in the right hand side of that functional constraint. This Rs. 2.6 change in profits that resulted from a unit change (increase) in the fertilizer is called the Shadow price, or Dual value. That is, the value of one additional unit of a scarce resource in LP is called shadow price. This shadow price for a constraint indicates the improvement in the objective function value that results from a one-unit increase in the right-hand side of the constraint. Sensitivity analysis thus, shows the changes in the optimal value of the objective function due to per unit change in the right hand side of a constraint. This analysis also guides the farmer in various aspects like: how much should the farmer is willing to pay for additional labour hours? Is it profitable to reduce the dosage of fertilizer? Note that, in the range of feasibility, the objective function value changes as follows:

Change in optimal value = (Shadow price/unit)(Change in the right hand side value of the constraint)

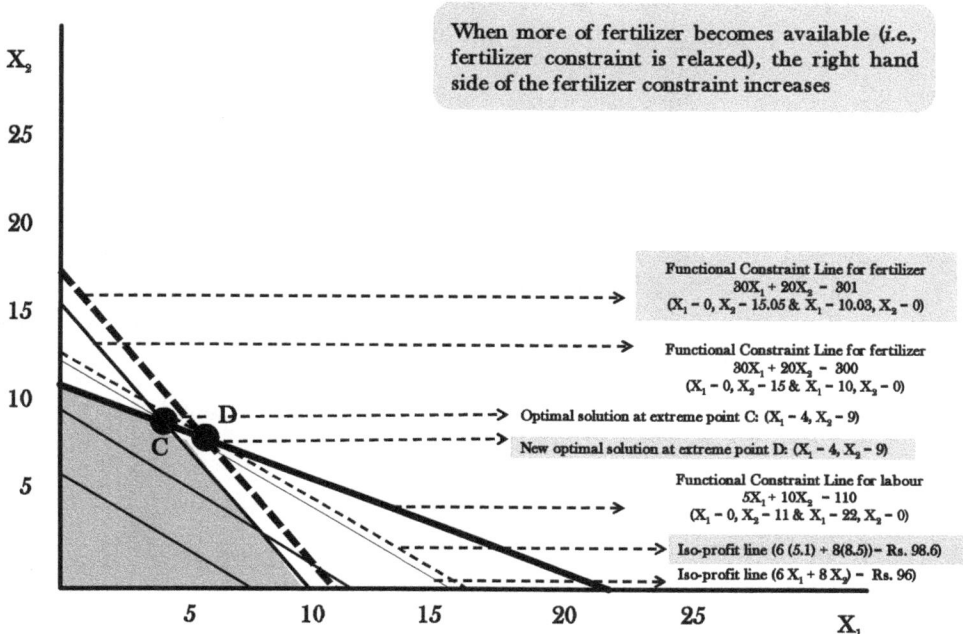

Figure 9.19.1: Finding Optimal Solution Based on Iso-Profit Line Approach.

The shadow price is valid only as long as the change in the right hand side is within the Allowable Increase and Allowable Decrease values. That is, in the above example, the shadow price of Rs. 2.6/unit is valid as long as the available fertilizer stays in a range within which all current corner points continue to exist. Similarly, sensitivity analysis can be worked out by changing one of the objective function coefficients. As the unit profit contribution of either product changes, the slope of the iso-profit lines also changes. The size of the feasible region, however, remains the same. That is, the locations of the corner points do not change. As in the earlier case of changing the right hand side value of the constraint, there is an allowable decrease and an allowable increase for each objective function coefficient over which the current optimal solution remains optimal. A new corner point becomes optimal, if an objective function coefficient is decreased or increased too much.

Thus, the shadow prices in a profit maximization problem indicate, how much total profits would rise per unit increase in the use of each input. Shadow prices thus, provide the imputed value or marginal valuation or worth of each input to the firm. If a particular input is not fully employed, its shadow price is zero because, increasing the input would leave profits unchanged. A firm should increase the use of the input as long as the MVP or shadow price of the input to the firm exceeds the cost of hiring the input. This shadow prices provide important information for planning and strategic decisions of the firm. Shadow prices are also used

☆ by many large corporations to correctly price the output of each division that is the input to another division, in order to maximize the total profits of the entire corporation,

☆ by Government to appropriately price some government services, and

☆ for planning in developing countries where the market system often does not function properly (*i.e.*, where input and output prices do not reflect their true relative scarcity).

The computer solution of the primal LP problem also provides the values of the shadow prices. Sometimes, it is also easier to obtain the optimal value of the decision variables in the primal problem by solving the corresponding dual problem.

Generalized Procedure of Simplex Method (Maximization Function)

1. Formulate the given LP problem in Standard form.
2. Convert each inequality in the set of constraints to equality by adding slack variable or disposable activity.
3. Create the initial simplex tableau.
4. Compute opportunity cost in the Plan:

   Σ(Contribution x Corresponding real activities)

   Σ(Contribution x Corresponding disposal activity values)
5. Compute shadow price (Z-C) in the Plan
6. Compute ratio in the Plan by employing the formula:

   Divide resource activity level values with corresponding real activities

7. Compute Value of the Programme in the Plan by employing the formula:

   Σ(Contribution x Corresponding resource activity level) for each row

8. Identify the column in the Plan that corresponds lowest shadow price or highest negative shadow price.

9. Identify the lowest ratio in the Plan. Select that row and divide all the elements in that row (key row) by the pivot element *i.e.*, the element that lies at the intersection between selected lowest shadow price column are selected lowest ratio row.

10. Delete that key row in the next plan.

11. Transfer all the calculated values as above in Step 9, in the next plan for the real activity corresponding to lowest shadow price.

12. The value of elements of non-key rows are calculated by employing the formula:

   $N=O-(I \times P)$, where O=Previous row value of that resource activity in preceding plan, I= Incoming row value in the current plan, P= Pivot value in the previous plan.

13. Repeat the same procedure as above from step 4 to 12 till the optimal plan is reached.

14. The criterion for optimal plan is that, 'when all the Z-C values of the row are either zero or positive'.

15. Compute the optimal solution by employing the values of resources activity levels of enterprises/products in the objective function.

16. Verify the optimal solution with the value of the programme.

ii. Cost Minimization Objective Function

In the previous section, we demonstrated the simplex method for solving LP problem with profit maximization objective function. The steps of simplex method that are discussed at the end of the previous section are common even for minimization problem, but with slight changes and the same can be witnessed from the following example:

Example 9.12

The Vitamins A_1 and A_2 are found in two different Foods X_1 and X_2. One unit of Food X_1 contains 2 units of Vitamin A_1 and 5 units of Vitamin A_2. One unit of Food X_2 contains 4 units of Vitamin A_1 and 2 units of Vitamin A_2. One unit of Food X_1 and Food X_2 costs Rs.3 and Rs. 2.25 respectively. The minimum daily requirement for a person of Vitamins A_1 and A_2 is 40 and 50 units respectively. Find the optimum mix of Foods X_1 and X_2 at the minimum cost, which makes the daily minimum requirement of Vitamins A_1 and A_2.

Solution

Step 1

The above information can be conveniently presented in the form of table as given below:

Restrictions	Restriction Level	Real Activities		Disposal Activities		Artificial Variables	
		Food X_1	Food X_2	Vitamin A1 (X_3)	Vitamin A2 (X_4)	A_1	A_2
Vitamin A_1	40	2	4	−1	0	1	0
Vitamin A_2	50	5	2	0	−1	0	1
Unit cost		3	2.25	0	0	M	M

Step 2

The above tabular form of LP problem can be conveniently expressed as mathematical equations. That is, translate the given data in the table into inequalities as given below.

Min Z $\quad 3X_1 + 2.25X_2$

Subject to

$2X_1 + 4X_2 \quad\quad \geq 40$ of Vitamin A_1

$5X_1 + 2X_2 \quad\quad \geq 50$ of Vitamin A_2

$X_1, X_2 \quad\quad\quad \geq 0$

Step 3

Then, all these inequalities are to be converted into equalities by subtracting surplus variables (X_3 and X_4) from the two '$\geq$' constraints as follows:

Min Z $3X_1 + 2.25X_2 + 0X_3 + 0X_4$

Subject to

$2X_1 + 4X_2 - 1X_3 + 0X_4 = 40$

$5X_1 + 2X_2 + 0X_3 - 1X_4 = 50$

$X_1, X_2, X_3, X_4 \geq 0$

X_3 and X_4 are surplus variables each for one variable X_1 and X_2 respectively *i.e.*, X_3 for X_1 and X_4 for X_2

The surplus variables represent the extra amount of Vitamin A_1 and Vitamin A_2 that exceed the minimum requirements specified in the constraints. A surplus variable is the difference between the total value of the true (decision) variables and the number (usually, total resource available) on the right-hand side of the equation. Thus, a surplus variable will *always* have a negative value. However, the simplex method requires that, the initial basic feasible solution be at the origin, where $X_1 = 0$ and $X_2 = 0$. Testing these solution values, we have:

$2X_1 + 4X_2 - 1X_3 + 0X_4 \quad\quad = 40$

$2(0) + 4(0) - 1X_3 + 0X_4 \quad\quad = 40$

$X_3 \quad\quad\quad\quad\quad\quad\quad\quad\quad = -40$

The idea of 'negative excess units of Vitamin A_1' is not meaningful and this also violates the non-negativity restriction of LP. To overcome this problem, we add an artificial variable to each of the functional constraints equations of Vitamin A_1 and Vitamin A_2 as shown below.

$2X_1 + 4X_2 - 1X_3 + 0X_4 + 1A_1 + 0A_2 = 40$

$5X_1 + 2X_2 + 0X_3 - 1X_4 + 0A_1 + 1A_2 = 50$

A_1 and A_2 are Artificial variables for each surplus variable. So, one 'artificial variable' is added to each of the 'greater-than-equal-to' constraints to ensure an initial basic feasible solution. These artificial variables are 'penalized' in the objective function by introducing a large positive coefficient 'M' for minimization problem.

Considering one of above equations *i.e.*, $2X_1 + 4X_2 - 1X_3 + 0X_4 + 1A_1 + 0A_2 = 40$

$2(0) + 4(0) - 0X_3 + 0X_4 + 1A_1 + 0A_2 = 40$

$A_1 \qquad\qquad\qquad\qquad = 40$

The use of artificial variable has no meaning, unlike surplus variable, as the former is simply used in the functional constraint equations only to give positive solution to the origin. That is, artificial variable is simply used to start the process of simplex method, but once the iterations were started, it has no use and thus, is discarded. These variables can be eliminated from the simplex tableau as and when they become zero (non-basic). So, the LP problem in standard form is presented as below:

Min Z $3X_1 + 2.25X_2 + 0X_3 + 0X_4 + MA_1 + MA_2$

Subject to

$2X_1 + 4X_2 - 1X_3 + 0X_4 + 1A_1 + 0A_2 = 40$

The above data are presented through matrices as given below:

$$[3 \quad 2.25 \quad 0 \quad 0 \quad M \quad M] \begin{bmatrix} X_1 \\ X_2 \\ X_3 \\ X_4 \\ A_1 \\ A_2 \end{bmatrix} - \text{Min Z}$$

Subject to

$$\begin{bmatrix} 2 & 4 & -1 & 0 & 1 & 0 \\ 5 & 2 & 0 & -1 & 0 & 1 \end{bmatrix} \begin{bmatrix} X_1 \\ X_2 \\ X_3 \\ X_4 \\ A_1 \\ A_2 \end{bmatrix} \begin{bmatrix} -40 \\ -50 \end{bmatrix}$$

$$\begin{bmatrix} X_1 \\ X_2 \\ X_3 \\ X_4 \\ A_1 \\ A_2 \end{bmatrix} \geq 0$$

$5X_1 + 2X_2 + 0X_3 - 1X_4 + 0A_1 + 1A_2 = 50$

$X_1, X_2, X_3, X_4, A_1, A_2 \geq 0$

X_3 and X_4 are surplus variables each for one variable $X-_1$ and X_2 respectively *i.e.*, X_3 for X_1 and X_4 for X_2

A_1 and A_2 are Artificial variables to bring negative value of surplus variable to positive values

Remember that, an artificial variable has no significance pertaining to the solution of the problem and it is used merely to find a solution mix in the first simplex tableau. Although artificial variables will always form part of the initial solution mix, the objective is to remove them as soon as possible by means of the simplex procedure. As long as an artificial variable still appears in the solution mix, the final solution has not yet been found. As any other variable, artificial variables are also included in the objective function, but the value attached to them creates another problem. In minimization problems, since the objective is to find the lowest cost possible, a very large value is allocated to artificial variables. This value is denoted by M, where 'M' is a very large positive value.

This expression of LP problem represent LP problem in Standard form. So, a LP problem is in standard form, if it seeks to *minimize* the objective function subject to the given constraints and representing in terms of surplus variables and artificial variables. Note that, if there are 'm' constraints in the given problem, the number of surplus variables and artificial variables added will be 'm' each. In this example, there are two constraints with respect to Vitamin A_1 and Vitamin A_2 and hence, two surplus variables X_3 and X_4; and two artificial variables X_5 and X_6 are added. It is at this point, we begin applying the Simplex method to solve the formulated LP problem.

Plan I

The initial simplex tableau for a minimization model is developed in the same way as prepared under maximization model, except for one difference. That is, in Z-C row, we consider the largest positive value to select the pivot column. Note that, across the top, the decision variables are listed first, then surplus variables and finally artificial variables.

Contri-bution	Resou-rce Activity	Resou-rce Activity Level	Real Activities		Surplus Variables		Artificial Variables		Ratio
			Food X_1	Food X_2	Vit A_1	Vit A_2	A_1	A_2	
M	Vit A1	40	2	4	−1	0	1	0	40/2 = 20
M	Vit A2	50	5	2	0	−1	0	1	50/5 = 10
Net income(C)			3	2.25	0	0	M	M	
Opportunity cost (Z)			7M	6M	−M	−M	M	M	
Shadow price (Z-C)			7M-3	6M-2.25	−M	−M	0	0	

In the above table:

Opportunity Cost (Z)

It is calculated by the formula:

Σ(Contribution x Corresponding real activities of Food X_1 and Food X_2)

(M x 2 + M x 5) = 7M (For column 4)

(M x 4 + M x 2) = 6M (For column 5)

Σ(Contribution x Corresponding disposal activity values of Vit A1 and Vit A2)

(M x (-1) + M x 0) = -M (For column 6)

(M x 0 + M x (-1)) = -M (For column 7)

Σ(Contribution x Artificial variable values of Vit A1 and Vit A2)

(M x 1 + M x 0) = M (For column 8)

(M x 0 + M x 1) = M (For column 9)

Ratio

To calculate Ratio, consider highest (positive) shadow price (*i.e.*,7M-3) and consider that column real activities of Food X_1. Divide resource activity level values of Vit A_1 and Vit A_2 (*i.e.,* column 3) with corresponding real activities of Food X_1 of highest shadow price column *viz.*, 2 and 5 (*i.e.,* column 4): *i.e.*, 40/2=20, 50/5=10 to workout Ratios.

Among the computed ratio values in Plan I, consider lowest ratio (i.e, 10) and eliminate that row (*i.e.*, Vit A_2 row) in the next plan (*i.e.,* Plan II). Now, replace that row (*i.e.*, Vit A_2 row) by employing the pivot value of the column with respect to highest shadow price (*i.e.*, 7M-3 shadow price column). So, considering the Vit A_2 row and column of the highest shadow price (7M-3) in Plan I, the pivot value is 5 *i.e.*, the intersection value of the selected row and selected column. Now, divide the entire eliminated Vit A_2 row values with the pivot value (5) and include them as Food X_1 row, as shown through Plan II. This is given by:

=50/5 = 10

=5/5   = 1

=2/5 = 2/5

=0/5   = 0

=-1/5   = (-1/5)

=0/5   = 0

=1/5 = 1/5

Transfer all the above calculated values as Food X_1 row values in Plan II.

Plan II

Contri-bution	Resource Activity	Resource Activity Level	Real Activities		Surplus Variables		Artificial Variables		Ratio
			Food X_1	Food X_2	Vit A_1	Vit A_2	A_1	A_2	
M	Vit A1	20*	0	16/5	−1	2/5	1	−2/5	20/(16/5) = 6.25
3	Food X_1	50/5 =10	5/5 = 1	2/5	0	−1/5	0	1/5	10/(2/5) = 25
Net income (C)			3	2.25	0	0	M	M	
Opportunity cost (Z)			3	16M/5+6/5	−M	2M/5+(−3/5)	M	−2M/5+(3/5)	
Shadow price (Z-C)			0	16M/5 −(1.05)	−M	2M/5−(3/5)	0	−7M/5+(3/5)	

*: To calculate non-key row values in Plan II of Vit A_1, the following formula will be used:

N=O-(I x P), where O=Previous row value of that resource activity in previous plan, I= Incoming row value in this plan (*i.e.*, Food X_1 values of row 2 in this current Plan II), P=Pivot value for Vit A_1 corresponding to the highest shadow price value (7M-3) column in the previous Plan I (*i.e.*, 2).

So, for Vit A_1 in Plan II:

$$N = 40\text{-}(10\text{x}2) \quad = 20$$
$$= 2\text{-}(1\text{x}2) \quad = 0$$
$$=4\text{-}(2/5)\,(2) \quad = 16/5$$
$$= \text{-}1\text{-}(0\text{x}2) \quad = \text{-}1$$
$$= 0\text{-}(\text{-}1/5)\,(2) \quad = 2/5$$
$$= 1\text{-}(0\text{x}2) \quad = 1$$
$$= 0\text{-}(1/5)\,(2) \quad = \text{-}2/5$$

Transfer the above calculated values for Vit A_1 row in Plan II.

After computing resource activity levels, real activities, disposal activities and artificial variables for Vit A_1 row, follow the same procedure as in I Plan, to compute opportunity cost values, shadow prices and ratios. That is,

Opportunity Cost (Z)

It is calculated by the formula:

Σ(Contribution x Corresponding real activities of Food X_1 and Food X_2)

(M x 0 + 3 x 1) = 3 (For column 4)

(M x (16/5) + 3 x (2/5)) = (16M/5)+(6/5) (For column 5)

Σ(Contribution x Corresponding disposal activity values of Vit A_1 and Vit A_2)

(M x (-1) + 3 x 0) = -M (For column 6)

$(M \times (2/5) + 3 \times (-1/5)) = (2M/5) + (-3/5)$ (For column 7)

Σ(Contribution x Corresponding Artificial variable values)

$(M \times 1 + 3 \times 0) = M$ (For column 8)

$(M \times (-2/5) + 3 \times (1/5)) = (-2M/5) + (3/5)$ (For column 9)

Ratio

To calculate Ratio, consider highest shadow price (*i.e.*,$((16M/5)-1.05)$ and consider that column real activities of Food X_2. Divide resource activity level values of Vit A_1 and Food X_1 (*i.e.*, column 3) with corresponding real activities of Food X_2 of highest shadow price column *viz.*, $(16/5)$ and $(2/5)$ (*i.e.*, column 5): *i.e.*, $20/(16/5)=6.25$, $10/(2/5)=25$.

Among the computed ratio values in Plan II, consider lowest ratio (*i.e.*, 6.25) and eliminate that row (*i.e.*, Vit A_1 row) in the next plan (*i.e.*, Plan III). Now, replace that row (*i.e.*, Vit A_1 row) by employing the pivot value of the column with respect to highest shadow price (*i.e.*,$((16M/5)-1.05)$. So, considering the Vit A_1 row and column of the highest shadow price $((16M/5)-1.05)$, the pivot value is $(16/5)$ *i.e.*, the intersection value of the selected row and selected column. Now, divide the entire eliminated Vit A_1 row values with the pivot value $(16/5)$ and include them as Food X_2 row, as shown through Plan III. This is given by:

$= 20/(16/5)$ $\qquad = 6.25$

$=0/(16/5)$ $\qquad = 0$

$=(16/5)/(16/5)$ $\qquad = 1$

$=-1/(16/5)$ $\qquad = -5/16$

$=(2/5)/(16/5)$ $\qquad = 1/8$

$=1/(16/5)$ $\qquad = 5/16$

$=(-2/5)/(16/5)$ $\qquad = -1/8$

Transfer all the above calculated values as Food X_2 row values in Plan III.

Plan III

Contri-bution	Resource Activity	Resource Activity Level	Real Activities		Surplus Variables		Artificial Variables	
			Food X_1	Food X_2	Vit A_1	Vit A_2	A_1	A_2
2.25	Food X_2	20/(16/5) = 6.25*	0	1	−5/16	1/8	5/16	−1/8
3	Food X_1	7.5	1	0	1/8	−1/4	−1/8	1/4
Net income (C)			3	2.25	0	0	M	M
Opportunity cost (Z)			3	2.25	−0.328	−0.469	0.328	0.468
Shadow price (Z-C)			0	0	−0.328	−0.469	0.328-M	0.468-M
Value of programme			36.5625					

*: To calculate non-key row values in Plan III of Food X_1, the following formula will be used:

N=O-(I x P), where O=Previous row value of that resource activity in previous plan,

I= Incoming row value in this plan (*i.e.*, Food X_2 values of row 1 in this Plan III),

P= P=Pivot value for Food X_1 corresponding to the highest shadow price value (16M/5 –(1.05) column in the previous Plan II (*i.e.*, 2/5).

So, for Food X_1 in Plan III:

N= O – (I x P)	= 10 – (6.25 x 2/5) = 7.5
= 1 – (0 x 2/5)	= 1
= 2/5 – (1 x 2/5)	= 0
= 0 – (- 5/16 x 2/5)	= 1/8
= -1/5 – (-1/8 x 2/5)	= -1/4
= 0 – (5/16 x 2/5)	= -1/8
= 1/5 – (-1/8 x 2/5)	= 1/4

Transfer all the above calculated values as Food X_1 row values in Plan III.

Value of the Programme

It is given by Σ(Contribution x Corresponding resource activity level) for each row *i.e.*, [(2.25*6.25)+(3*7.5)] = 14.0625 + 22.5 = 36.56.

Criteria for Stopping Computation of Plans

To arrive at the optimal solution, the criterion is that, when all the Z-C values (*i.e.*, Shadow price values) are either zero or negative for real activities and surplus variables (*i.e.*, Z-C row contains no positive values for real activities and surplus variables). So, Plan III gives the optimal solution. Thus, considering Plan III, select 7.5 units of Food X_1 and 6.25 units of Food X_2 and by doing so, we can minimize the cost to the tune of Rs. 36.56 (also indicated by the Valuation of programme). That is, given objective function:

Min Z $3X_1 + 2.25X_2$

= 3(7.5)+2.25(6.25) = Rs.36.56

To summarize, the adjustments necessary to apply the simplex method to a minimization problem are as follows:

☆ Transform all '≥' constraints to equalities by subtracting a surplus variable and adding an artificial variable.

☆ Consider highest positive shadow price to select the pivot column

Note that, although the above discussed diet example model included only '≥' constraints, it is possible for a minimization problem to also have '≤' and '=' constraints in addition to '≥' constraints. Similarly, it is possible for a maximization problem to have '≥' and '=' constraints in addition to '≤' constraints. Problems that contain a combination of different types of inequality constraints are referred to as Mixed constraint problems. So, in case of mixed constraint problems, we have to employ slack variables, surplus variables and artificial variables and the same is discussed here under.

Thus, the simplex technique involves generating a series of solutions in tabular form, called tableaus. By inspecting the bottom row of each tableau, one can immediately tell, if it represents the optimal solution. Each tableau corresponds to a corner point of the feasible solution space. The first tableau corresponds to the origin. Subsequent tableaus are developed by shifting to an adjacent corner point in the direction that yields the highest (smallest) rate of profit (cost). This process continues as long as a positive (negative) rate of profit (cost) exists. Thus, in this method, the computational routine is an iterative process. To *iterate* means to repeat; *i.e.,* in working toward an optimum solution, the computational routine is repeated over and over, following a standard pattern. Successive solutions are developed in a systematic pattern until the best solution is reached. Each new solution will yield a value of the objective function as large as or larger than the previous solution. This important feature assures us that we are always moving closer to the optimum answer. Finally, the method indicates when the optimum solution has been reached (Sami, 2007).

Merits of Simplex Method

This Simplex method is the most widely used algebraic procedure for solving LP problems. This method is a general-purpose LP algorithm widely used to solve large scale problems. Although it lacks the intuitive appeal of the graphical approach, its ability to handle problems with more than two decision variables makes it extremely valuable for solving problems often encountered in production/operations management. Thus, simplex method offers an efficient means of solving more complex LP problems.

Complications in Simplex Method

As discussed earlier under graphical approach, a LP problem may have different type of solutions corresponding to different situations. Here, the same will be discussed in the context of Simplex method:

☆ Equalities instead of inequalities for constraints.

☆ Decision variables unrestricted in signs.

☆ Zero constants on the right-hand side of one or more constraints.

☆ Some or all decision variables must be integers.

☆ Non-positive constants on the right-hand side of the constraints.

☆ More than one optimal solution *i.e.,* multiple solutions such that, there is no unique optimal solution (Table 9.5.1).

☆ The constraints are such that, no feasible solution exists (Table 9.5.1).

☆ The constraints are such that, one or more of the variables can increase without limit and never violate a constraint *i.e.,* the solution is unbounded (Table 9.5.1).

Table 9.5.1: Possible Complications in the Application of Simplex Method

Cases	How to Recognize them in Simplex Tableau
Multiple optimal solutions	If the index of a variable not contained in the solution mix is zero in the final tableau, it means that, there is more than one optimal solution. Mathematically, the inclusion of this variable in the solution mix will not change the value of the objective function.
Degeneracy	One or more constraints are redundant – as a result of this, two equally small non-negative ratios may occur in the table when the pivot row is to be identified. If the incorrect one is selected, the only problem is that, an extra iteration will be carried out. This degeneracy refers to the situation in which a LP problem has a basic feasible solution with at least one basic variable equal to zero. This can occur at formulation or if there is a tie for the minimizing value in the ratio test to determine the leaving variable. Note that,
	☆ When degeneracy occurs, an optimal solution may have been attained even though some Z-C values are <0. Thus, the condition that, Z-C $\geq$ 0 is sufficient for optimality, but not necessary.
	☆ If the number of basic variables is fewer than the number of constraints in a solution, the solution is said to be degenerate.
	☆ A zero constant term for one or more basic variables in any iteration of the simplex solution would be a clear indication of a degenerate solution.
	Note that, the normal simplex procedure cannot solve a degenerate problem. Advanced methods are available to solve degenerate problems.
Infeasibility	This case is easily recognized, if in the final tableau, at least one of the artificial variables still exists in the solution mix, whilst all the indices indicate that an optimal solution has been found.
Unbounded solutions	When identifying the pivot row, all the ratios will be either negative or ∞. It means that, one or more variables can increase indefinitely without the constraints being exceeded in a maximization problem.

☆ Some or all of the coefficients and right-hand-side terms are given by a probability distribution rather than a single value.

Limitations of Simplex Method
They include:

☆ Inability to deal with multiple objectives

☆ Inability to handle problems with integer variables

VII. LP Problems Involving Slack, Surplus and Artificial Variables

Having understood the concept of formulation of LP problem for both maximization and minimization functions, it is essential to learn to formulate the LP problem involving both slack and surplus variables. By this time we are aware that, in simplex procedure:

☆ All equations must be equalities.

☆ All variables must be present in all equations.

☆ In the case of '≤' constraints, slack variables are added to the actual variables to make the equation an equality.

☆ In the case of '≥' constraints, surplus variables and artificial variables are used to make the equation an equality.

Consider the following LP problem:

$$\text{Min } Z = 5X_1 + 7X_2$$

Subject to

$$X_1 + X_2 = 4500$$
$$X_1 \leq 2000$$
$$X_2 \geq 800$$
$$X_1, X_2 \geq 0$$

In the above example, there are three constraints *viz.*, one equality, one 'smaller than or equal to' and one 'greater than or equal to'. The model should now be modified as follows:

$$X_1 + X_2 = 4500$$
$$X_1 + S_1 = 2000$$
$$X_2 - S_2 = 800$$
$$X_1, X_2, S_1, S_2 \geq 0$$

where S_1 is a slack variable and S_2 is a surplus variable.

As explained earlier, the presence of a surplus variable causes a problem when drawing the first simplex tableau because of its negative value. To overcome this, we add an Artificial variable (a variable that has a positive value denoted by Ai) to the equation. The above LP model is thus rewritten before using simplex procedure.

$$\text{Min } Z\ 5X_1 + 7X_2 + 0S_1 + 0S_2 + MA_1 + MA_2$$

Subject to

$$1X_1 + 1X_2 + 0S_1 + 0S_2 + 1A_1 + 0A_2 = 4500$$
$$1X_1 + 0X_2 + 1S_1 + 0S_2 + 0A_1 + 0A_2 = 2000$$
$$0X_1 + 1X_2 + 0S_1 - 1S_2 + 0A_1 + 1A_2 = 800$$
$$X_1, X_2, S_1, S_2, A_1, A_2 \geq 0$$

VIII. Transportation Problem

The transportation problem is one of the sub-classes of LP problem, where the objective is to transport various quantities of a single homogeneous product that are initially produced or stored at various places (called factories or plants or sources or origins or supply origins), to different destinations (say, warehouses) in such a way that, the total transportation cost is minimum. Prof. F.I. Hitchaxic developed the basic transportation problem in 1941. However, George B. Dantzig in 1951 applied the concept of LP in solving the transportation models to ensure optimality. Thus, transportation problems or models are primarily concerned with the optimal (best possible or lowest cost) way in which a homogeneous product produced at different factories can be transported to a number of destinations (also called demand destinations). So, transportation model is basically an extension of LP model. This model can be solved by a procedure called transportation technique. The main objective in a transportation problem is to fully satisfy the destination requirements within the operating production capacity constraints at the minimum possible cost. Whenever there is physical movement of goods from the point of production to the final consumers through a variety of channels of distribution (wholesalers, retailers, distributors etc.), there is a need to minimize the cost of transportation, so as to increase the profit on sales. Transportation problems arise in all such cases. This model aims at providing the answer to the producer in ascertaining, how many units of a particular product should be transported from each supply origin to each demand destinations so that, the total prevailing demand for the firm's product is satisfied, while at the same time the total transportation costs are minimized.

A. Requirements of Transportation Model

They include:

☆ Supply at each source or origin

☆ Demand at each destination

☆ Unit cost of transportation of good from each source to each destination

☆ Since single (homogeneous) commodity is involved, each destination can receive its requirement from different sources

B. Assumptions of Transportation Model

The important assumptions include:

☆ The total cost of transportation is directly proportional to the number of units of commodity shipped or transported.

☆ Unit cost of transportation varies with the distance across each source and each destination.

☆ The commodity transported from different sources to different demand destinations is homogeneous.

☆ The transportation problem applies to situations, where a single commodity is to be transported from various sources of supply (origins) to various demand destinations.

C. Formulation of Transportation Model

Mathematically a transportation problem is nothing but a special LP problem in which the objective function is to minimize the cost of transportation subjected to the demand and supply constraints. The transportation model can be presented in the form of a networking model (Figure 9.20). The line joining the source and destination represents the route through which commodity is shipped or transported. Let there

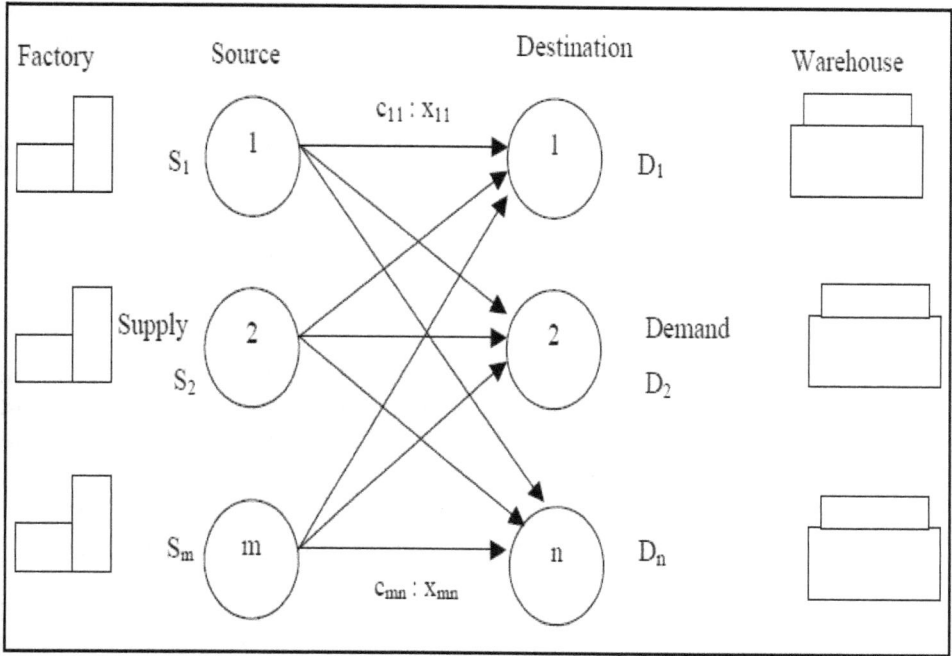

Figure 9.20: Transportation Networking Model.

be '*m*' sources of supply S_1, S_2,............S_m having ai (i = 1,2,...m) units of supplies respectively to be transported to '*n*' number of destinations *i.e.*, d_1, d_2.........d_n with b_j (j = 1,2....n) units of requirements respectively. Let C_{ij} be the cost for shipping or transport for one unit of the commodity from source i, to destination j for each route. If Xij represents the units shipped per route from source i to destination j, then the problem is to determine the transportation schedule, which minimizes the total transportation cost of satisfying supply and demand conditions. The transportation problem can be stated mathematically as a LP problem as below:

$$\text{Min } Z = \sum_{i=1}^{m}\sum_{j=1}^{n} Cij\, Xij \qquad\qquad \textit{Linear Objective Function}$$

Subject to constraints

$$\sum_{j=1}^{n} Xij \leq ai \qquad (i = 1 \text{ to } m) \qquad\qquad \textit{Supply Constraint}$$

The above equation specifies that, the total shipments from the sources cannot exceed the supply.

$$\sum_{i=1}^{m} Xij \leq bj \qquad (j = 1 \text{ to } n) \qquad\qquad \textit{Demand Constraint}$$

The above equation specifies that, the total shipments must satisfy the demand.

$Xij \geq 0$ *Non-negativity constraint*

$$\sum_{i=1}^{m} ai$$ *Total Supply from different Sources*

$$\sum_{j=1}^{n} bj$$ *Total demand from different destinations*

The above model infers that,

- ☆ The formulation of transportation problem is similar to LP problem formulation. Here, the objective function is the total transportation cost that is to be minimized and the constraints are the supply and demand available at each source and destination respectively.
- ☆ Let the supply at i^{th} source is a_i and demand at the destination j is b_j.
- ☆ C_{ij} is the unit cost of transporting a good from i^{th} source or origin to j^{th} destination.
- ☆ X_{ij} refers to number of units of commodity or good shipped or transported from i^{th} source to j^{th} destination.
- ☆ Linear objective function implies, total cost of transporting the product from different sources to different destinations is minimized.
- ☆ Supply constraints indicate the relationship between origin capacity of plants and product to be received by the destinations.
- ☆ The demand constraints indicate the relationship between destination requirements and product to be shipped from plants or origins.
- ☆ Non-negativity constraint implies, no negative shipment is permitted.

Keeping the above items in view, we can now formulate LP model representing transportation model assuming a firm with three plants (sources) located at different places *viz.*, Mumbai (O_1), Chennai (O_2) and Bangalore (O_3). The total output (supply) from these three plants or sources or factories is absorbed by four destinations like D_1, D_2, D_3 and D_4. In the Table 9.6, X_{11} represent number of units of commodity transported from 1st source to 1st destination. Similarly, X_{24} represent number of units of commodity transported from 2nd source to 4th destination and so on. In general, Xij represent number of units of commodity transported from i^{th} source to j^{th} destination. C_{12} represent unit cost incurred in transporting the commodity from 1st source to 2nd destination. Similarly, C_{24} represent unit cost incurred in transporting the commodity from 2nd source to 4th destination and so on. In general, Cij represent unit cost of transporting the commodity from i^{th} source to j^{th} destination.

From the above information and Table 9.6, the mathematical (LP) model for transportation problem can be expressed as given below:

Table 9.6: General Format of Transportation Model

Sources	Destinations				Capacity of source
	D1	D2	D3	D4	
Mumbai (O1)	C_{11} X_{11}	C_{12} X_{12}	C_{13} X_{13}	C_{14} X_{14}	b1
Chennai (O2)	C_{21} X_{21}	C_{22} X_{22}	C_{23} X_{23}	C_{24} X_{24}	b2
Bangalore (O3)	C_{31} X_{31}	C_{32} X_{32}	C_{33} X_{33}	C_{34} X_{34}	b3
Destination requirement	d1	d2	d3	d4	Σbi Σdi

$$\text{Min } Z = C_{11}X_{11}+C_{12}X_{12}+C_{13}X_{13}+C_{14}X_{14}+C_{21}X_{21}+C_{22}X_{22}+C_{23}X_{23}+C_{24}X_{24}+C_{31}X_{31}+C_{32}X_{32}+C_{33}X_{33}+C_{34}X_{34}$$

Subject to

$X_{11}+X_{12}+X_{13}+X_{14}$	$= b_1$	*(Total capacity of Source O_1)*
$X_{21}+X_{22}+X_{23}+X_{24}$	$= b_2$	*(Total capacity of Source O_2)*
$X_{31}+X_{32}+X_{33}+X_{34}$	$= b_3$	*(Total capacity of Source O_3)*
$X_{11}+X_{21}+X_{31}$	$= d_1$	*(Destination D_1 total requirement)*
$X_{12}+X_{22}+X_{32}$	$= d_2$	*(Destination D_2 total requirement)*
$X_{13}+X_{23}+X_{33}$	$= d_3$	*(Destination D_3 total requirement)*
$X_{14}+X_{24}+X_{34}$	$= d_4$	*(Destination D_4 total requirement)*

Transportation models are solved manually within the context of a *tableau*, as in the simplex method. The tableau for our wheat transportation model is shown through Table 9.7. Each cell in the tableau represents the amount transported from one source to one destination. Thus, the amount placed in each cell is the value of a decision variable for that cell. For example, the cell X_{11} at the intersection of row 2 (Mumbai Source) and column 2 (Destination, D1 (Visakhapatnam)) represents the decision variable. The smaller value within each cell (upper right hand corner in each cell) refers to the unit transportation cost for that route. For example, in the above cell at the intersection of row 2 (Mumbai Source) and column 2 (Destination, D1

(Visakhapatnam)), the value, Rs. 160, is the cost of transporting one unit of product from Mumbai to Visakhapatnam. Along the outer rim of the tableau across each column and row are the total supply and total demand constraint (quantity) values, which are referred to as rim requirements.

D. Characteristics of Transportation Model

The above discussion on the formulation of transportation model reveals the following characteristics

☆ A product is transported from a number of sources to a number of destinations at the minimum possible cost.

☆ Each source is able to supply a fixed number of units of the product, and each destination has a fixed demand for the product.

☆ The LP model has constraints for supply at each source and demand at each destination.

☆ All constraints are equalities in a balanced transportation model, where supply equals demand.

☆ Constraints contain inequalities in unbalanced transportation models where, demand is more than supply or supply is more than demand.

Example 9.13

The following example was used to demonstrate the formulation of the transportation model. A food processing firm has four plants in Mumbai, Chennai, Bangalore and Delhi. The product produced at these four plants is to be transported to five major destinations in India *viz.*, D_1, D_2, D_3, D_4 and D_5. Each source is able to supply the following units of product to the destinations on a monthly basis:

Plant (Source)	Supply (Units)
Mumbai	500
Chennai	575
Bangalore	610
Delhi	645

Each destination demands the following number of units of product per month:

Destination	Demand (Units)
D_1	410
D_2	540
D_3	390
D_4	440
D_5	550

The cost of transporting one unit of product from each plant (source) to each destination differs according to the distance and rail system. These costs are shown in the following table:

Plant (Source)	Destination				
	D_1	D_2	D_3	D_4	D_5
Mumbai	5	11	8	9	10
Chennai	7	9	10	7	9
Bangalore	6	10	12	5	8
Delhi	4	8	7	11	7

The problem is to determine, how many units of product to transport from each source to each destination on a monthly basis in order to minimize the total cost of transportation. The LP model for this problem is formulated in the equations as given below:

$$\text{Min } Z = 5X_{11} + 11X_{12} + 8X_{13} + 9X_{14} + 10X_{15} + 7X_{21} + 9X_{22} + 10X_{23} + 7X_{24} + 9X_{25} + 6X_{31}$$
$$+ 10X_{32} + 12X_{33} + 5X_{34} + 8X_{35} + 4X_{41} + 8X_{42} + 7X_{43} + 11X_{44} + 7X_{45}$$

Subject to

$X_{11} + X_{12} + X_{13} + X_{14} + X_{15}$	$= 500$	(Total capacity of Source, Mumbai (O_1))
$X_{21} + X_{22} + X_{23} + X_{24} + X_{25}$	$= 575$	(Total capacity of Source, Chennai (O_2))
$X_{31} + X_{32} + X_{33} + X_{34} + X_{35}$	$= 610$	(Total capacity of Source, Bangalore (O_3))
$X_{41} + X_{42} + X_{43} + X_{44} + X_{45}$	$= 645$	(Total capacity of Source, Delhi (O_4))
$X_{11} + X_{21} + X_{31} + X_{41}$	$= 410$	(Destination D_1 total requirement)
$X_{12} + X_{22} + X_{32} + X_{42}$	$= 540$	(Destination D_2 total requirement)
$X_{13} + X_{23} + X_{33} + X_{43}$	$= 390$	(Destination D_3 total requirement)
$X_{14} + X_{24} + X_{34} + X_{44}$	$= 440$	(Destination D_4 total requirement)
$X_{15} + X_{25} + X_{35} + X_{45}$	$= 550$	(Destination D_5 total requirement)

$Xij \geq 0$

In this model, the decision variables Xij represent the number of units of product transported from each source, 'i' (*where,* i=1,2,3 and 4), to each destination,'j' (where j=1,2,3,4 and 5). The objective function represents the total transportation cost incurred in moving the product from different sources to different destinations. Each term in the objective function reflects the cost of the units transported for one route. For example, if 50 units of product are transported from Mumbai to Destination D1, the cost of Rs.5 is multiplied by X_{11}=50, which equals to Rs. 250. The first four constraints in the above LP model represent the supply constraints at each source; the last five constraints represent the demand constraints at each destination. As an example, consider the first supply constraint and this constraint represents the units of product transported from Mumbai to all five destinations. The amount transported from Mumbai plant is limited to the 500 units of product available. Note that, this constraint (as well as all others) is an equation rather than an inequality because, all the units of product available (supply=2330 units) will be needed to meet the total demand (=2330 units). In other words, the five destinations demand, 2330 units of product, which is the exact amount that can be supplied by the four sources (=2330 units). Thus, all that can be supplied will be, in order to meet demand. This type of model, in which supply exactly equals demand, is referred to as a Balanced transportation model. This balanced model will be used to demonstrate the solution of a transportation problem.

E. Balanced and Unbalanced Transportation Models

As mentioned above, the model in which total supply from the sources is equal to total demand by the destinations is called Balanced transportation model (Table 9.7). This is given by:

$$\text{Min } Z = \sum_{i=1}^{m}\sum_{j=1}^{n} C_{ij} X_{ij} \qquad \text{\textit{Linear Objective Function}}$$

Subject to constraints

$$\sum_{j=1}^{n} X_{ij} \leq a_i \quad (i = 1 \text{ to } m) \qquad \text{\textit{Supply Constraint}}$$

The above equation specifies that, the total shipments from the sources cannot exceed the supply.

$$\sum_{i=1}^{m} X_{ij} \leq b_j \quad (j = 1 \text{ to } n) \qquad \text{\textit{Demand Constraint}}$$

The above equation specifies that, the total shipments must satisfy the demand.

$$X_{ij} \geq 0 \qquad \text{\textit{Non-negativity constraint}}$$

$$\sum_{i=1}^{m} a_i \qquad \text{\textit{Total Supply from different Sources}}$$

$$\sum_{j=1}^{n} b_j \qquad \text{\textit{Total demand from different destinations}}$$

So, in case of balanced transportation model:

$$\sum_{i=1}^{m} a_i = \sum_{j=1}^{n} b_j$$

Supply (from various sources) are written in the rows, while a column is an expression for the destination's demand. In general, if a transportation problem has 'm' rows and 'n' columns, then the problem is solvable, if there are exactly (m + n −1)

Table 9.7: Balanced Transportation Model (Demand = Supply)

Sources	Destinations		Capacity ('000 tonnes)
	D_1 (Visakhapatnam)	D_2 (Hyderabad)	
Mumbai (O_1)	160 X_{11}	400 X_{12}	2000
Chennai (O_2)	200 X_{21}	200 X_{22}	3000
Bangalore (O_3)	204 X_{31}	136 X_{32}	2400
	4600	2800	7400 (Total Supply)
Destination-wise Demand	d_1	d_2	7400 (Total Demand)

basic (allocated or filled cells) variables. However, in reality demand may exceed the supply or supply may exceed the demand thereby, leading to unbalanced transportation. In such cases, we re-formulate the model so that, supply gets equal to the demand or demand gets equal to supply thereby, resulting in balanced transportation model.

i. When Demand Exceeds the Supply

In such case, a dummy plant is created (Table 9.8 and Table 9.9), so as to make it a Balanced transportation model. The shipment of product from dummy plant to any destination is allowed. Unit cost of transportation from dummy plant to any destination is zero.

ii. When Supply Exceeds the Demand

In such case, we add dummy destination (Table 9.10 and Table 9.11). Shipment of product from the origins to the dummy destination is allowed. Unit cost of transportation from any source to dummy destination is zero.

Thus, when total supply from sources equals to total demand from destinations, then it is a Balanced transportation model, otherwise it is an unbalanced model. The unbalanced model can be balanced by adding a dummy supply source (row) in case, when demand is greater than supply or by adding a dummy demand destination (column), when supply is greater than demand.

Table 9.8: Unbalanced Transportation Model (Demand > Supply).

Sources	Destinations		Capacity ('000 tonnes)
	D₁ (Visakhapatnam)	D₂ (Hyderabad)	
Mumbai (O1)	160 X_{11}	400 X_{12}	2000
Chennai (O2)	200 X_{21}	200 X_{22}	3000
Bangalore (O3)	204 X_{31}	136 X_{32}	2400
	5100 ↓	3500 ↓	7400 (Total Supply)
Destination-wise Demand ('000 tonnes)	d_1	d_2	8600 (Total Demand)

Table 9.9: Balancing Unbalanced Transportation Model (Demand > Supply) by Introducing Dummy Source (Plant)

Sources	Destinations		Capacity ('000 tonnes)
	D₁ (Visakhapatnam)	D₂ (Hyderabad)	
Mumbai (O1)	160 X_{11}	400 X_{12}	2000
Chennai (O2)	200 X_{21}	200 X_{22}	3000
Bangalore (O3)	204 X_{31}	136 X_{32}	2400
Dummy source (O4)			1200
	5100 ↓	3500 ↓	8600 (Total Supply)
Destination-wise Demand ('000 tonnes)	d_1	d_2	8600 (Total Demand)

Table 9.10: Unbalanced Transportation Model (Demand < Supply)

Sources	Destinations		Capacity ('000 tonnes)
	D_1 (Visakhapatnam)	D_2 (Hyderabad)	
Mumbai (O1)	160 X_{11}	400 X_{12}	2000
Chennai (O2)	200 X_{21}	200 X_{22}	3100
Bangalore (O3)	204 X_{31}	136 X_{32}	2900
	4600	2800	8000 (Total Supply)
Destination-wise Demand ('000 tonnes)	d_1	d_2	7400 (Total Demand)

Table 9.11: Balancing Unbalanced Transportation Model (Demand < Supply) by Introducing Dummy Destination

Sources	Destinations		Dummy destination	Capacity ('000 tonnes)
	D_1 (Visakhapatnam)	D_2 (Hyderabad)		
Mumbai (O1)	160 X_{11}	400 X_{12}		2000
Chennai (O2)	200 X_{21}	200 X_{22}		3100
Bangalore (O3)	204 X_{31}	136 X_{32}		2900
	4600	2800	600	8000 (Total supply)
Destination-wise demand ('000 tonnes)	d_1	d_2	d_3	8000 (Total demand)

F. Things to Remember for Solving Transportation Problem

Now, let us go in-depth for solving transportation problem to obtain initial feasible solution and testing for its optimality. Before going into details, the following are the points to remember:

☆ The number of positive allocations in the cells of transportation matrix must be equal to (m+n-1). But, when the number of positive allocations at any stage of feasible solution is less than the required number (m+n-1), then the solution is said to be degenerate, otherwise non-degenerate.

☆ Cell in the transportation table having positive allocation will be called occupied cell, otherwise empty or non-occupied cell.

G. Initial Feasible Solutions in Transportation Problems

In a transportation problem, an initial feasible solution can be generated by several alternative methods. However, there are three common methods *viz.*, North-West Corner (NWC) Rule, Assignment by Inspection/Judgement or Least Cost Method (LCM) or Minimum Cell Cost Method and Vogel's Approximation Method (VAM) and they are discussed here under with reference to the following example:

Example 9.14

A food processing firm has three plants at Mumbai, Chennai and Bangalore. The product produced at these three plants is to be transported to three major destinations in India *viz.*, D_1, D_2 and D_3. Each source is able to supply the following units of product to the destinations on a monthly basis:

Plant (Source)	Supply (Units)
Mumbai	150
Chennai	175
Bangalore	275
Total Supply	600

Each destination demands the following number of units of product per month:

Destination	Demand (Units)
D_1	200
D_2	100
D_3	300
Total Demand	600

The cost of transporting one unit of product from each plant (source) to each destination differs according to the distance and rail system. These costs are shown in the following table:

Plant (Source)	Destination		
	D_1	D_2	D_3
Mumbai	6	8	10
Chennai	7	11	11
Bangalore	4	5	12

The problem is to determine how many units of product to transport from each source to each destination on a monthly basis in order to minimize the total cost of transportation.

Answer

The LP model for this problem is formulated in the equations as given below:

Min $Z = 6X_{11}+8X_{12}+10X_{13}+7X_{21}+11X_{22}+11X_{23}+4X_{31}+5X_{32}+12X_{33}$

Subject to

$X_{11}+X_{12}+X_{13}$	$= 150$	(Total capacity of Source, Mumbai (O_1))
$X_{21}+X_{22}+X_{23}$	$= 175$	(Total capacity of Source, Chennai (O_2))
$X_{31}+X_{32}+X_{33}$	$= 275$	(Total capacity of Source, Bangalore (O_3))
$X_{11}+X_{21}+X_{31}$	$= 200$	(Destination D_1 total requirement)
$X_{12}+X_{22}+X_{32}$	$= 100$	(Destination D_2 total requirement)
$X_{13}+X_{23}+X_{33}$	$= 300$	(Destination D_3 total requirement)

$Xij \geq 0$

The above problem can be represented through Transportation Tableau (Table 9.12) for easy understanding and it is solved by the three methods *viz.*, NWC Rule, LCM or Minimum Cell Cost Method and VAM.

i. The North-West Corner (NWC) Rule

It is one of the simplest methods, which provides an initial feasible solution to a transportation problem. This method developed by Dantzig and Charnes and Cooper named it as the 'NWC Rule'. The steps involved in this method (Table 9.13) are as under:

☆ *Step 1:* As the name of the rule itself suggests, first select the upper-left or the NWC cell of the transportation matrix.

☆ *Step 2:* Allocate as many units to this cell as possible considering the capacity of the source and the destination requirement. In the upper-left corner cell (*i.e.,* second row-second column (2,2)), the capacity of the source is 150 units, but the destination requirement is 200 units. So, allocate all the 150 units to the upper-left corner cell (2,2) so that, the source capacity is fulfilled, but not the destination requirement. Since destination requirement is not fulfilled, move down the same (second) column and allocate remaining 50 units in (3,2) cell so that, the destination requirement of D_1 is fulfilled. Note that, the allotment of product units should be in tune with the destination

Table 9.12: Transportation Tableau (Matrix)

Sources	Destinations			Capacity of source
	D1	D2	D3	
Mumbai (O1)	6	8	10	150
Chennai (O2)	7	11	11	175
Bangalore (O3)	4	5	12	275
Destination requirement	200	100	300	600 / 600

Table 9.13: North-West Corner Rule

Sources	Destinations			Capacity of source
	D1	D2	D3	
Mumbai (O1)	6 **150**	8	10	150
Chennai (O2)	7 **50**	11 **100**	11 **25**	175
Bangalore (O3)	4	5	12 **275**	275
Destination requirement	200	100	300	600 / 600

requirement. That is, the allocation is of such magnitude that, the capacity of the (first) source is exhausted or the requirement of (first) destination is satisfied or both. So, allot 200 units from the sources Mumbai and Chennai to the (2,2) and (3,2) cells as per the destination D_1 requirement.

☆ *Step 3:* After exhausting the demand for the second column, move along *i.e.*, horizontally to the next cell in the third row and third column (*i.e.*, 3,3). That is, after fulfilling the demand requirement for the second column (ie. (2,2) and (3,2) cells), move horizontally to (3,3) cell *i.e.*, in the third row and third column. Then repeat the above Step 2. That is, since the destination requirement for column 2 (*i.e.*, for D_1) was completely fulfilled, now allot 100 units (*i.e.*, 175-50=125) of second source (Chennai) to destination D_2, as per the destination requirement of D_2 (=100 units). So, by now, demand requirement of destination D_2 is completely fulfilled.

☆ *Step 4:* After exhausting the demand for the third column, move along *i.e.*, horizontally to the next cell *i.e.*, in the third row and fourth column (*i.e.*, 3,4). That is, after fulfilling the demand requirement for the third column (ie. (3,3 cell)), move horizontally to (3,4) cell *i.e.*, in the third row and fourth column. Then repeat the above Step 3. That is, since the destination requirement for column 3 was completely fulfilled, now allot the remaining 25 units (*i.e.*, 175-(100+50)=25) of second source (Chennai) to destination D_3, as per the destination requirement of D_3 (=300 units). So, by now, the source capacity of Chennai (*i.e.*, 175 units) was completely fulfilled.

☆ *Step 5:* After allotting 25 units of product to cell (3,4) now move vertically down to cell (4,4) and allot remaining 275 units from source O_3 (Bangalore) so that, both source O_3 capacity (275 units) and destination requirement of D_3 (300 units) are fulfilled.

Thus, in NWC Rule, the number of units of product allocated in the cell is the most possible, *subject to* the supply and demand constraints for that cell. The largest possible allocation is made to the cell in the upper left hand corner of the tableau, followed by allocations to adjacent feasible cells. Note that, the procedure of allocation of units of product to the cells is continued till the total quantity that is available (source capacity) is fully allocated to the various cells, as required (demand requirement).

☆ The total transportation cost of this solution is computed by substituting the cell allocations (*i.e.*, the amounts transported) into the objective function. So, total transportation cost by employing the formula:

Σ(Allocated units to each destination x Unit transportation cost incurred for transporting the product to each destination)

$= \text{Min } Z = 6X_{11}+8X_{12}+10X_{13}+7X_{21}+11X_{22}+11X_{23}+4X_{31}+5X_{32}+12X_{33}$

$= 6(150)+8X_{12}+10X_{13}+7(50)+11(100)+11(25)+4X_{31}+5X_{32}+12(275) = $ Rs.5925

Thus, the methodology of this method revolves around the following two points:

☆ Note that, if the requirement of destination D_2 is satisfied (say, 3,3 cell), but the capacity of the source (third row, Chennai) is not exhausted, move to right in the same row and make allocation in the next cell (3,4), which exhausts the capacity of that source (third row, Chennai) or satisfy the requirement of third destination or both.

☆ On the other hand, if the capacity of the source (say, second row, Mumbai) is exhausted and the requirement of first destination is unsatisfied (say, 2,2), then move down the column and make second allocation (in 3,2) that satisfies the requirement of first destination or exhaust the origin capacity of second source or both.

☆ This process is repeated till the source capacity and destination requirement are matched.

☆ The number of cells occupied in the transportation matrix are equal to (m+n-1), where 'm'=number of rows (Sources) and 'n'= number of columns (Destinations). Since, there are three sources (rows) and three destinations (columns) in this example, there are (3+3-1)=5 occupied or filled cells in the transportation tableau or matrix (Table 9.13).

ii. Assignment by Inspection or Judgement or LCM or Minimum Cell Cost Method

This method is quicker in obtaining initial feasible solution, as it reduces the number of calculations required to be done compared to NWC rule. The following steps are involved in this method:

☆ *Step 1:* In the transportation matrix, first allocation is made to the cell having lowest shipping cost per unit.

☆ *Step 2:* The least cost cell is filled as much as possible taking the capacity of the source and destination requirement.

☆ *Step 3:* When the smallest cost is not unique *i.e.*, there are other cells having the same smallest cost, select any cell which has this smallest cost.

☆ *Step 4:* The second allocation is to be made in the same column or row to another cell having next least cost in view of the remaining capacity of source and destination requirement.

☆ *Step 5:* Eliminate that row or the column, when either the supply is exhausted or demand is satisfied.

☆ *Step 6:* Follow the same process across the columns and rows till total demand and supply are exhausted.

☆ *Step 7:* Compute the total transportation cost by employing the formula:

Σ(Allocated units to each destination x Unit transportation cost incurred for transporting the product to each destination)

In the given Table 9.14,

☆ The cell that enjoys lowest transportation cost per unit of product is (4,2) *i.e.*, Rs.4/unit and thereby, allocate the supply as per the destination demand *i.e.*, 200 units from source O_3 (Bangalore).

Table 9.14: Assignment by Inspection or Judgement Method or LCM

Sources	Destinations			Capacity of source
	D₁	D₂	D₃	
Mumbai (O₁)	6	8 25	10 125	150
Chennai (O₂)	7	11	11 175	175
Bangalore (O₃)	4 200	5 75	12	275
Destination requirement	200	100	300	600 600

☆ Since the total destination requirement of D₁ (200 units) is fully met, now consider the next lowest unit shipping cost *i.e.,* Rs.5 in the (4,3) cell and allocate remaining 75 units from source O₃ (Bangalore) and by this allocation, the source capacity is exhausted, but destination D₂ demand is not completely fulfilled.

☆ So, now, look at the next lowest shipping cost per unit (Rs.8) in the same column 3 (*i.e.,* 2,3), as its destination demand D₂ is not completely fulfilled and thereby, allocate the supply as per the remaining destination demand *i.e.,* 25 units from source O₁ (Mumbai). Since the total destination requirement of D₂ (100 units) is fully met, now look at next lowest shipping cost per unit (Rs.10) of the fourth column *i.e.,* 2,4 (as the columns 2 and 3 destination requirements are already fulfilled).

☆ Since the total destination requirement of D₂ (100 units) is fully met, now consider the next lowest unit shipping cost *i.e.,* Rs.10 in the (2,4) cell and allocate remaining 125 units from source O₁ (Mumbai) and by this allocation, the source capacity is exhausted, but destination D₂ demand is not completely fulfilled.

☆ So, now, look at the next lowest shipping cost per unit (Rs.11) of (3,4) and thereby, allocate the supply as per the destination demand *i.e.,* 175 units from source O₂ (Chennai). By this allocation, both destination demand of D₃ (300 units) is fully met and source capacity (Chennai) is fully exhausted.

Thus, the procedure of allocation of units of product is to be followed across the columns and rows till total demand and supply are exhausted.

☆ Total transportation cost can be computed by employing the formula:

Σ(Allocated units to each destination x Unit transportation cost incurred for transporting the product to each destination)

$= \text{Min } Z = 6X_{11} + 8X_{12} + 10X_{13} + 7X_{21} + 11X_{22} + 11X_{23} + 4X_{31} + 5X_{32} + 12X_{33}$

$= 6X_{11} + 8(25) + 10(125) + 7X_{21} + 11X_{22} + 11(175) + 4(200) + 5(75) + 12X_{33} = \text{Rs.}4550$

The above analysis infers that, the LCM method will provide a solution with a lower cost than the NWC solution because, the former considers lower cost in the allocation process. It is, therefore, quite natural that, a lower cost will be attained using the LCM method and is closer to the optimal solution and fewer subsequent iterations will be required to achieve the optimal solution.

iii. Vogel's Approximation Method (VAM)

This method is more accurate compared to the above two methods. This method yields a very good initial feasible solution, which sometimes may be the optimal solution. It takes into account not only least cost Cij, but also the costs that just exceed Cij. Although this method takes more time when compared to the earlier two methods in looking for initial feasible solution, but it reduces the time in reaching the optimal solution. This method is based on the concept of penalty cost or regret. If a decision maker incorrectly chooses from several alternative courses of action, a penalty may be suffered (and the decision maker may regret the decision that was made). In a transportation problem, the courses of action are the alternative routes, and a wrong decision is allocating to a cell that does not contain the lowest cost. The following is the procedure involved in this method:

Step 1: From the given data in the transportation matrix, compute penalty for the row and column data by subtracting the least cost element from the next least cost element in the same row or same column. So, penalty is the difference between the smallest and the next smallest cost in the same row and same column.

Step 2: Identify the column or row with largest penalty and in that column or row consider the least transportation cost cell. In case of a tie, select the row or column having minimum transportation cost. If a tie persists, then select the row or column having the maximum possible assignments or you may simply select any row or column in case of a tie without considering minimum costs etc.

Step 3: Allocate as much as possible to the least cost cell in the selected column (with largest penalty) from the corresponding capacity (supply) of the source.

Step 4: Adjust demand and supply by subtracting the transported units from the respective destination requirement of the selected column and respective capacity of the source of the selected row.

Step 5: Cross out the satisfied row or column.

Step 6: In the next iteration, delete that row or column for which the demand is equal to supply.

Step 7: Repeat the iterations with the same procedure discussed in the above steps till, total demand from the destinations (total destination requirement) is equal to total supply from the sources (total capacity). That is, stop the iteration, when there is only one row (source) or one column (destination).

Step 8: At the end *i.e.* check that the total number of filled cells = (m + n–1), where 'm'=number of rows (Sources) and 'n'= number of columns (Destinations). Only then, the initial solution would be feasible.

The above discussed procedure is followed now to solve the given problem for achieving lowest possible total transportation cost for transporting the product across several destinations from different plants or sources (Tables 9.15 to 9.20). In this example, in I iteration, since the penalty is highest (considering both rows and columns) with reference to Chennai source (O_2) *i.e.*, 4, the allocation of 175 units is made in the least cost transportation cell *i.e.* (3, 2) of that row. So, in the II iteration, the Chennai source (O_2) is deleted, as for that source, the capacity is completely satisfied. In II iteration, the penalty is highest with reference to destination D_2 *i.e.*, 3 and accordingly the allocation of 100 units is made in the least cost transportation cell *i.e.* (3, 3) of that column. Now, since the destination requirement of D_2 is completely fulfilled, that column is deleted in the III iteration. In the III iteration, the penalty is highest for Bangalore source (O_3) *i.e.*, 8 and accordingly the allocation of 25 units is made in the least cost transportation cell *i.e.* (3, 2) of that row. Since the source capacity of Bangalore O_3 was not completely exhausted (*i.e.*, 175-25 = 150), that source was still continued in the IV iteration with the balance capacity of 150 units. In the IV iteration, since there is only column of Destination D3, the iterations were stopped

Table 9.15: Vogel's Approximation Method – Transportation Tableau (Matrix)

Sources	Destinations			Capacity of source
	D1	D2	D3	
Mumbai (O1)	6	8	10	150
Chennai (O2)	7	11	11	175
Bangalore (O3)	4	5	12	275
Destination requirement	200	100	300	600 600

Table 9.16 : Vogel's Approximation Method (I Iteration)

Sources	Destinations			Capacity of source	Penalty
	D1	D2	D3		
Mumbai (O1)	6	8	10	150	8-6=2
Chennai (O2)	7 175	11	11	~~175~~	**11-7=4**
Bangalore (O3)	4	5	12	275	5-4=3
Destination requirement	~~200~~ 25	100	300	425 425	
Penalty	6-4=2	8-5=3	11-10=1		

Table 9.17: Vogel's Approximation Method (II Iteration)

Sources	Destinations			Capacity of source	Penalty
	D1	D2	D3		
Mumbai (O1)	6	8	10	150	8-6=2
Bangalore (O3)	4	5 100	12	~~275~~ 175	5-4=1
Destination requirement	25	~~100~~	300	325 325	
Penalty	6-4=2	**8-5=3**	12-10=2		

Table 9.18: Vogel's Approximation Method (III Iteration)

Sources	Destinations		Capacity of source	Penalty
	D1	D3		
Mumbai (O1)	6	10	150	10-6=4
Bangalore (O3)	4 25	12	~~175~~ 150	12-4=8
Destination requirement	~~35~~	300	300 300	
Penalty	6-4=2	12-10=2		

and the allocations made above are shown in Table 9.20 and transportation cost was computed (Rs.5125).

In the IV iteration (Table 9.19), no more penalty can be worked out for rows (or columns in some cases) and thereby, this is the final iteration for the problem. Further, the total demand from the destination D_3 (*i.e.,* total destination requirement) is equal to total supply from the sources (total capacity).

Table 9.19: Vogel's Approximation Method (IV Iteration)

Sources	Destination	Capacity of source	Penalty
	D3		
Mumbai (O1)	10	150	
Bangalore (O3)	12	150	
Destination requirement	300 300	300	
Penalty			

Table 9.20: Vogel's Approximation Method – Allocation Matrix and Cost of Shipping

Sources	Destinations			Capacity of source
	D1	D2	D3	
Mumbai (O1)	6	8	10	150
Chennai (O2)	7 175	11	11	175
Bangalore (O3)	4 25	5 100	12	275
Destination requirement	200	100	300	600 600

Cost of shipping = Min $Z = 6X_{11}+8X_{12}+10X_{13}+7X_{21}+11X_{22}+11X_{23}+4X_{31}+5X_{32}+12X_{33}$
$= 6X_{11}+8X_{12}+10X_{13}+7(175)+11X_{22}+11X_{23}+4(25)+5(100)+12X_{33}$ = Rs.5125

Now, transfer all the data pertaining to allocated units into the least cost cells right from I iteration to IV iteration and the same is shown as Allocation matrix (Table 9.20). This facilitates the calculation of transportation cost by using the following formula:

Σ(Allocated units to each destination x Unit transportation cost incurred for transporting the product to each destination)

Cost of shipping = Min $Z = 6X_{11}+8X_{12}+10X_{13}+7X_{21}+11X_{22}+11X_{23}+4X_{31}+5X_{32}+12X_{33}$

$= 6X_{11}+8X_{12}+10X_{13}+7(175)+11X_{22}+11X_{23}+4(25)+5(100)+12X_{33}$ = Rs.5125

H. Criteria to Identify Initial or Basic Feasible Solution

The solution obtained by any of the above three methods must fulfill following conditions:

☆ The solution must be feasible, *i.e.*, it must satisfy all the supply and demand constraints. This is called Rim condition.

☆ The number of positive allocations must be equal to (m+n–1), *where,* 'm' is number of rows and 'n' is number of columns.

The solution that satisfies both the above mentioned conditions is called a non-degenerate initial (basic) feasible solution.

I. Test for Optimality

An optimality test can be performed to find whether the obtained feasible solution is optimal or not. For testing the optimality, first the feasible solution must satisfy:

☆ Number of allocations equal to (m+n-1), where 'm' is the number of rows and 'n' is the number of columns. In the solution derived (Table 9.14 – being the lowest transportation cost (Rs. 4550) achieved under LCM), the number of filled (allocated) cells are five in number and this is equal to (m+n-1)=(3+3-1=5). Hence, optimality test can be performed.

☆ Further these (m+n-1) allocations should be in independent positions. That is, a close look at the feasible solution (Table 9.14) of the problem indicates that, all the allocations are in independent positions, as it is impossible to increase or decrease any allocation without either changing the position of the allocations or violating the row and column restrictions. For example, if the allocation in cell (2,3) is changed from (25) to (35), then the allocation in cell (2,4) must be changed from (125) to (115) in order to satisfy the row restriction. Similarly the allocation in cell (4,3) must be changed from (75) to (65) in order to meet the column restriction. Likewise, the row restriction for (4,2) should also be adjusted. A simple rule for allocations to be in independent positions is that, the occupied (allocated) cells do not form a closed loop. This closed loop is not seen in the Table 9.14 of feasible region. This closed loop is exemplified through Table 9.21.

Table 9.21: Allocated Cells Forming a Loop Implying NOT a Feasible Solution

Sources	Destinations			Capacity of source
	D₁	D₂	D₃	
Mumbai (O₁)	6	8	10	150
Chennai (O₂)	7 ← 124	11 136 ↑	11	260
Bangalore (O₃)	4 ↓ 59	5 110 ↓	12	169
Destination requirement	183	236	160	579 / 579

Since, the above two conditions are satisfied, now employ procedure for testing the optimality of feasible solution. Two methods are commonly used for this purpose *viz.*, Stepping-Stone Method and Modified Distribution (MODI) Method. Among the above three methods for computing the initial feasible solution, LCM yielded lowest transportation cost (Rs.4550) compared to NWC Rule Method and VAM and hence, the feasible solution derived from LCM will be considered to test for its optimality.

i. Stepping-Stone Method

Consider the Table 9.14, which gives the first feasible solution for the problem under consideration by employing LCM. Let us start with any arbitrary empty cell, say (4,4) and allocate '+1' unit to this cell (Table 9.22). In order to keep up the column 4 restriction, '-1' must be allocated to cell (3,4). In order to keep up the row 3 restriction, '+1' must be allocated to cell (3,3). Consequently, '-1' must be allocated to cell (4,3) in order to keep up the column 3 restriction. The net change in transportation cost as a result of this perturbation is calculated as given below and this is called the Evaluation of empty cell.

$$=(+1\times12)+(-1\times11)+(+1\times11)+(-1\times5) = +7$$

The rules of thumb are:

☆ When there are 'm' rows and 'n' cells, the total number of empty cells is given by: $(m-1)(n-1)$. In this case, the number of empty cells are $(3-1)(3-1)=4$.

Table 9.22: Stepping Stone Method to Test for Optimality Considering LCM

Sources	Destinations			Capacity of source
	D1	D2	D3	
Mumbai (O1)	6	8 25	10 125	150
Chennai (O2)	7	11 175 (+1)	11 (-1)	175
Bangalore (O3)	4 200	5 75 (-1)	12 (+1)	275
Destination requirement	200	100	300	600 / 600

☆ Cell evaluations must be worked out for all these empty cells. If any cell evaluation is negative, the cost can be still reduced so that, the initial feasible solution under consideration can be improved and thereby, the obtained initial feasible solution is not optimal. On the other hand, if all cell evaluations are positive or zero, the initial feasible solution obtained is considered optimal.

In the above case, the Stepping Stone method proved cell evaluation is positive (+7) and even for other empty cells and thereby, the obtained feasible solution is optimal.

ii. MODI Method

In MODI method, cell evaluations of all the occupied cells are calculated simultaneously and only one closed path for the most negative cell is traced, unlike in Stepping Stone Method. Thus, MODI method is more time-saving compared to the Stepping Stone Method. The methodology involved in this method is discussed here under through the following steps:

Step 1

Set up a cost matrix (Table 9.23) with reference to the unit costs associated with the cells for which allocations have been made (*i.e.* filled or occupied cells).

Step 2: Determination of Row and Column Values for Occupied Cells

For this, in the obtained feasible solution through LCM (Table 9.14), consider the unit costs of the occupied (filled) cells with respect to each column and each row. Let 'Ui' be the row value and 'Vi' be the column value and assume, 'U1'=0, then

Table 9.23: Step 1: MODI Method or The 'u-v' Method – Cost Matrix for Occupied Cells

Sources	Destinations		
	D_1	D_2	D_3
Mumbai (O_1)		8	10
Chennai (O_2)			11
Bangalore (O_3)	4	5	

U2+V3=8. So, 0+V3=8 ————→ V3=8

U2+V4=10. So, 0+V4=10 ————→ V4=10

U3+V4=11. So, U3+10=11 ————→ U3=1

U4+V2=4. So, -3+V2=1 ————→ V2= 4

U4+V3=5. So, U4+8=5 ————→ U4= -3

The above calculations for each row and column are shown along the borders of the Table 9.24.

Table 9.24: Step 2 - Determination of Row and Column Values for Occupied Cells

			4	8	10
	Sources		**Destinations**		
			D₁	D₂	D₃
0	Mumbai (O₁)			8	10
1	Chennai (O₂)				11
-3	Bangalore (O₃)		4	5	

Step 3

Fill the empty cells with the sums of Ui+Vi. This gives the Implicit costs of empty cells.

Z22 = U2+V2=0+4=4

Z32 = U3+V2= 1+4=5

Z33 = U3+V3= 1+8=9

Z44 = U4+V4= -3+10= 7

The above calculations are shown through Table 9.25.

Step 4: Computation of Opportunity Cost of Empty Cells

This is given by:

Opportunity cost = Implicit cost – Actual cost. That is, this Step 4 includes the subtraction of empty cell values of original cost matrix (Table 9.14) from implicit cost

Table 9.25: Step 3 - Determination of Implicit Costs of Empty Cells.

Sources	Destinations		
	D₁ (4)	D₂ (8)	D₃ (10)
Mumbai (O₁) — 0	4		
Chennai (O₂) — 1	5	9	
Bangalore (O₃) — -3			7

matrix of empty cells in Step 3 (Table 9.25). The resulting matrix is called Cell evaluation matrix. So,

$Z_{22}-C_{22} = 4-6 = -2$

$Z_{32}-C_{32} = 5-7 = -2$

$Z_{33}-C_{33} = 9-11 = -2$

$Z_{44}-C_{44} = 7-12 = -5$

The above calculations are shown through Table 9.26.

The rule of thumb is, if the opportunity cost values of all empty cells are either zero or negative (non-positive), it implies optimal solution. From the above calculations, since all the opportunity cost values of empty cells are negative, it implies an optimal solution. So, the objective function with reference to LCM *i.e.*,

$= \text{Min } Z = 6X_{11}+8X_{12}+10X_{13}+7X_{21}+11X_{22}+11X_{23}+4X_{31}+5X_{32}+12X_{33}$

$= 6X_{11}+8(25)+10(125)+7X_{21}+11X_{22}+11(175)+4(200)+5(75)+12X_{33} = \text{Rs.}4550$

is an optimal solution.

J. Generalized Procedure to Solve a Transportation Problem

The solution algorithm to a transportation problem can be summarized into the following steps:

Table 9.26: Cell Evaluation Matrix

Sources	Destinations		
	D_1	D_2	D_3
Mumbai (O_1)	-2		
Chennai (O_2)	-2	-2	
Bangalore (O_3)			-5

Step 1

Formulate the problem and set up in the matrix form. As discussed earlier, the formulation of transportation problem is similar to LP problem formulation. Here, the objective function is the total transportation cost that is to be minimized and the constraints are the supply available at each source and demand at each destination.

Step 2

Obtain an initial basic feasible solution. This initial basic solution can be obtained by using any of the following methods:

- ☆ NWC Rule
- ☆ LCM
- ☆ VAM

Step 3

The solution obtained by any of the above three methods must fulfill the following conditions:

- ☆ The solution must be feasible, *i.e.* it must satisfy all the supply and demand constraints. This is called Rim condition.
- ☆ The number of positive allocations/filled cells/occupied cells must be equal to (m+n−1), *where,* 'm' is number of rows and 'n' is number of columns.

Step 4

Test the initial basic feasible solution for its optimality: Use the following two methods to test the optimality of obtained initial basic feasible solution:

☆ Stepping Stone Method

☆ MODI Method

If the solution is optimal then stop, otherwise, determine a new improved solution.

K. Merits of LP Technique

LP is an important branch of applied mathematics that solves a wide variety of optimization problems. This technique finds place in various applications like:

☆ In production planning and scheduling problems. In these problems, we determine the number of units of different products, which should be produced and sold by a firm when each product requires a fixed manpower, machine hours, labour hours per unit of product, warehouse space per unit of the output etc., in order to make maximum profits.

☆ In aircraft and crew scheduling. The airline industry uses LP to optimize profits and minimize expenses in their business. Airlines needed to consider, how many people would be willing to pay a higher price for a ticket if they were able to book their flight at the last minute and have substantial flexibility in their schedule and flight times. The airline also needed to know how many people would only purchase a low price ticket, without an in-flight meal. Through LP, airlines were able to find the optimal breakdown of how many tickets to sell at which price, including various prices in between. Airlines also need to consider plane routes, pilot schedules, direct and indirect flights, and layovers.

☆ LP is important in managerial decision making. The reason is that, it helps the business firm in minimizing the costs and maximizing the profits. It also guides the manager to work under limitations and conditions.

☆ In solving staffing problems like the number of staff needed in colleges, hospitals, mines, hotels and other types of businesses.

☆ In the field of marketing. This technique is used in the selection of the best advertising medium among a number of media.

☆ In solving the diet problems through minimizing the cost and this is very useful for hospitals. In these problems, we determine the amount of different kinds of constituents/nutrients which should be included in a diet, so as to minimize the cost of the desired diet such that, it contains a certain minimum amount of each constituent/nutrients.

☆ In addressing transportation problems. That is, we determine a transportation schedule in order to find the cheapest way of transporting a product from plants/factories situated at different locations to different markets.

☆ Farm managers use LP to increase the revenue of their operations, like what to produce, how much of it and what to use it for.

☆ Amusement parks use LP to make decisions about queue lines.

☆ In other different areas such as finance (resolving situations of capital budgeting, financial planning and so on), product mix problems (problems based on blending resources to produce an item, management must decide the quantity of each product), multiple plant location studies (the new location will be, where the total production and distribution cost will be minimized), maximizing material utilization (determine the combination of cuts that will meet requirements for the amounts of the different sizes with a minimum trim loss) etc.

Above all these applications, another remarkable characteristic of LP technique is that, it has the adapting facility to reality, which allows solving, by computer programs, problems with thousands of variables and constraints. It also allows sensitivity analysis. That is to say it, helps to analyze, what happens to the results when we change the coefficients of the objective function and/or in the constraints. That is, the manager can ascertain, how changes affect the optimal solution to the original LP problem. (The range of values over which the current solution will remain optimal, despite the change of the coefficients, is called range of optimality).

Thus, considering the above applications of LP, it serves as an important part of operations research and continues to make the world more economically efficient.

L. Demerits or Limitations of LP Technique

Though LP enjoys wider applications across various fields like theory of firm's production, in inter-regional trade, in general equilibrium analysis, in welfare economics, in development planning etc., it suffers from the following limitations:

☆ It involves laborious mathematical calculations to determine the given objective function. Hence, it demands analytical skills on the part of the researcher to run the computer software programme to perform huge number of mathematical calculations.

☆ Even if the objective function is clearly specified, it may not be so easy to find out various technological, financial, marketing and other constraints that may be operative in pursuing the given function.

☆ Given a specified objective function and a set of functional constraints, the latter may not be directly expressible as linear inequalities.

☆ LP technique is based on the assumption that, there exists linear relationship between inputs and outputs. This means that, inputs and outputs can be added, multiplied and divided. However practically, the relations between inputs and outputs are mostly non-linear.

☆ LP technique assumes perfect competition both in product and factor markets. But, perfect competition is only a myth.

☆ The LP technique is based on the hypothesis of constant returns. However, in reality, there are either diminishing or increasing returns, which a firm experiences in its production programme.

☆ Mostly, LP models present trial and error solutions and it is difficult to find out optimal solutions to the various economic complexities.

☆ LP technique assumes that, in objective function, proportionality implies that, the marginal rate of contribution to the objective (maximization or minimization) for each variable is assumed to remain constant throughout the entire range of activity levels in the problem. That is, variables cannot be multiplied or divided by other variables, cannot be raised to an exponent other than 1, or be arguments of other functional relationships (say, sin X or log X). However, this may not always hold true in the real world. Economies of scale, for instance, reflect variations in costs and profit margins as production levels change. Price discounting for certain preferred customers also violates the proportionality assumption. Similarly, in functional constraints, proportionality implies that, resource usage per variable is assumed constant throughout the entire operational range of the problem. But, in many situations, the manager might get a volume discount such that, the price per unit of product goes down, if he purchase more quantity of a product. These discounts are often nonlinear, which that a LP model is either inappropriate or is really an approximation of the real world problem.

☆ LP technique assumes linearity of the variables both in the objective function and in functional constraints. The broader implication of linearity is that, the variables are assumed to be mutually independent. In other words, the products are assumed to be neither complements nor substitutes of each other and there is no interaction between the variables. Clearly, this may not be the case in the actual system, in which case majority of the products are either substitutes or complements of each other and thereby, the linearity assumption would be violated.

☆ Factors such as uncertainty, weather conditions etc., are not taken into consideration. That is, when using LP, there is no way to deal with uncertainty. We formulate the problem with the assumption that, we know all of the values for costs, profits, constraints etc. But, in real-life problems, these variables often are unknowns. Methods such as *chance constrained programming* or *linear programming under uncertainty* can be used in these situations.

☆ Only one single objective is dealt with, while in real life situations, problems come with multi-objectives.

☆ Parameters are assumed to be constants, but in reality they may not be so.

☆ As per the assumption of LP model, the solution variables can have any value, but in some cases, the variables may have only integer values. For example, if a machinery manufacturing firm aims at, how many processing machines have to be produced, then only integer values of decision variables are meaningful.

☆ LP model does not take into account the influence of time on both objective function and functional constraints.

To conclude, a comparative picture between *pros* and *cons* about LP reveal that, LP is the most used program in the management area, despite it has several arguments against it. There are sound reasons, which take us to select this method for solving various management problems owing to the complexity of the problems that can be handled.

M. Concept of Optimality

The earlier discussion under factor-product relationship, factor-factor relationship and product-product relationship and the discussion under LP technique commonly highlight the concept of 'optimality' in the production programme. In all the above concepts, optimality implies utilization of resources more efficiently in a production programme, so as to achieve either cost minimization or profit maximization or both. Besides the above decision making areas, the concept of optimality also arises with reference to consumer behaviour and firm's behaviour under different forms of market competition (perfect and imperfect market competitions). Let us now refresh the concept of optimality in the above decision making areas.

1. Decision Making by Consumer

a. Consumer's Equilibrium when the Commodity is Available Free of Cost to the Consumer

If the commodity is freely available to the consumer, he will not hesitate to consume the same commodity till he reaches the point of maximum satisfaction. That means, he will consume the same commodity till the point of satiety, which occurs when Marginal Utility (MU) is equal to zero or Total Utility (TU) is maximum. In case of certain commodities, the point of satiety is reached quickly, while in others, it takes more time.

b. Consumer's Equilibrium when Commodity is Priced to the Consumer

Case-1: One-Commodity Consumer's Equilibrium

On the other hand, if the commodity is not available at free of cost to the consumer, which is the common practical situation, the consumer tries to attain maximum satisfaction taking into consideration several aspects like MU derived from each unit of the commodity, price of the commodity, MU of money, MU derived from the commodity in terms of money (MU derived from the commodity/MU of money), MU of expenditure (MU derived from the commodity/Price of the commodity), prices of the substitutes etc. So, in this case, the consumer will not consume the commodity till the point of satiety. Rather, he will go on consuming the commodity units, as long as, MU derived from the commodity in terms of money is higher than price of the commodity or MU of expenditure is higher than MU of money. The consumer will reach the point of equilibrium or attain maximum satisfaction when MU derived in terms of money is equal to the price paid for each unit of the commodity or MU of expenditure is equal to MU of money. Since, the consumer is rational, he will not pay more for the commodity than the MU received in terms of money from each unit of the commodity. As the consumer knows, if he goes on consuming the commodity, the MU derived from each unit of the commodity diminishes, and hence, he will be very

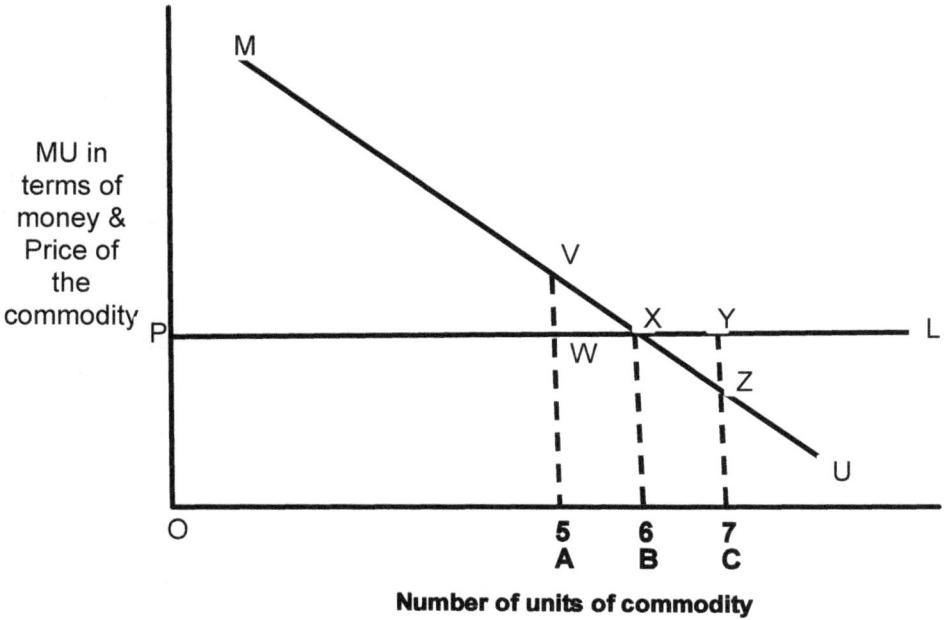

Figure 9.21: Point of Consumer's Equilibrium.

careful in allocating the resources on the commodity and he stops purchasing the commodity when the MU derived in terms of money is equal to its price. The same is explained through the Figure 9.21.

In the Figure 9.21, along X-axis, number of units of commodity and along Y-axis, price and MU derived from the commodity in terms of money are taken. As the MU diminishes continuously, due to continuous consumption of the same commodity, the MU curve (in terms of money) is a continuous downward sloping curve from left to right. Since the price of the commodity is constant at a given point of time, it is represented by a straight line 'PL' parallel to X-axis and the price is OP per unit. The consumer purchases the first five units of the commodity, since the MU derived in terms of money from each unit of the commodity is higher than the price paid for the commodity, OP. At fifth unit of the commodity, the MU derived in terms of money is VA and price paid is OP. So, he is left over with a surplus satisfaction of VW over the price paid for the commodity. At the sixth unit of the commodity, the MU derived in terms of money, BX is equal to price paid for the commodity, OP. So, this is the point of consumer's equilibrium or the point of maximum satisfaction to the consumer and at this point, there is no surplus satisfaction to the consumer. If the consumer consumes seventh unit of the commodity, he derives the MU in terms of money as CZ, but he pays the same price OP and thereby, he incurs loss of YZ, as the MU derived in terms of money from the seventh unit is less than price paid for the commodity. Since consumer is rational, he is not prepared to consume beyond sixth unit of the commodity, as the MU in terms of money still diminishes below the price of the commodity. So, the consumer reaches the point of equilibrium at sixth unit of the commodity and thereby, he stops consuming at OB units or six units of the commodity.

If the consumer consumes OA units of commodity, he is left over with surplus satisfaction of VWX. If he consumes OB unit of commodity, there is scope for realizing this left over surplus satisfaction, VWX. So, at sixth unit of commodity or consuming OB units of commodity, the consumer derives maximum satisfaction, as there is no scope for surplus satisfaction or left over satisfaction. On the other hand, if the consumer consumes seventh unit of the commodity, as mentioned earlier, the price paid for the commodity is more than MU derived from the commodity in terms of money and thereby, he incur loss in satisfaction to the tune of XYZ. So, moving in either way from OB unit or from sixth unit of the commodity, will lead to diminution of total satisfaction. So consumer's equilibrium refers to the situation, in which a consumer gets maximum satisfaction for the given level of income and price of the commodity. In the words of Alfred Marshall, '*consumer's equilibrium is that state of consumer's demand, which he thinks to be the best and which he does not want to alter*'. The above explanation can be summarized in the following way:

At OA Units of Purchase Cf commodity

Total satisfaction gained by the consumer = OMVA

Total cost incurred by the consumer in purchasing the commodity = OPWA

Surplus satisfaction enjoyed by the consumer = PMVW

Surplus satisfaction left over with the consumer = VWX

At OB Units of Purchase of Commodity

Total satisfaction gained by the consumer = OMXB

Total cost incurred by the consumer in purchasing the commodity = OPXB

Surplus satisfaction enjoyed by the consumer = PMX

Surplus satisfaction left over with the consumer = 0 (zero)

At OC Units of Purchase of Commodity

Total satisfaction gained by the consumer = OMZC

Total cost incurred by the consumer in purchasing the commodity = OPYC

Loss in satisfaction = XYZ

So, based on the above analysis, we can derive the point of consumer's equilibrium from the formulae given below.

Method 1

The point of consumer's equilibrium is when MU of expenditure is equal to MU of money

$$\text{Consumer's equilibrium} = \frac{\text{MU of the commodity A}}{\text{Price of the commodity A}} = \text{MU of money} \qquad \textit{Equation 9.1}$$

The above equation 9.1 can be written as,

$$\text{Consumer's equilibrium} = \frac{MU_A}{P_A} = MU_M$$

In the above equation 9.1, the left side portion represents MU of expenditure or Weighted MU.

Method 2

The point of consumer's equilibrium is when MU derived in terms of money is equal to price of the commodity. So,

$$\text{Consumer's equilibrium} = \frac{MU \text{ of the commodity A}}{MU \text{ of money}} = \text{Price of the commodity A}$$

Equation 9.2

The above equation 9.2 can be written as,

$$\text{Consumer's equilibrium} = \frac{MU_A}{MU_M} = P_A$$

In the above equation 9.2, the left side portion represents MU derived in terms of money.

Method 3

There is another way of expressing the point of consumer's equilibrium *i.e.*, through studying the net gain in the consumption of commodity. That means, larger the net gain between TU in terms of money and total expenditure, greater is the satisfaction derived by the consumer.

Case 2: Two Commodities or More than One Commodity Consumer's Equilibrium

The same principle, as discussed above, also applies, if the consumer deals with more than one commodity to arrive at the point of consumer's equilibrium or the point of maximum satisfaction. For example, if the consumer deals with two commodities A and B, the prices of the two commodities are P_A and P_B, MUs derived from the two commodities is MU_A and MU_B and assumed constancy of MU of money is MU_M, then the point of consumer's equilibrium in case of two commodities is given by the following methods:

Method 1

If the consumer deals with more than one commodity, he will be in equilibrium when he equalizes the MU of expenditure or weighted MUs of all commodities and the consumer will go on purchasing commodities till the MU of expenditure of each commodity becomes equal to the MU of money to him.

$$\text{Consumer's equilibrium} = \frac{MU \text{ of the commodity}}{\text{Price of the commodity}} = MU \text{ of money}$$

Equation 9.1

The above equation 9.1 can be written as,

$$\text{Consumer's equilibrium} = \frac{MU_A}{P_A} = MU_M \qquad \textit{for commodity A}$$

$$\text{Consumer's equilibrium} = \frac{MU_B}{P_B} = MU_M \qquad \textit{for commodity B}$$

In the above equations, the left side portion represents MU of expenditure.

So, the point of consumer's equilibrium in dealing with both the commodities A and B is given by the formula:

$$\frac{MU_A}{P_A} = \frac{MU_B}{P_B} = MU_M \qquad \text{Equation 9.3}$$

This is called Two commodity equilibrium or Principle of Proportionality. The above equation 9.3 implies that, in case of two commodities A and B, the consumer derives maximum satisfaction when MU of expenditure on both the commodities are equal to MU of money.

In the above equation, if $(MU_A/P_A) > (MU_B/P_B)$, then the consumer will go on substituting commodity A in place of commodity B. This results in fall in MU_A due to its excessive consumption and finally MU_A/P_A decreases and gets equal to MU_B/P_B and the consumer reaches the point of equilibrium. But, it is important that, the point of equality between MU_A/P_A and MU_B/P_B can be achieved not only once but also at different levels of expenditure. This is influenced by the size of money income with the consumer.

If the consumer deals with more than two commodities, then the point of equilibrium will be given by,

$$\frac{MU_A}{P_A} = \frac{MU_B}{P_B} = \frac{MU_C}{P_C} = \frac{MU_N}{P_N} = MU_M \qquad \textit{Equation 9.4}$$

The above equation can be expressed as

$$\frac{MU_A}{MU_B} = \frac{P_A}{P_B} \text{ and } \frac{MU_B}{MU_C} = \frac{P_B}{P_C} \text{ and so forth} \qquad \textit{Equation 9.5}$$

This indicates that, if the consumer deals with more than one commodity, he will be in equilibrium when he equalizes the ratios of MUs of commodities with the ratio of corresponding prices for each pair of commodities consumed.

Method 2

If the consumer deals with more than one commodity, he will be in equilibrium when he equalizes the MU derived from the commodities in terms of money with their respective prices.

$$(MU_A/MU_M) = P_A \qquad \textit{Consumer's equilibrium for commodity A}$$

where, (MU_A/MU_M) is MU derived from commodity A in terms of money.

$(MU_B/MU_M) = P_B$ *Consumer's equilibrium for commodity B*

where, (MU_B/MU_M) is nothing but MU derived from commodity B in terms of money.

Method 3

There is another way of expressing the point of consumer's equilibrium *i.e.* through studying the net gain across the consumption of commodities. That means, larger the net gain between TU in terms of money and total expenditure across the commodities, greater the satisfaction derived by the consumer.

2. Decision Making by Producer

i. Optimization of Output through Increasing Resource Use Efficiency

As discussed under Chapter 2, let us remember that, Stage II is called as 'Rational stage' or 'Optimal stage' because, there is a possibility of optimization of output. At which particular point, the farmer will decide to produce depends upon the various factors like, output he would like to produce, price of the factor he has to pay, price of the product in the market etc. The criteria to optimize the output in this stage can be studied both from the output side and input side.

Output side: 1. MC=MR

2. MPP=Factor-Product Price Ratio: $[(\Delta Y/\Delta X)=(P_X/P_Y)] = MPP * P_Y = P_X$ So,

$VMP = P_X$

(where P_X = Price of factor, Fertilizer)

Input side: $MVP_X=MFC_X = [(\Delta TR/\Delta X) = (\Delta SRTVC/\Delta X)]$

Thus, the level of input usage within Stage II at which the farmer can maximize the profits all depends upon how many units of output the farmer can sell, the price of the product, and the monetary costs of employing the variable input.

Inequality between MR and MC or MVPx (VMP) and MFCx (or P_x)

Case 1: MR>MC or MVPx (VMP)>MFCx (or P_x)

This case is observed in the first stage of production function and the farmer is advised to increase the input usage, so that MC or MFC_X increases and becomes equal to MR or MVPx (VMP) respectively to attain optimality in the production programme. Similarly, with increase in input usage, MPP decreases thereby, MVPx (VMP) falls and gets equal to P_X and this optimality is achieved in Stage II.

Case 2: MR<MC or MVPx (VMP)<MFCx (or P_x)

This case is observed in the third stage of production function and the farmer is advised to reduce the input usage so that, MC or MFC_X decreases and becomes equal to MR or MVPx (VMP) respectively to attain optimality in the production programme. Similarly, with decrease in input usage, MPP increases thereby, MVPx (VMP) rises and gets equal to P_X and this optimality is achieved in Stage II.

ii. Cost Minimization in Production Programme

LCC of factors can be achieved in the following two ways:

a. Cost Minimization for a given Level of Output

Here, the farmer tries to minimize the cost to produce a given level of output in the production programme. Three important conditions are essential to achieve point of LCC of resources:

☆ The iso-cost line should be tangent to the isoquant from below

☆ Slope of the iso-cost line should be equal to the slope of isoquant

☆ Isoquant should be convex to the origin

Recall now the values of the slopes of these two curves. The slope of isoquant indicates MRTS of these two resources *i.e.* $MRTS_{MF} = \Delta F/\Delta M$. The slope of iso-cost line indicates prices ratio of manure and fertilizer *i.e.*, P_M/P_F. So, the point of LCC is given by:

$$MRTS_{MF} = \Delta F/\Delta M \ (= MPP_M/MPP_F) = P_M/P_F \qquad \textit{Equation 9.6}$$

Thus, the LCC of resources occurs at the point, where the MRTS of the resources is inversely equal to the ratio of their prices or the ratio of MPP of resources is directly equal to the ratio of their prices. This simply tells the farmer that, the LCC of manure and fertilizer is such that, equal increments of output should be obtained for the last rupee spent on each of the inputs.

b. Output Maximization for a given Cash Outlay and Prices of the Resources

The other way of attaining the optimal combination of factors is maximizing the output for a given level of cash outlay with the farmer and for the given prices of the two resources. So, again at the point of tangency of iso-cost line and isoquant, all the three necessary conditions mentioned above are to be fulfilled for achieving optimization of resources usage.

iii. Profit Maximization for a given Level of Resources

Economic efficiency in product-product relationship is attained when the physical concept ($MRPS_{PM}$) is integrated with the economic concept (price ratio of products). Thus, the OPC can be determined by imposing the PPC map on iso-revenue line. Three important conditions must be fulfilled to arrive at the point of optimum combination of products. They include,

☆ The iso-revenue line should be tangent to the PPC from above

☆ Slope of the iso-revenue line should be equal to the slope of PPC

☆ PPC should be concave to the origin *i.e.*, the MRPS of paddy for maize ($MRPS_{FM}$) must be increasing at the point of equilibrium.

Recall now the values of the slopes of these two curves. The slope of PPC indicates MRPS of paddy for maize and slope of iso-revenue line indicates price ratio of two products and the point of OPC is explained below.

Slope of the PPC= $MRPS_{PM} = (\Delta M)/(\Delta P)$

Slope of the iso-revenue line = (P_P/P_M)

So, the point of profit maximization is when the slope of the PPC is equal to the slope of the iso-revenue line and this is given by,

$$(\Delta M)/(\Delta P) = (P_P/P_M) \text{ or } MRPS_{PM} = (P_P/P_M)$$
Equation 9.7

So, at the point of OPC, the slope of PPC is equal to the slope of iso-revenue line or the $MRPS_{PM}$ is inversely equal to the price ratio of paddy and maize. The point of OPC can also be stated that, the rate (MRPS) at which the farmer is willing to substitute paddy for maize is inversely equal to the price ratio between paddy and maize.

3. Decision making by the Firm under Perfect and Imperfect Market Competitions

To achieve the optimality, the firm aims at the equality of MR and MC and this will guide to optimize the output or maximize the profits. MR indicates the additional revenue the firm gets in selling additional unit of output and MC indicates the additional cost incurred by the firm in producing the additional unit of output. The rules of thumb are:

☆ The firm attains equilibrium, when MR=MC

☆ When MR>MC, the firm should continue the production programme to increase the output, so that MC rises and thereby, the equality between MR and MC is ensured.

☆ When MR<MC, the firm has to reduce the output, so that MC falls and thereby, the equality between MR and MC is ensured.

The above rules of firm's equilibrium imply that, the firm will not produce an additional unit of output, which involves more MC compared to MR earned from the same. In other words, the firm will produce an additional unit of output. only when the MR earned from that unit is more than MC incurred in producing the same. So, the firm continues to produce more units of output and attains optimum level of output at the point, where MR = MC. According to Stonier and Hague, *'a firm will be in equilibrium when it is earning maximum money profits. But, the money profits of a firm will always be maximized when its marginal revenue equals the marginal cost'.* In the graphical illustration of the MR and MC approach (Figures 7.17 and 7.18), the equality between MRC and MC curve will not be the only sufficient condition for the firm's equilibrium, but the firm must also satisfy the second order condition *i.e.,* the MC curve should cut the MR curve from below, while MC curve is rising upward. Thus, the two important conditions for the firm's equilibrium include,

☆ MR= MC

☆ MC curve should cut the MR curve from below, while rising upward.

This approach is applicable to study the firm's equilibrium both under perfect and imperfect market competitions and the same was already discussed in Chapter 7.

4. LP Technique

We already know, a LP problem consists of a linear objective function to be maximized or minimized subject to certain constraints in the form of linear equations or inequalities. The above concepts to attain optimality in the production programme are based on marginal analysis. This is where, the concept of LP technique differs from the above marginal approach and this also contribute to its superiority over them and the same can be highlighted from the following points:

☆ Marginalism or Marginal approach of optimality assumes continuous production function and factor inputs are substitutable. But, in case of LP technique, the decision maker chooses a finite number of production processes and they are less flexible for substitution compared to marginal analysis.

☆ In marginal analysis it is assumed that, the firm produces a single product, whereas the concept of LP technique can be applied to multi-factor and multi-product concepts.

☆ In marginal approach, the concepts of cost minimization and profit maximization are analyzed in terms of linear equalities. However, in LP technique, the functional constraints are expressed as linear inequalities to derive the values of the decision variables in the objective function.

☆ In the marginal approach, the graphical analysis for optimization is in terms non-linear curves. However, in LP technique, the graphical solution for optimization is studied in terms of linear curves.

☆ Unlike marginal approach, LP technique provides corner solution for optimization in the estimated feasible region.

☆ Unlike marginal approach, LP technique addresses the concept of shadow price analysis.

Exercise

1. Let us assume a case of feeding farm animals. Animals need:

   14 units of nutrient A,

   12 units of nutrient B, and

   18 units of nutrient C.

   Two feed grains are available, X and Y.

   A bag of X has 2 units of A, 1 unit of B, and 1 unit of C.

   A bag of Y has 1 unit of A, 1 unit of B, and 3 units of C.

   A bag of X costs Rs. 2. A bag of Y costs Rs.4.

   Minimize the cost of meeting the nutrient requirements.

2. A firm uses wood and labor to produce tables and chairs. The unit profit for tables is Rs.6, and unit profit for chairs is Rs.8. There are 300 board feet (bf) of wood available, and 110 hours of labor available. It takes 30 bf and 5 hours to make a table, and 20 bf and 10 hours to make a chair. The following table contains the information for the LP problem.

Resource	Table (X 1)	Chair (X 2)	Available
Wood (bf)	30	20	300
Labor (hr)	5	10	110
Unit profit	Rs. 6	Rs. 8	

Maximize the profits of a firm in manufacturing tables and chairs by using graphical method.

3. Let us assume a profit maximizing firm producing three products with the following objective function and functional constraints:

    Max $Z = 5X1 + 2X2 + X3$

    Subject to

    $X1 + 3X2 - X3 \leq 6$,

    $\qquad X2 + X3 \leq 4$,

    $3X1 + X2 \leq 7$,

    $X1, X2, X3 \geq 0$.

    Maximize the profits of a firm by employing Simplex method.

4. Let us assume a profit maximizing firm producing two products with the following objective function and functional constraints:

    Max $8X1 + 5X2$ (Weekly profit)

    Subject to

    $2X1 + 1X2 \leq 1000$ (Plastic)

    $3X1 + 4X2 \leq 2400$ (Production Time)

    $X1 + X2 \leq 700$ (Total production)

    $X1 - X2 \leq 350$ (Mix)

    $Xj > = 0, j = 1,2$ (Non-negativity)

    Maximize the profits of a firm by employing both Graphical method and Simplex method.

5. Presume an industry manufactures two commodities M1 and M2. Each unit of commodity M1 supplies Rs.30 to profit and each unit of commodity M2 supplies Rs.40 to profits. The manufacture of these commodities requires inputs X, Y and Z and their available volume are 14, 10 and 4 respectively. Assumed that, the manufacture of one commodity M1 procures 2 units of input X, 1 unit of input Y and does not require input Z and the manufacture of one unit of commodity M2 requires 2 units of input X, 2 units of Y and 4 units of Z. Derivate the above problem into LP and solve it with simplex method.

6. Let us assume a profit maximizing firm producing two products with the following objective function and functional constraints:

Maximize $Z = 6X_1 + 4X_2$

Subject to:

$2X_1 + 3X_2 \leq 120$ (Labour)

$2X_1 + X_2 \leq 60$ (Capital)

where, $X_1, X_2 \geq 0$

7. Solve the LP problem using Simplex method. Determine the following:
   a. What is the optimal solution?
   b. What is the value of the objective function?
   c. Which constraint has excess resources and how much?

   Max $Z = 5X_1 + 6X_2$

   Subject to :

   $2X_1 + X_2 \leq 2000$

   $X_1 \leq 800$

   $X_2 \leq 200$

   where, $X_1, X_2 \geq 0$

8. A firm manufactures two types of T-shirts, one with collar and another without collar. Each T-shirt with collar yields a profit of Rs. 20, while each T-shirt without collar yields Rs. 30. Shirt with collar requires 15 minutes of cutting and 25 minutes of stitching. Shirt without collar requires 10 minutes of cutting and 20 minutes of stitching. The full shift time is available for cutting in an 8 hour shift, but only 6 hours are available for stitching. Formulate the problem as an LP model to maximize the profit.

9. A company makes two products (X and Y) using two machines (A and B). Each unit of X that is produced requires 50 minutes processing time on machine A and 30 minutes processing time on machine B. Each unit of Y that is produced requires 24 minutes processing time on machine A and 33 minutes processing time on machine B. At the start of the current week, there are 30 units of X and 90 units of Y in stock. Available processing time on machine A is forecast to be 40 hours and on machine B is forecast to be 35 hours. The demand for X in the current week is forecast to be 75 units and for Y is forecast to be 95 units. Company policy is to maximize the combined sum of the units of X and the units of Y in stock at the end of the week.

   ❖ Formulate the problem of deciding how much of each product to make in the current week as a linear program.

   ❖ Solve this linear program graphically.

10. A company is involved in the production of two items (X and Y). The resources need to produce X and Y are two-fold, namely machine time for automatic processing and labour time for hand finishing. The table below gives the number of minutes required for each item:

	Machine Time	Labour Time
Item X	13	20
Item Y	19	29

The company has 40 hours of machine time available in the next working week, but only 35 hours of craftsman time. Machine time is costed at Rs. 10 per hour worked and labour time is costed at Rs. 2 per hour worked. Both machine and labour idle times incur no costs. The revenue received for each item produced (all production is sold) is Rs. 20 for X and Rs.30 for Y. The company has a specific contract to produce 10 items of X per week for a particular customer.

☆ Formulate the problem of deciding how much to produce per week as a linear program.

☆ Solve this linear program graphically.

11. Solve the following LP problem by graphical method:

Maximize $5X_1 + 6X_2$

Subject to:

$X_1 + X_2 \leq 10$

$X_1 - X_2 \geq 3$

$5X_1 + 4X_2 \leq 35$

$X_1 \geq 0$

$X_2 \geq 0$

12. A diet is to contain at least 4000 units of carbohydrates, 500 units of fat and 300 units of protein. Two foods A and B are available. Food A costs Rs. 2 per unit and food B costs Rs.4 per unit. A unit of food A contains 10 units of carbohydrates, 20 units of fat and 15 units of protein. A unit of food B contains 25 units of carbohydrates, 10 units of fat and 20 units of protein. Formulate the problem as an LP problem, so as to find the minimum cost for a diet that consists of a mixture of these two foods and also meets the minimum requirements.

13. In the production of 2 types of products, a firm uses 3 machines A, B and C. The time required to produce the first type of product is 6 hours, 8 hours and 12 hours in machines A, B and C respectively. The time required to make the second type of product is 8 hours, 4 hours and 4 hours in machines A, B and C respectively. The maximum available time (in hours) for the machines A, B, C are 380, 300 and 404 respectively. The profit on the first type of product is Rs.5, while that on the second type of product is Rs.3. Find the number of products of each type that should be produced to get maximum profit.

14. Use Simplex Method for solving the LP problem:

    Maximize $\quad Z = f(X,Y) = 3X + 2Y$

    Subject to:

    $2X + Y \le 18$

    $2X + 3Y \le 42$

    $3X + Y \le 24$

    $X \ge 0, Y \ge 0$

15. A firm has 3 factories located in Delhi, Mumbai and Chennai, which produce the same product. There are four major warehouses situated at Visakhapatnam, Vijayawada, Warangal and Hyderabad. As an average daily product supply from Delhi, Mumbai and Chennai is 30, 40, and 50 units respectively. The average daily requirement of this product at Visakhapatnam, Vijayawada, Warangal and Hyderabad is 35, 28, 32, 25 units respectively. The cost (Rs.) of transportation per unit of product from each factory to each district centre is given in the following table. The problem is to determine the number of units of product to be transported from each factory to different warehouses at minimum cost.

Factories	Visakhapatnam	Vijayawada	Warangal	Hyderabad	Supply
Delhi	6	8	8	5	30
Mumbai	5	11	9	7	40
Chennai	8	9	7	13	50
Demand	35	28	32	25	

16. A firm produces a product at plants in Kurnool and Chittoor. The product is then transported to two outlets located in Vijayawada and Hyderabad. The cost per unit (Rs.) of transporting product from each of the two plants to the two outlets is as follows:

From	To	
	Vijayawada	Hyderabad
Kurnool	40	65
Chittoor	70	30

The plant at Kurnool can supply 250 units of product per week; the plant at Chittoor can supply 400 units of product per week. Vijayawada outlet has a demand of 300 units of product per week and the outlet at Hyderabad demands 350 units of product per week. The firm wants to know the number of units of product to transport from each plant to each outlet in order to minimize the total shipping cost. Solve this transportation problem.

17. A food processing firm in three cities produce the following amounts of product:

Location	Weekly Production (tons)
City A	150
City B	210
City C	320
	680

This firm from three cities supply the product to four warehouses, where they have the following demand:

Location	Weekly Demand (tons)
Warehouse 1	130
Warehouse 2	70
Warehouse 3	180
Warehouse 4	240
	620

Shipping costs (Rs/unit) of product are as follows:

From	To			
	1	2	3	4
A	14	9	16	18
B	11	8	7	16
C	16	12	10	22

a. Set up a transportation tableau for this problem and determine the initial solution. Identify the method used to find the initial solution.

b. Solve this problem using MODI.

c. Formulate this problem as a general linear programming model.

10

Economic Analysis of Agricultural Projects

Gittinger (1972) defined project as *'a whole complex of activities involved in using resources to gain benefits'*. He (1982) further opined that, *'project' as. an investment activity upon which resources – costs – are expended to create capital assets that will produce benefits over an extended period of time and which logically lends itself to planning, financing, and implementing as a unit. A specific activity, with specific starting point and specific ending point, intended to accomplish a specific objective. The smallest operational element prepared and implemented as a separate entity in a national plan or program. Generally unique in that it is not a segment of an ongoing program, although it may be a 'time slice' – a portion lasting several years – of a long-term program. Or, put more succinctly, 'the whole complex of activities for which money will be spent in expectation of returns'.* So, a project can be defined as an investment activity, in which the financial resources are spent, so as to create durable capital assets that provide benefits for an extended period of time. A project may also be defined as a set of activities, which aim at achieving specific objectives within a stipulated period of time and budget. While there are several definitions of project in the literature, one of the best has been offered by Tuman

(1983), who states: *'A project is an organization of people dedicated to a specific purpose or objective. Projects generally involve large, expensive, unique, or high risk undertakings which have to be completed by a certain date, for a certain amount of money, with some expected level of performance. At a minimum, all projects need to have well defined objectives and sufficient resources to carry out all the required tasks.'* As defined in 'A Guide to the Project Management Body of Knowledge' (PMI, PMBOK® Guide, 2000), *'a project is a temporary endeavor undertaken to create a unique product or service. Temporary means that every project has a definite beginning and a definite end. Unique means that the product or service is different in some distinguishing way from all other projects or services'.* Declerck *et al.* (1983 and 1997), defined *'a project is a whole of actions limited in time and space, inserted in, and in interaction with a politico-socio-economic environment, aimed at and tended towards a goal progressively redefined by the dialectic between the thought (the project plan) and the reality'.* The projects are often considered as 'cutting edges of development' and 'building blocks of an investment plan'.

The above definitions also infer that, the word 'project' has different connotations in different contexts. In one context, project means a location specific activity with specific objectives, time and cost limitations and of non-repetitive nature. In the context of financing and banking, a project is considered as an investment activity, in which financial resources are used for creating capital assets that produce benefits over a fairly longer period of time. In this context, cultivation of paddy, wheat, maize etc., by the farmer will not represent a project, as their cultivation will not lead to the creation of durable capital assets, there is no long term investment in the production programme and the returns are not extended for a fairly longer period of time. However, if the farmer goes for mango plantation or setting up of a poultry farm, it represents a project, as it fulfills all the above three financial and banking criteria. Hence, project is sometimes called as 'Capital expenditure' or 'Capital investment' or 'Capital project'. Another term used is 'Scheme', but a scheme is smaller in scale than a project.

I. Project vs Programme

The above explanation infers, what a 'Project' is. 'Programme' refers to set of projects representing various sectors of the economy for achieving overall development. For example, 'Integrated Rural Development Programme' is an anti-poverty programme that aims at alleviating poverty among rural population. To alleviate poverty among them, various activities or projects are executed representing various sectors like health, sanitation, agriculture, irrigation, electricity, education etc. The following points further highlight the differences between a project and a programme:

☆ Project is micro in its scope, whereas programme is macro in its scope.

☆ Projects are specific in its objective(s), whereas in a programme, there are broader goals.

☆ Project is of shorter duration when compacted to a programme for its completion.

☆ Objective(s) of the project must fit into the broad frame work of the programme.

- ☆ The goals of the programme will be achieved through formulation of several projects each with specific objectives.
- ☆ Project is more precisely defined, unlike a programme.
- ☆ Unlike programme, project will have a specific clientele.

II. Project Cycle or Project Life Cycle

The way in which projects are planned and executed follows a sequence that has become known as the project cycle. The cycle starts with the identification of a project or an idea and develops that idea into a working plan that can be implemented and finally evaluated. So, the cycle that a project passes right from initial conceptualization stage to the final evaluation stage is called 'Project cycle'. That is, the cycle of a project begins with project identification stage and ends with project evaluation stage to verify, how best the project met the planned objectives. The project cycle consists of the following stages (Figure 10.1):

1. Conception or Identification
2. Preparation or Formulation
3. Analysis or Appraisal
4. Implementation
5. Monitoring
6. Evaluation

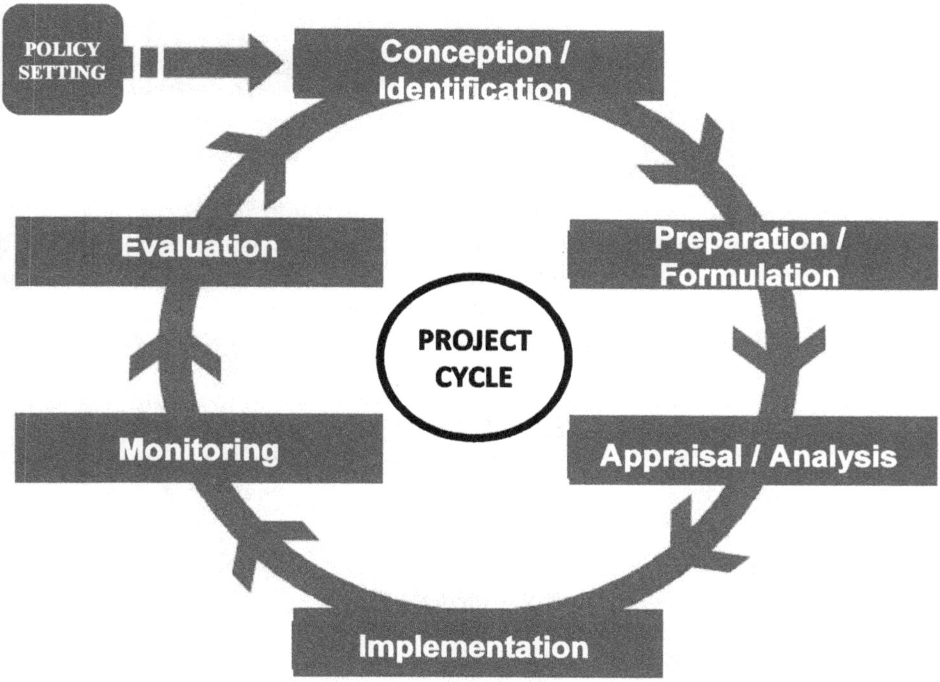

Figure 10.1: Phases of Project Cycle.

A project is considered as a cycle because, each phase not only arises from the preceding phase, but also leads into the succeeding phase. The idea behind studying the project cycle is that, it indicates the number of sequential processes that are involved right from the identification of a project to its final evaluation. The project cycle, in general, is characterized by:

☆ Each phase in the cycle defines the key decisions, information requirements and responsibilities.

☆ Each phase in the cycle is progressive *i.e.* each phase needs to be completed for the commencement of next phase.

☆ Experiences gained from each project cycle enable the project manager to build and design future programmes and projects.

1. Conception or Identification

Project identification is the most crucial and sensitive stage of project cycle, as it leads to the key decisions on project choice, concept and content. Most projects enter the first phase of the project cycle with little or no structure. Ideas that start in the back of the mind of the researcher or project manager start to bubble up into potential projects. An agricultural project can be identified from one or more of the following sources:

☆ Based on the programmes and policies of the Government drafted in the Five Year Plan.

☆ Survey should be conducted at farmers' level to identify and prioritize their problems and the top most problem can be selected for formulating the project.

☆ By formulating special projects, which fits into the broad framework of the programmes like IRDP, DPAP, NATP, NAIP etc.

☆ Net work projects arising out of on-going projects.

In recent years, major donor agencies (such as the World Bank) place much emphasis on project identification as an important element in the overall success of the project. After identifying the project, it is essential to plan for both cost estimation and benefit estimation. Among these two, cost estimation can be easily planned because, the expenditure pattern in the project can be drawn in advance.

Different Types of Costs Incurred in the Project

The various costs incurred in the project include:

☆ *Direct Costs or Primary Costs*: These are the costs related to the provision of infrastructural facilities in the project. Examples include: construction office buildings, farm sheds, cattle sheds etc.

☆ *Indirect Cost or Secondary Costs*: These are the costs related to the provision of other (fringe) benefits to the project staff like construction of schools to staff children, hospitals, staff quarters etc., in the project area.

☆ *Project Costs:* These are the costs incurred towards operation and maintenance of the project. Examples include, purchase of sprinklers, drip irrigation system, pesticides, fertilizers etc.

☆ *Social Costs*: These costs refer to technological externalities in the project area and spillovers from the project. Examples include, pollution problems, health hazards to individuals around the project site etc.

In the context of cost structure, it is essential now to differentiate between production cost and an investment cost. A production cost in one enterprise may be an investment cost in the other. For example, fertilizer is a production cost in the cultivation of paddy, but the same is an investment cost in a mango plantation project, as the same input has to be applied for several successive years in the project and the cash inflows will be there for a fairly longer period of time after a gestation period. Thus, the only difference, which distinguishes these two costs is the time span during which the income is generated.

Different Types of Benefits Realized from the Project

The benefits realized from the project can be categorized into Tangible benefits and Intangible benefits.

☆ *Tangible benefits:* These are the benefits that can be measured or worked out. Benefits like, increase in income, increase in yield etc., fall under tangible benefits.

☆ *Intangible benefits:* These are the benefits, which cannot be measured or quantified, but can be realized by the society or beneficiaries. Benefits like improved managerial ability of the farmers, proper income distribution in economy, improved standard of the living of the beneficiaries etc., fall under tangible benefits.

In identification phase, it is also very important to see that, whether the project is implemented in the prioritized area or not. In this phase, the implementation agency:

☆ Explain the context in which the project is being identified.

☆ Conducts a review about similar works accomplished at different locations or states or countries.

☆ Defines the goals and objectives of the project and its scope in-detail.

☆ Plan about different resources that are required to execute the project in the ensuing future.

☆ Identify and screen the activities to be carried out in the project.

☆ Recommend the sequence of steps to be taken to develop the project.

☆ Consult the intended beneficiaries and the relevant stakeholders to gain primary background information about the project.

☆ Analyze the possible constraints they may face in the execution of project and the identification of options to address them.

☆ Study the relevance of selected project to the ultimate beneficiaries in the project area. Of course, the identification and selection of beneficiaries for the project will be studied in the ensuing Formulation phase.

2. Preparation or Formulation

The following are the important aspects that are to be taken into consideration for formulation of projects:

> ☆ *Organizational aspects:* It is related to the proper placement of staff in the project, demarcation of authority, linking of authority, assigning duties and responsibilities to the staff members etc.

> ☆ *Managerial aspects:* These aspects evaluate the managerial capacity of the manager, who is responsible for implementing the project. In formulating agricultural projects, managerial skills of the entrepreneur count much, as he has to identify the right beneficiaries for smooth execution of the project at the grass root level. This is so important because, even if a proven technology is chosen for the project, it may fail due to lack of or inadequate managerial capability on the part of the project manager. It is important for the funding agency to judge the managerial capability of the project manager and also his financial capability (worth).

> ☆ *Economic aspects:* It refers to estimation of costs incurred and benefits derived by the beneficiaries of the project.

> ☆ *Financial aspects:* It refers to the source of finance, interest rates, adequacy of credit, timeliness of supply of credit, procedural formalities to obtain loan, conditions to be followed for securing the loans etc.

> ☆ *Commercial aspects:* It refers to the arrangement for supply of inputs for the initiation and operation of the project, prospects for marketing of project output both in domestic and international markets, strengthening of backward linkages (related to supply of inputs, labour and such other items, which go into the production process) and forward linkages (linkages necessary after the production process is completed *i.e.*, related to transportation, processing, storage and marketing of the output) of the project etc. However, the nature of the linkage changes along with the nature of the project. For example, processed milk is a forward linkage in case of a dairy plant, whereas it is a backward linkage for an ice-cream factory.

> ☆ *Technical aspects:* It is related to soil type, soil health problems (like soil salinity, alkalinity, acidity etc), irrigation and drainage facilities available, pests and disease problems, scope for mechanization in the project site etc.

> ☆ *Social aspects:* It is related to traditions, customs and habits of the beneficiaries.

The important objectives of project preparation or formulation are to demonstrate that the identified project is:

> ☆ in accordance with the programmes and policies framed by the Government

> ☆ prioritized problem is being addressed to safeguard the intended beneficiaries' interests.

> ☆ both operationally and managerially workable

> ☆ technically feasible

☆ economically and financially viable

☆ sustainable

☆ restore ecological balance through minimizing social costs

☆ provide sufficiently accurate estimates of costs and expected benefits

Thus, during the formulation phase, the project ideas that are framed earlier are developed into operational plans. Detailed consultations will be done with the beneficiaries and other stakeholders towards planning and feasible execution (whether the decisions are likely to succeed) of the methodology of the project such that, the project benefits can be sustained (whether it is likely to generate long term benefits for the beneficiaries) in the project area. On the basis of this assessment, a decision is made on to proceed to the next phase. This phase is the analysis of the project, where the project is appraised both for technical feasibility and economic viability of the investment and this also forms the basis for seeking funds for the project from the funding agencies.

3. Appraisal or Analysis

The students must note that, appraisal of the project will be done even before the implementation of the project. The appraisal will be done for project by the specialists taking into consideration the proposed costs and proposed benefits of the project. When costs and benefits have been identified, priced and valued, the project manager is ready to determine, whether the project is to be accepted or rejected. There is no one best technique for estimating project worth (although some are better than others, and some are especially deficient). The techniques of project appraisal can be conveniently categorized into two major categories *viz.,* Undiscounted and Discounted. Undiscounted techniques include Ranking by Inspection, Pay Back Period (PBP), Proceeds per rupee (unit) outlay and Average annual proceeds per rupee (unit) outlay. Discounted techniques include Net Present Value (NPV), Benefit-Cost Ratio (BCR), Internal Rate of Return (IRR), Modified IRR (MIRR), Net Benefit-Investment (N/K) Ratio (NBIR) and Profitability Index (PI). Both these techniques are discussed in-detail in the ensuing pages. Generally, discounted measures will be followed to estimate the discounted net benefits and rate of return from the project. This appraisal enables the project manager to analyze about the technical feasibility, economic viability and financial viability of the investment. Managerial aspects also play an important role in appraising the project. The appraisal of the project will be done by the donor agency (say, Banks) to assess, whether the project is within their risk profile and whether it fall within the scope of the agency and budgets within the limits to be funded. Since, the project is appraised based on the proposed costs and benefits, it falls under *ex ante assessment* of a project and is the key element in the decision as to whether or not to proceed with a project. So, the appraisal of the project is to establish, whether a project is worthwhile in the light of its costs in terms of resource commitments and the project's expected benefits. Project appraisal also involve the consideration of alternative projects (the *with* option(s)) or alternatively, by comparison with the status quo (that is, the *do-nothing* option). Note that, in reality, a project will be appraised number of times in the project cycle (Figure 10.2). Even

| Conception/Identification | • Does the project fit within the programmes and policies formulated by the Government?
• Is the project falls in prioritized area of investment? |

| Preparation/Formulation | • Is the project logically sound enough?
• Is the framed goals and objectives of the project are relevant, effective and efficient?
• Whether the project is relevant to the beneficiaries at significant note? |

| Appraisal/Analysis | • Is the project technically feasible?
• Is the project economically viable?
• Is the project financially viable?
• Is the project benefits are sustainable?
• Does the project have comparative advantage above others? |

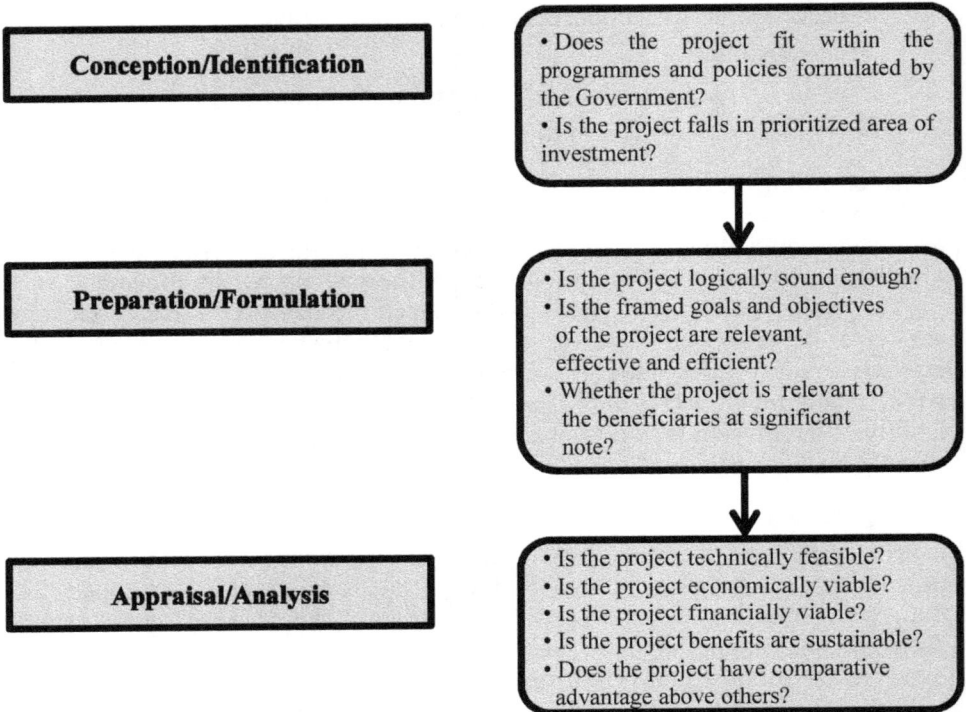

Figure 10.2: Process of Appraisal in a Project Cycle.

after initial identification phase, the project will be appraised, whether to continue it towards the preparation or formulation phase and during formulation phase, the project will be appraised to know, whether or not the project will be proposed for funding.

Thus, project appraisal involves the comparison of costs and benefits. If (discounted) benefits exceeds (discounted) costs, the project could be considered for acceptance Otherwise, it is not. That is, project appraisal means a pre-investment analysis of a project to determine whether the project should be implemented or not. This appraisal of project is necessitated because, the resources or means are limited as compared to the needs of the society. As a result, any investment undertaken implies depriving other projects resources. Hence, it is very important to appraise each project before investment decision so that, scarce resources are utilized in the best possible ways. In other words, before allocation of resources for a particular project, the decision making authority must convince itself that the proposed project is the best and most economical way of achieving the desired objective (in terms of socio-economic benefits). For this and for ensuring economic use of resources, we have to appraise each project very minutely from different angles.

4. Implementation

A project that is considered to be worthwhile at the appraisal phase qualifies for implementation. This is the most crucial phase of the project after studying the technical feasibility, economic viability and financial viability of the project, as it represents the action stage. Note that, *'not until one implements a project, it remains an intention'*. If the project is found favourable in terms of technical feasibility, economic viability and financial viability, it will be implemented in the project site. This phase marks the initiation of the execution of project work through coordinating activities and people for the assignment to be done. Thus, this phase is the period in which the project is actually conducted and the planned activities are carried out. The implementation phase can be conveniently categorized into three sub-periods:

☆ *Investment period:* During this period, major investment of the project will be done for the execution of the project at project site. It generally ranges from few months to few years.

☆ *Development period:* It generally refers to gestation period of the project. Gestation period is the time period between the initial investment in the project to the commencement of cash inflow into the project. This gestation period often consumes more time, but the implementation agency must make all efforts to minimize the gestation period.

☆ *Full production period:* It refers to the time period during which the cash inflow starts into the project. The implementation agency should ensure that, the returns should increase over a period of time and they must be sustained.

5. Monitoring

Monitoring refers to supervision of the project on the project site, so as to ascertain whether the project is moving on the desired lines or not. Monitoring concerns making observations of what is occurring in the project. This phase of the project starts even from the implementation phase, where extensive data are collected, compiled and analyzed to check the progress of the project execution from time to time. This monitoring is done by the implementing agency. This enables the project manager to check, whether any extra expenditure has been incurred in the project than the proposed costs, to check any irregularities in the project and to set the things right in the project. This makes to keep up the quality of the work that is going on, to ensure that the project is heading in the right direction, that progress is made towards the objectives, problems are spotted early and to reassess the risks of the project. Thus, monitoring involves timely collection, compilation and analysis of data, so as to ascertain whether the project is moving in the planned direction or not. The results and learning from the monitoring has to be fed back into the project design and adjustments or improvements where necessary have to be made. This phase is considered important in the project, as in practice, nothing will go completely as planned and few activities are carried out within the estimated time. So, monitoring is a continuous process for the duration of the project. The knowledge and skills required for monitoring are the same as for assessment and analysis.

6. Evaluation

Evaluation is often the last phase of the project cycle, but at the same time, the beginning of the next phase *i.e.* extension of the same project or for identifying the new project. It refers to the final checking or verification of the project regarding its contribution of benefits to the beneficiaries (Figure 10.2.1). So, evaluation is a means of determining success or failure and it addresses two important things *viz.*, what has been achieved and how well it has been achieved. Generally, evaluation of the project can be done by four ways:

☆ *Ex-ante evaluation:* It refers to evaluation of the project even before its implementation through analyzing the proposed costs and benefits.

☆ *Ex-post evaluation:* It refers to evaluation of the project at the end of its implementation through analyzing the actual costs and benefits.

☆ *Mid-course evaluation:* In this method, project evaluation is done at middle/ half of its period.

☆ *Concurrent evaluation:* In this method, evaluation is done periodically or very frequently during its implementation.

Among the above four evaluations methods, concurrent evaluation is more desirable because, the project can be efficiently checked for its implementation throughout the project cycle. All World Bank-assisted projects are now subjected to an *ex-post* audit. It allows for re-working of the estimates of both discounted and undiscounted measures to see, how far the actual costs and benefits influences the sustainability perspective of the long-term investment. Generally, the evaluation of project is done by an outside agency. This evaluation also helps both the donor

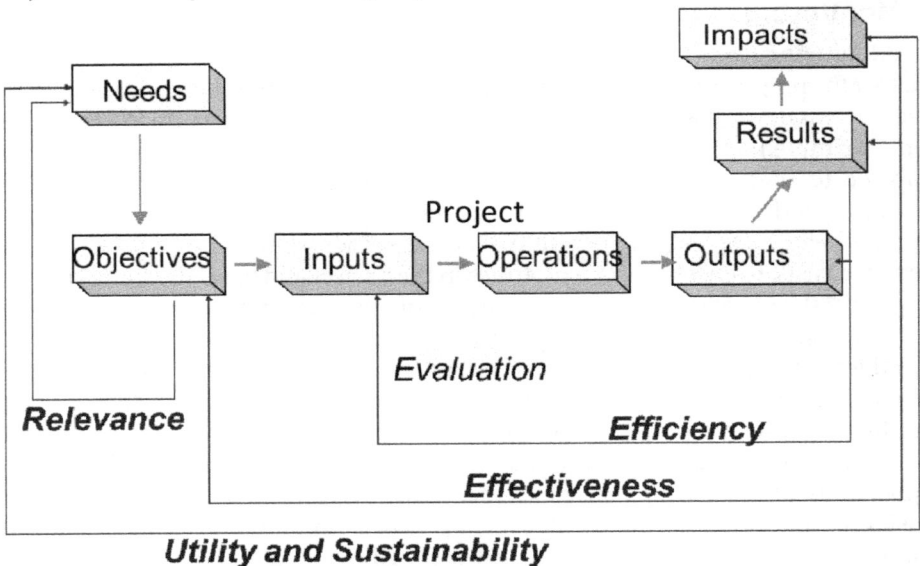

Courtesy: IPA Funds Programme Management 12-19 sept. 2011

Figure 10.2.1: The General Evaluation Critera of an Agricultural Project.

agency and implementation agency to identify elements of strength and weakness, success or failure. These results are valuable in planning future projects and in attempts to avoid repeating or committing similar mistakes. Thus, the results of the evaluation process need to be disseminated. This is why Baum (1982) described the evaluation system as '*a gold mine of information, supplementing and complementing that provided by the broader stream of project supervision reports*'. Some projects are re-visited several years later, when they should have reached full development in order to make a more definitive *impact evaluation*.

Besides external evaluation by an outside agency, staff of the project can do internal evaluations periodically. Sometimes, evaluation can also be a joint one with staff from the project and personnel from the outside agency. Irrespective of the agency involved in evaluating the project, the purpose of the evaluation can be two-fold *viz.*, to assess the actual results of an activity and/or to assess what has been learnt from the project. The following could be examined during a formative evaluation:

☆ To what extent have the objectives been achieved? And at what costs? If objectives were not met, then why?

☆ What are the strategies and actions used to achieve the formulated objectives? Which were the strengths in the strategies or actions? Which were the weak points?

☆ Are objectives still valid or do these needs to be adapted?

☆ Are the costs in proportion to the benefits?

The above discussion infers the following characteristics of different phases of a project life cycle:

☆ The project is divided into several distinct phases.

☆ Each phase is marked by a number of deliverables or phase outputs.

☆ Usually one phase consists of several sub-phases or activities.

☆ The phases are progressive *i.e.*, each phase should have 'phase exit' or completion point that allow the next phase to be tackled with success.

☆ A technical review should be carried out at the end of each phase.

Criteria for Selection of a Project

The following are the different criteria that will be taken into consideration for selection of the project:

☆ *Work selection criterion*: It refers to the selection of project site for implementation of project so that, the objectives of project can be fulfilled efficiently.

☆ *Priority criterion:* It refers to the project that must fall in the priority area of development.

☆ *Financial criterion:* It refers to the availability and use of funds in the project.

☆ *Supply criterion:* It refers to the supply of inputs like labour, resources, machinery into the project etc.

☆ *Social criterion:* It refers to fulfillment of certain social objectives like increase in employment opportunities, restoration of ecological balance etc.

☆ *Benefit criterion:* It refers to both tangible and intangible benefits offered by the project.

☆ *Economic viability criterion:* It refers to higher net benefits offered by the project.

☆ *Technical feasibility criterion:* It refers to applicability of modern technology in the execution of project.

☆ *Rate of return criterion:* It refers to returns derived for each rupee invested in the project.

IV. Features or Characteristics of Project

They include:

☆ Project will have a specific, preordained goal or set of goals.

☆ Project will have a specific location for its execution.

☆ Project will have a specific time period for its completion.

☆ Project can be measured in terms of costs and returns.

☆ Project can be evaluated for its net benefits.

☆ Project will have some risks and uncertainties in its implementation.

☆ Project aims at maximization of resource use efficiency.

☆ Project will have a definite target group or clientele.

☆ Project is a living entity *i.e.* it deals with human beings.

☆ It should have a well-defined time sequence of investment and production activities.

☆ Project will have a defined beginning and end (specified time to completion).

☆ Project will have a series of complex or interrelated activities.

☆ Project will have a limited budget (Pinto and Slevin (1988).

☆ Risk and uncertainty is highest at the beginning stages of a project and reduces thereafter, as the project continues.

Thus, when we think of an agricultural project, it implies, project is an investment activity, where we expend capital resources to create a producing asset from which we can expect to realize benefits over an extended period of time. Often, project is a specific part of a larger, less precisely defined 'programme'. Normally a project will have an area of geographic concentration, a specific clientele group, a well-defined time sequence for investment and production activities, a specific group of activities, benefits which can be identified and estimated and finally analyzed for their economic and financial results.

V. Project Appraisal Techniques

As discussed earlier, project is appraised for its net benefits even before its implementation considering proposed costs and benefits. This project appraisal involves a detailed study about the project with reference to technical feasibility, economic viability and financial viability of the project investment. This appraisal is done by financing (funding) agency to ascertain, whether it has to finance for the investment or not?

☆ *Technical feasibility:* The study about technical feasibility of the project investment will be done with reference to:

❖ Location of the project in the context of its access to raw materials, man power, transport facilities, communication facilities, market for the output of the project etc.

❖ Scope for the adoption of modern technology in the project.

❖ Availability of plant equipment for the project.

☆ *Economic viability:* The study about economic viability of the project investment will be done with reference to:

❖ Increased net cash flows into the project

❖ Generation of employment opportunities at the country (macro) level

❖ Contribution of the project to the National Income.

☆ *Financial viability:* The study about financial viability of the project investment will be done with reference to:

❖ Cost estimates of the project.

❖ Sources of the finance to the project, rates of interest etc.

❖ Profitability of the investment (*i.e.*, earning of profits by the project should be started within reasonable period of time).

❖ Repayment capability of the project investment from the cash inflow it enjoys.

❖ Contribution of project investment in terms of increase in income and employment opportunities at the beneficiary (micro) level.

Broadly, there are two techniques for appraising the project *viz.*, Undiscounted technique and Discounted technique (Figure 10.2.1).

A. Undiscounting Technique

In this technique, time value of money is not taken into consideration in estimating the net returns and rate of return from the project during its life time. The various measures under this undiscounting technique include:

i. Ranking by Inspection

Based on this method, projects are ranked based on the initial investment and net cash flow stream in the project. The following two instances may arise considering above two parameters *i.e.*, initial capital investment and net cash flow in the project.

☆ Two projects A and B having similar initial capital investment and same net value of cash inflows, but project A earns for more period compared to project B. In this case, project A is preferred over project B.

☆ Two projects A and B having similar initial capital investment and same net value of cash inflows, but the net cash inflows in project B are more in

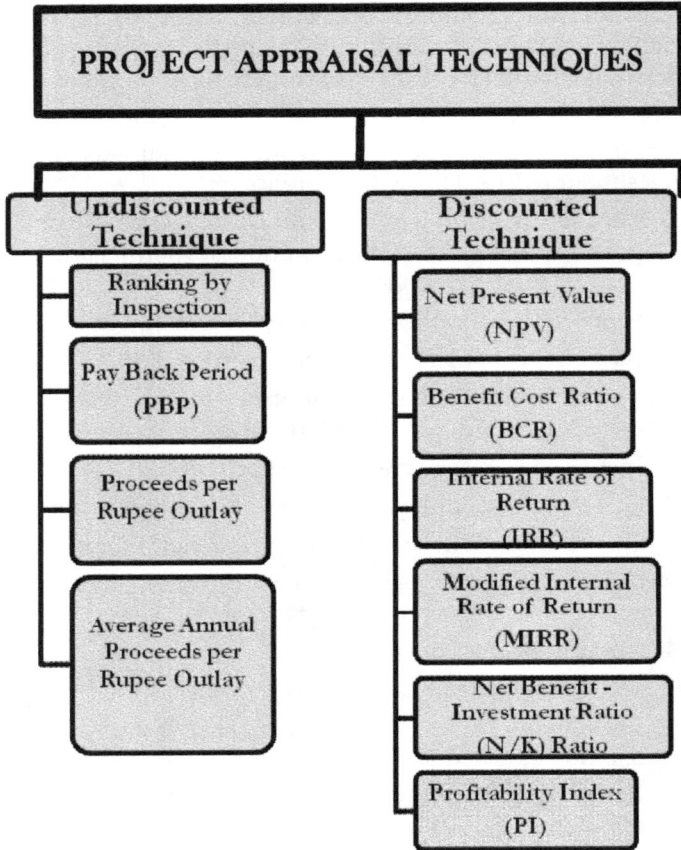

Figure 10.2.1: Classification of Project Appraisal Techniques.

earlier years than project A. In such case, project B is preferred over project A.

Thus, judging or ranking projects based on mere inspection does not seem appropriate.

ii. Pay Back Period (PBP)

It refers to the number of years taken by the project to completely cover its investment from the annual cash inflows or returns. It is, otherwise, defined as the length of time from the beginning of the project until the net value of the incremental production stream reaches the total amount of capital investment (Net value of incremental production = Value of incremental production less operation and maintenance cost, production cost etc). The formula used to compute PBP is given by:

$P = I/R$

where, P=PBP (years), I = Initial investment of the project, R = Annual cash inflows or returns from the project

When two projects have same rate of return and involve same amount of risk, then the investment decision will be taken based on the PBP. In employing this measure, the projects will be ranked based on the lowest magnitude of the estimate *i.e.*, the project with lowest PBP is more preferred over the projects that have higher PBPs. This measure assess the time required for the cumulative income (arising from the investment) to equal the initial cost of the investment. This measure is used to highlight those investments that are not viable *i.e.*, investments that never achieve payback. This measure is also used to select the most appropriate source of finance. For example, investments having a short PBP would require short-term finance. Note that, PBP is a 'break-even' type measure. The decision rule is that, accept the project, if the PBP is less than some preset limit. The pay-back rule says that, *'if the calculated PBP is less than or equal to some pre-specified PBP, then accept the project, otherwise reject it'*.

Example 10.1

Two investments each needing an initial capital of Rs.10,000, but resulting in different patterns of net cash flows as shown below.

Year	Project A	Project B
0 (Investment)	(10,000)	(10,000)
1	3,000	1,000
2	3,000	2,000
3	3,000	3,000
4	3,000	4,000
5	3,000	6,000
Total	15,000	16,000
PBP (yrs)	3.3	4.0

The students must note that, if the annual net cash flow (cash inflow-cash outflow) is the same for each year of the investment, the PBP is simply calculated by dividing the amount of the investment by the annual net cash flow (Rs.10,000/Rs.3,000 = 3.3 years) *i.e.*, for Project A. On the other hand, if the annual net cash flow is irregular during each year of the investment, the PBP is assessed by taking the year, where the net cash flow is equal to the cost of the investment. In this example, for Project B, the total net cash inflow is equal to investment at 4th year *i.e.* (1,000 + 2,000 + 3,000 + 4,000) = Rs.10,000. So, the cumulative net cash flow covers the investment in the fourth year and hence, PBP=4 years. So, Project A is preferred over Project B because, it has the shorter PBP. So, according to this criterion, the shorter the PBP for recovery of investment, the more profitable is the project.

Example 10.1.1

Assume a machine costs Rs.600,000. It produces a product such that, each unit generate a profit of Rs.5 on an output of 60,000 units per year. Compute PBP.

Solution

Given, total number of units produced/year = 60000

Also given, profit/unit = Rs.5

So, total annual profit = 5*60000 = Rs.300000

So, PBP = I/R = 600000/300000 = 2 years

Merits of PBP

They include:

☆ PBP is a widely used investment criterion.

☆ This method is very useful in evaluating the profits which involve high uncertainty.

☆ PBP helps the business firm to analyze when their capital investment will be recovered from the net cash inflows and this guides them regarding the payment of dividends.

☆ This measure is simple and easy to work out.

☆ PBP is useful measure for the firm, which suffers from liquidity crisis. This is because, such firm will be more interested in quick return of funds rather than profitability, which PBP also emphasizes.

Demerits of PBP

They include:

☆ It is a measure of project's capital recovery, not profitability. That is, it does not consider, how profitable a project will be, but considers how quickly the outlay will be recovered.

☆ Further, this method is biased against long-term projects and followed only, when capital investment is small.

☆ This undiscounted measure suffers from the limitation that, it ignores the cash flows arising after the PBP has occurred as well as the timing of the income flows. That is, this method considers that, the money received during earlier life of the investment is more valuable than money received later. In the above example, in investment B, the measure ignores the higher cash inflows after 4th year (*i.e.*, in 5th year). That is, this **measure** fails to consider earnings after the PBP. Consider another example, if there are two projects A and B with the same PBP, then by mere inspection, it is difficult to rank these projects. However, if project B continues to earn even after PBP, which is not the case for project A, then project B is to be considered. So, PBP method alone does not rank the projects, as it ignores the cash flow in the project after PBP. Further, say if both projects A and B enjoy same PBP (5 years each), but project A enjoys higher cash inflow in the earlier years than project B, then project A is to be considered for selection. This is because, the higher cash inflow of project A in earlier years is more desirable, as these earlier cash inflow can be re-invested earlier and thus, they are more valuable. This further emphasizes that PBP does not take into consideration the timing of cash inflows of the project.

☆ This measure is inferior to discounted cash flow techniques because, it ignores the time value of money.

Discounted PBP

A variant of the PBP measure is the discounted PBP in which, the procedure is same as in undiscounted PBP discussed above, but both costs and returns are discounted considering a discount factor. For the data given through Table 10.1 for Project A, considering the undiscounted cash flow, the PBP is 4 years after starting the project. However, considering the discounted cash flows (where Present Worth of Costs (PWC) and Present Worth of Benefits (PWB) are calculated), the PBP is between 4 and 5 years after starting the project.

Table 10.1: Computation of Discounted PBP

Year	Incr Costs (Rs.)	Incr Benefits (Rs.)	Net Incr Benefits (Rs.)	Df @ 10 per cent = $1/(1.1)^y$	NPV (Rs.)	Cumulative Net Cash Flow after Discounting
1	10000		−10000	0.909	−9090.91	−9090.91
2		3000	3000	0.826	2479.34	−6611.57
3		3000	3000	0.751	2253.94	−4357.63
4		4000	4000	0.683	2732.05	−1625.57
5		4000	4000	0.621	2483.69	858.11
6		5000	5000	0.564	2822.37	
7		2000	2000	0.513	1026.32	
8		3000	3000	0.467	1399.52	

Note that, PBP may be regarded roughly as the reciprocal of IRR, when the annual net cash inflow is constant throughout the duration of the project and the duration is fairly long. Though discounted PBP is a useful performance indicator to appraise the project's anticipated performance, it should never be used as the sole appraisal method.

c. Proceeds per Rupee of Outlay

It is the ratio between the total net cash inflow from the project to initial investment in the project. The projects are ranked based on the highest magnitude of the estimate. This is given by:

Proceeds per Rupee Outlay= R/I

where, R = Total net cash inflows or net returns from the project, I = Initial investment in the project. So, the higher the proceeds per rupee of the outlay, the higher the economic viability of the project. This criterion, however, does not take into consideration the time value of money. Further, this method also does not take into consideration the timing of cash inflow into the projects, as the project with earlier cash inflow is better than the project with long gestation period.

d. Average Annual (Net) Proceeds per Rupee of Outlay

In this method, first average annual net proceeds will be worked out by dividing the total net cash inflow from the project with total number of years (duration) of the project. Later, the average annual net cash inflow will be divided by initial investment of the project, to workout average annual net proceeds per rupee outlay. If average annual net proceeds per rupee of outlay are high, the project will be economically justified for implementation. This is given by:

Average Annual (Net) Proceeds per Rupee Outlay= (R/N)/I

where, R = Total net cash inflows or net returns from the project, N=Number of years (duration) of project, I = Initial investment of the project.

Average Annual Net Proceeds per Rupee Outlay expressed in percentage implies Simple Rate of Return (SRR) from the project investment. Average annual (net) proceeds can also be computed as flows:

= (Total Cash inflows excluding depreciation - Initial Investment) / Investment life

So, SRR (%) = (Average annual (net) proceeds / Initial Investment) * 100

This SRR is commonly used undiscounted criterion for project evaluation. It basically expresses the average annual net profits (Average Annual Net Cash Inflows) as a percentage of initial investment over the investment's expected life. The calculated SRR should be compared with the investor's Required Rate of Return (RRR) to judge the profitability of the investment. The project investment will be accepted, if SRR >.RRR, otherwise it will be rejected. In case of several projects for comparison, the project with highest SRR should be selected for investment.

This method suffers from a serious drawback that, it shows more bias towards short-lived projects. Say for example, there are two projects A and B. For project A, the total net cash inflow is Rs.20 lakhs and is for 2 years duration and for project B, the total net cash inflow is Rs.21 lakhs and is for 3 years duration and both the projects have same capital investment of Rs.20 lakhs each. In this example, project B seems to be better by mere inspection, as it yields more net cash inflow compared to project A. However, by employing this method, project A ranks much better than project B.

Thus, in undiscounted technique, discounted values of costs and returns are not considered. Further, Opportunity Cost of Capital (OCC) is not taken into consideration (OCC refers to, what rate of return can the firm earns if that money was used elsewhere). So, this technique is considered less realistic compared to discounted technique. Further, these undiscounted measures will not take into consideration the timing of cash inflows into the project. Hence, the concept of 'discounting' of net cash inflows or discounting of costs and discounting of benefits separately gives the right picture for analyzing the economic viability of project investment and for ranking of different project investments even of different durations.

B. Discounting Technique

In this technique, we take time value of money into consideration, unlike in Undiscounting technique. Before going into the details of discounting technique, let us discuss about the time value of money. There is a popular phrase that, '*A dollar today is worth more than a dollar a year from now*'. The same concept applies in choosing between investment projects. Those projects that promise earlier returns are more preferred to those that promise late returns. That means, a dollar received now is more valuable than a dollar received a year from now, because of the simple reason that, if you have a dollar today, you can put it in the bank and can have more than a dollar a year from now due to earning interest. In general, people prefer benefits or cash now to benefits or cash later for reasons which include:

☆ They desire to consume goods now rather than delay in their enjoyment

☆ They can invest the cash now in other lucrative opportunities *i.e.,* say on other enterprises or simply save the money in the bank

☆ The expectation of future benefits may have various risks and uncertainties

☆ Inflation will reduce the value of future benefits.

So, considering that the dollar today is more worthy than dollar in the future, we need some means of weighing cash inflows that are received at different times so that, they can be compared. By discounting technique, we can adjust the value of a dollar received any number of years from now to its present value so that, it can be compared with the value of a dollar in hand today. By discounting the future values of cash inflows to the present value, it will enable the project manager to compare the present investment with other competing investments *i.e.,* helps to ascertain the OCC.

The opposite of discounting technique is compounding technique, where we compute the future value of present worth of money in its future date so that, it can be compared with the value of a dollar in hand today. Thus, in compounding technique, we estimate the future value of present money. Assume that, if a bank pays 5 per cent interest on a deposit of Rs. 100 today, it will be worth Rs. 105 in one year from now. This can be expressed in mathematical terms by means of the following formula or equation:

$$F_1 = P (1 + i)^1$$

where, F_1 = Balance at the end of one year period, P = Amount saved/invested in the current period, and 'i' = Rate of interest per year (per cent).

So, $F_1 = 100(1+0.05)^1 = Rs.105$

Example 10.2

If a saving is made now of Rs. 100 in a bank, to earn interest at 5 percent, then P = Rs. 100 and i = 0.05. Under these conditions, F_1 = Rs. 105, the amount to be received in one year. The amount of Rs. 100 is the present value of money saved and its future value is Rs. 105 after one year due to earning interest. This Rs. 105 is also known as the compounded value of the present value of money saved in the bank (Rs. 100) or Rs. 100 is known as the discounted value of the future Rs. 105 receipt. So, Rs. 100 represents the value in present terms of Rs. 105 to be received a year from now, when the interest rate is 5 percent. When, if Rs. 105 is left in the bank for a second year, then at the end of the second year, the original Rs. 100 deposit will have grown to Rs. 110.25 by the following way:

Original deposit	Rs. 100.00
Interest for the first year (Rs. 100 × 0.05)	5
Balance at the end of the first year	105
Interest for the second year (Rs. 105 × 0.05)	5.25
Balance at the end of the second year	Rs. 110.25

Notice that, the interest for the second year is Rs.5.25, as compared to only Rs.5.00 for the first year. The reason for the greater interest earned during the second year is that, during second year, interest is being paid on *interest*. That is, the Rs.5.00 interest earned during the first year has been left in the account and has been added to the original Rs. 100 deposit, when computing interest for the second year. This is known as the compound interest. In this case, the compound is annual. Interest can also be compounded on a semi-annual, quarterly, monthly, or even more frequent basis. The more frequently compounding is done, the more rapidly the balance will grow. So, we can determine the future value of present money balance in an account after 't' periods of compounding using the following formula:

$Ft = P(1 + i)^t$

where, t = number of periods.

If t = 2 years and the interest rate is 5 percent per year, then the balance in two years will be as follows: $F_2 = 100(1 + 0.05)^2 = $ Rs. 110.25.

The above discussion on compounding can be viewed from the reverse direction, which implies the discounting technique *i.e.* we estimate the present value of future income. That means, in the earlier example, if we receive Rs. 110.25 after two years from now at an interest rate of 5 percent, its present value will be Rs. 100. We use the following formulae for discounting:

$P = Ft/(1 + i)^t$

Considering another example, assume that, you are going to receive Rs. 200 two years from now from an investment. That means, the future value of the sum after two years is Rs. 200. Since, this is the amount that you will be receiving after two years, its present value is computed as follows (assume, i=5 per cent):

In this example, Ft = Rs. 200 (the amount to be received in future), i = 0.05 (the annual rate of interest), and t=2 (the number of years in the future that the amount is to be received)

$P = Ft/(1 + i)^t$

$P = 200/(1 + 0.05)^2$

$P = $ Rs. 200/1.1025

$P = $ Rs. 181.40

As shown by the computation above, the present value of Rs. 200 to be received two years from now is Rs.181.40, if the interest rate is 5 percent. In effect, Rs.181.40 received right now is equivalent to Rs. 200 received after two years, if the rate of interest is 5 percent. That is, Rs.181.40 and Rs. 200 are just two ways of looking at the same thing. This process of finding the present value of a future cash flow is called discounting. This concept of present value is of central importance in economic analysis. We know that, benefits and costs from projects may not accrue immediately, but rather over a period of time. Since a dollar received today is worth more than a dollar received in the future, future streams of costs and benefits must be reduced to a present-day value. The difference between present and future dollar values is dependent upon the interest or discount rate. For example, the higher the interest rate, the more a dollar will return in the future, if loaned with interest. This logic can also be reversed so that, if future costs and benefits are known, and the interest rate is given, their present value can be calculated by the process of discounting. The concept of discounting is exemplified through Table 10.1.1. It is clear that, with increase in discount factor, the PWC in a project will decline. Since, no discounting is followed, the undiscounted cost structure lie parallel to the X-axis *i.e.,* remains same for the entire life of the project (Figure 10.3). From the above discussion, it is clear that, 'i' refers to interest (discount) rate, (1+i) refers to compounding factor and $1/(1+i)$ refers to discounting factor.

Table 10.1.1: Relation between Discount Factor and Present Worth

Year	Actual Value of Costs	Discount Factor 10 per cent = $(1/(1.10)^t)$	PWC	Discount Factor 15 per cent = $[1/(1.15)^t]$	PWC
1	1000	0.909	909.091	0.870	869.565
2	1000	0.826	826.446	0.756	756.144
3	1000	0.751	751.315	0.658	657.516
4	1000	0.683	683.013	0.572	571.753
5	1000	0.621	620.921	0.497	497.177
6	1000	0.564	564.474	0.432	432.328
7	1000	0.513	513.158	0.376	375.937
8	1000	0.467	466.507	0.327	326.902
9	1000	0.424	424.098	0.284	284.262
10	1000	0.386	385.543	0.247	247.185

Discount Rate

In the above example, we have discounted Rs. 200 to its present value of Rs. 181.40, when the rate of interest is 5 percent. This 5 percent interest that we have used to find the present value is called the Discount Rate. This employment of discount factor to estimate the future value of present cash flows (Compounding) and present value of future cash flows (Discounting) is a common practice in agricultural projects appraisal decisions. Note that, the basic formula for discounting can be applied regardless of the length of the time horizon. Selection of an interest or discount rate greatly influences the economic viability of the project. So, there has been considerable controversy regarding the selection of appropriate discount rate. Lower interest rates will make projects appear more worthwhile and will favour long-lived projects over short-lived ones. In fact, there is no simple rule for choosing a discount rate. Two main approaches are used in selecting proper discount rates for project investments *viz.*, OCC and Social Discount Rate (SDR) or Social Rate of Discount (SRD) of time preference.

☆ *OCC:* Before discussing OCC, it is essential to re-collect once again about the term opportunity cost. This term 'opportunity cost' is a simple and general term which will be used in any normal day to day situation. For example, a consumer has two options for lunch ie., rice and wheat, and he can have only one of the two. So, the consumer will normally choose the one that gives him more satisfaction. If he chose rice, he will lose the satisfaction which he would derive in having wheat (and *vice versa*). So, the amount of satisfaction the consumer realizes in having wheat is his opportunity cost for having rice and *vice versa*. The same concept can be used for studying the OCC. This OCC implies the alternative (rate of) return that project investors forgo in undertaking the current investment. That is, the OCC is the expected rate of return forgone by bypassing other potential investment activities (the lost opportunity) in choosing a particular project investment. It is usually referred to more succinctly as the cost of capital. This implies, OCC is the rate of return that can be expected to be earned on an alternative project that has the same level of risk as the project being considered for selection. So, the OCC is the rate that the project investor could get, if he did not take on the project being analyzed. The OCC approach suggests that, the discount rate should reflect the cost of funds withdrawn from the private sector of the economy. OCC also corresponds to the rate of return on investment elsewhere in the economy. Therefore, the discount rate should be equivalent to current market interest rate.

☆ *SRD or SDR:* This is the interest rate at which a section of the society will save the money in economy or the society prefers present consumption over future consumption. SDR of 12 per cent is widely used for discounting measures. However, the popular choice of discount factor in some countries ranges from 8 – 15 percent. Generally, the SDR is lower than the OCC.

The most difficult part in economic and financial appraisal of projects is to choose a discount rate. The project investor should see it as a choice between an opportunity of investing in the project and opportunity of investing in the next best opportunity in the economy. That is, in other words, instead of giving a green light to the project, the project investor always analyze the rate of return from various alternative capital investments. Note that, the rate of discounting varies with the capital position of the farmers. The discount rate will be lower for the farmer with unlimited capital than for a farmer with limited capital. If the (discounted) rate of return of the project is higher than the OCC, then we can advise the farmers to go for current investment. So, in discounting technique, discounted cash flows *i.e.,* discounted cash inflows or discounted benefits or discounted returns or PWB and discounted cash outflows or discounted costs or discounted costs or PWC will be taken into consideration rather than absolute cash flows into the project during its life time. Also note that, depreciation in the project will be automatically taken into consideration in discounting technique. Thus, the discount rate to be used in project analysis has to be based on OCC or the weighted cost of borrowing. The discount rate can be of two types *viz.*, real and nominal. The real discount rate could be expressed as the discount rate after adjusting inflation rate. This is given by:

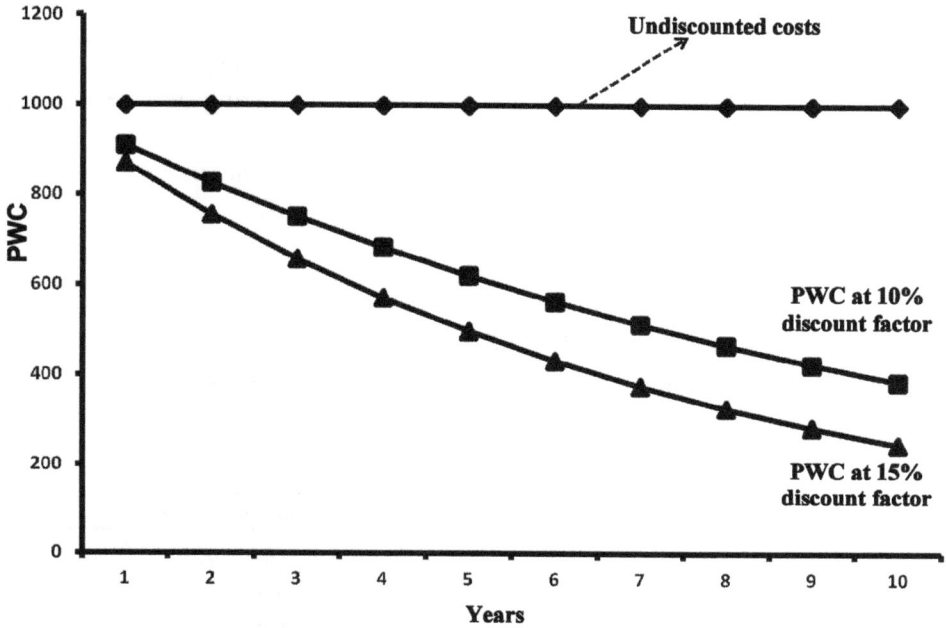

Figure 10.3: Relation between Discount Factor and Present Worth.

1+ Real Interest Rate = (1+Nominal Interest Rate)/(1+Inflation Rate)

In Indian conditions, in general, for agricultural and rural development projects, a rate of 15 per cent was considered appropriate and was advised for computing discounted measures of appraisal.

Example 10.2.1

Assume that, a farmer has entered into agreement to take an acre of land for lease at a cost of Rs.8,000 next year, increasing at 3 per cent a year (the forecasted inflation rate) for 3 additional years (4 years total). If discount rate is 10 per cent, what is the present value cost of the lease?

Solution

Considering nominal figures:

Year	Cash Flow (Nominal Figures)	Present Value @10 per cent
1	8000	$8000/(1.10)^1 = 7272.73$
2	$8000*(1+0.03)^1 = 8240.00$	$8240/(1.10)^2 = 6809.92$
3	$8000*(1+0.03)^2 = 8487.20$	$8487.20/(1.10)^3 = 6376.56$
4	$8000*(1+0.03)^3 = 8741.82$	$8741.82/(1.10)^4 = 5970.78$
		Total Present Value = Rs. 26429.99

From the above table, it is clear that, the total present value of taking land for lease for four years amounts to Rs. 26429.99 and this is calculated without considering the inflation rate. Now, assume the given inflation rate and adjust the discount factor (*i.e.,* real interest rate) to compute the total present value of taking land for lease for four years. As per the formula given above:

1+ Real Interest Rate = (1+Nominal Interest Rate)/(1+Inflation Rate)

= (1+(10/100))/(1+(3/100))

= 1.10/1.03

1+ Real Interest Rate = 1.06796

So, Real interest rate = 0.06796 = 6.796 per cent

Now, employ the above adjusted discount factor (Real interest rate) to inflation rate to compute the total present value of taking land for lease for four years. So, considering real figures:

Year	Cash Flow (Nominal Figures)		Present Value @ 10 per cent
1	$8000/(1+0.03)^1$	= 7766.99	$7766.99/(1.068)^1$ = 7272.73
2	$8240/(1+0.03)^2$	= 7766.99	$7766.99/(1.068)^2$ = 6809.92
3	$8487.20*(1+0.03)^3$	= 7766.99	$7766.99/(1.068)^3$ = 6376.56
4	$8741.82*(1+0.03)^4$	= 7766.99	$7766.99/(1.068)^4$ = 5970.78
			Total Present Value = Rs. 26429.99

Thus, after adjusting the discount factor considering the inflation rate, the total present value of taking land for lease for four years is Rs. 26429.99.

Since costs and benefits occur during the life time of a project and money has time value, it is essential to place current and future costs and benefits on an equal basis for comparison. This is done by assuming a discount factor to estimate the present values of future costs and benefits. Thus, discounting technique take into account the time-value of money or Principle of time preference. By this technique, we can 'reduce' the future benefits and costs to their present worth. So, this technique permits us to determine, whether to accept or reject the project for implementation that have cash outflows and cash inflows during the life time of the project. The various measures under this discounted technique include:

i. Net Present Value (NPV)/Net Present Worth (NPW)

NPV of an investment is defined as sum of discounted net benefits of a project over a period of time. That is, it is simply the summation of differences between PWB and PWC during each year of the project. NPV is also called as Discounted net cash flow method, as it uses the discounting method of analysis. This method considers the time value of money and the stream of cash flows over the entire life of the investment, unlike PBP. The word 'net' in NPV is a reminder that, there is a cash flow at time t=0. Hence, 'net' means 'net of the cost *now*'. The following are the formulae employed to compute NPV:

$$\sum_{t=1}^{n}(B_t - C_t)/(1+i)^t$$

$$\sum_{t=1}^{n}N_t/(1+i)^t$$

$$\sum_{t=1}^{n}[(B_t - C_t) * \{1/(1+i)^t\}]$$

$$NPV = [N_1/(1+i)^1] + [N_2/(1+i)^2] + [N_3/(1+i)^3] + \text{———————} + [N_t/(1+i)^t]$$

where, Bt : Discounted benefits or cash inflows or PWB

Ct : Discounted costs or cash outflows or PWC

Nt : Discounted Net benefits

i : Market rate of interest

t: Time period of project (1,2,3 — n years)

Note that, the NPVs of the project are additive. Additive in the sense, to compute NPV of an investment of 5 years period, the NPV of cash flows will be added for the five years period and that cumulative value indicates the NPV of the investment. Similarly, if the firm has two projects A and B, then the NPV of the combined investment is: $NPV_A + NPV_B$

Criteria for Selection of Projects Based on NPV

☆ For a single project, a positive NPV indicates acceptability. For multiple (competing) projects, the project with the highest NPV should receive highest priority. Thus, NPV must be positive for making the project investment (Table 10.2). If NPV is negative, it is better to drop the project. That is, projects with negative NPV values should be rejected because, the present value of the stream of benefits is insufficient to recover the present value of stream of costs of the project. So, do not accept any project unless it generates a positive NPV, when discounted by the OCC.

Table 10.2: Decision about Project Selection Based on NPV

NPV	Meaning	Decision
NPV > 0	Investment would add value to the firm	Project may be accepted
NPV < 0	Investment would subtract value from the firm	Project should be rejected
NPV = 0	No gain-No loss to the firm	Project is break even and hence, the project manager will be indifferent in his decision, whether to accept or reject the project. This project adds no monetary value.

☆ Higher the NPV value is desirable. That is, project with highest NPV value should be selected. If there are several independent and mutually exclusive projects (if, among a number of projects, the firm can only choose one, then the projects are said to be mutually exclusive. For example: Suppose you have the choice of modifying an existing machine or replacing it with a brand new one. You could not do both and produce the desired amount of output. So, the acceptance of one project precludes accepting the other. Similarly, the option of a firm is to (a) expand its existing plant or (b) build a new one on a separate site in order to increase production capacity. In such mutually exclusive projects, the project that offers the higher NPV and IRR would be picked. Since a firm usually has limited financial resources with substantial opportunity cost, it is not feasible to do both. Hence, these projects are considered mutually exclusive. In case of mutually exclusive projects, the economic decision is to go with NPV and not IRR. The NPV measure will rank projects in order of descending NPV values. Note that, regarding independent projects, they are evaluated as if you can invest in both projects. Therefore, a project with a positive NPV will also have an IRR higher than the OCC. The decision rule for independent projects is the same regardless of the measure used to evaluate profitability. That is, for independent investments (and if cash flows are conventional), then both the IRR and NPV methods lead to the same accept and reject decisions. However, as mentioned above in case of mutually exclusive projects, you can't take on both projects and you can choose only one. When deciding to pick between these two mutually exclusive projects, the NPV and IRR decision rules (assuming both are profitable) can be in conflict because of time horizon and cash flow differences between the two projects. For example, if two projects are mutually exclusive, a short project (Project B) might have IRR=19 per cent and NPV=13,000 and a long project (Project A) might have IRR=14 percent and NPV=22500. So, the decision between these projects may be complicated, but as a general rule, you should pick the project with the higher NPV thereby, maximizing firm value.

☆ NPV is an absolute measure and not a relative measure and hence, we cannot compare one project with another project based on NPV values because, it does not give or indicate the rate of return earned from the each rupee investment. So, no ranking of acceptable projects is possible with the NPV criterion, being an absolute measure and not relative measure. In this context, the next discounted measure *i.e.,* BCR gives the rate of return earned from the each rupee investment in the project (Table 10.3).

☆ The selection of the discount rate affects the result of the investment appraisal. When a higher discount rate is used, the NPV decreases and *vice versa*. At some higher discount rate, the NPV values would be zero, and at an even higher rate, it could become negative.

✰ Compared to other investment appraisal techniques such as the BCR and IRR (discounting measures) and the PBP (undiscounted measure), the NPV is viewed as the most reliable measure to support investment decisions. As discussed above, in choosing between two projects A and B, the NPV measure may suggest that, project A is preferable, while the IRR measure may suggest project B is preferable. In such case, the result indicated by the NPV measure is more reliable. But, in some cases, a smaller project with a lower NPV may be more attractive due to a higher BCR. So, it is essential to use other discounting measures, which also yield useful additional information to assess the economic viability of the project.

✰ When the implementation agency faces a budget constraint *i.e.,* it has to select the project(s) within the limit of a fixed budget, choose that subset of the available projects, which maximizes the NPV.

Merits of NPV

✰ The NPV is the most widely accepted criterion for selecting between projects

✰ NPV is the most straightforward discounted cash flow measure of the project.

✰ The value of NPV suggests, how much a project is adding in value terms to an existing entity or how much value the project is creating.

✰ A positive NPV means that, the project is expected to add value to the firm and will therefore, increase the wealth of the owners.

✰ Since the goal of project is to add value or increase owner's wealth, NPV is a direct measure of how well this project will meet the goal.

✰ Unlike BCR, NPV has units of currency such as Rupees or Dollars. So, one is able to know the impact in terms of value that the project would create.

✰ NPV is a single measure, which takes the amount and timing of cash flows into account.

✰ NPV measure is the superior method for mutually exclusive projects.

✰ The NPV method has the advantage that the end result of the computations is expressed in Rupees and not in a percentage.

✰ It can be used in situations, where the required rate of return varies over the life of the project.

But, NPV suffers from the limitations that, it is only an absolute measure (not a relative measure like BCR and IRR) and only comparable between projects, if the initial investment is the same.

Example 10.3

Assume a project with the following costs and benefits (Figures in Rs. Crores). Compute the NPV of the investment, assuming discount factor: 10 per cent.

Year	Incremental Costs (Rs.)	Incremental Benefits (Rs.)	df 10% (1/(1+1.10)ʸ)	Method 1		Method 2	
				PWC (Rs.)	PWB (Rs.)	Net (Incremental) Benefits (NB) (Rs.)	PW of NB or NPV (Rs.)
1	2.840	0.000	0.909	2.582	0.000	−2.840	−2.582
2	10.250	0.000	0.826	8.471	0.000	−10.250	−8.471
3	11.460	0.000	0.751	8.610	0.000	−11.460	−8.610
4	8.370	0.000	0.683	5.717	0.000	−8.370	−5.717
5	4.210	0.000	0.621	2.614	0.000	−4.210	−2.614
6	2.090	0.000	0.564	1.180	0.000	−2.090	−1.180
7	2.140	6.440	0.513	1.098	3.305	4.300	2.207
8	2.510	12.320	0.467	1.171	5.747	9.810	4.576
9	3.750	16.740	0.424	1.590	7.099	12.990	5.509
10	2.910	15.450	0.386	1.122	5.957	12.540	4.835
11	1.060	30.710	0.350	0.372	10.764	29.650	10.392
12	1.030	70.260	0.319	0.328	22.387	69.230	22.059
			TOTAL	34.855	55.259		20.404

$$\text{NPV} = 55.259 - 34.855 = \text{Rs. } 20.404$$

Example 10.4

Suppose, there are two project investments A and B. The first pays the net benefits of Rs. 210 in the first year, but nothing in next year. The second investment B pays the net benefits of Rs. 100 in the first year, and Rs. 115 in next year (*i.e.*, a total of Rs. 215). Now, among these two investments, the second investment appears to be better. But, the NPV of investments (projects) show otherwise, as it all depends upon the discount rate. If the discount rate is 5 percent, then computing NPV will give:

NPV of Investment A: $= [210/(1+0.05)^1] + [0/(1+0.05)^2]$ = Rs. 200

NPV of Investment B: $= [100/(1+0.05)^1] + [115/(1+0.05)^2]$ = Rs. 199.5

Thus, though the second investment B pays out a greater sum, after discounting, the first investment looks like a better choice.

Example 10.5

Assume the following projects with their NPVs. Which projects are rejected for investment?

Project A: NPV (+ Rs.70,000)

Project B: NPV (− Rs.50,000)

Project C: NPV (+ Rs. 100,000)

Project D: NPV (- Rs. 25,000)

Solution

Only projects A and C are acceptable and projects B and D are rejected. Among A and C, project C is more preferred, as it enjoys higher NPV.

Example 10.6

Following are the four projects along with their NPVs. If budget constraint is Rs.4 lakhs, choose that subset of the available projects.

Project E: NPV (+ Rs.60,000)

Project F: NPV (+ Rs.400,000)

Project G: NPV (+ Rs. 150,000)

Project H: NPV (+ Rs. 225,000)

Solution

Since budget constraint is Rs.4 lakhs, combinations EF, FG and FH are impossible, as they cost too much. Combinations GH, EG and EH are within the budget. GH combination with NPV of Rs.375,000 is more preferred, as its NPV is highest.

Example 10.7

Assume the following projects are mutually exclusive and select the project for investment.

Project I: NPV Rs.300,000

Project J: NPV Rs.700,000

Projects K: NPV Rs. 600,000

Solution

Projects J should be chosen because, it has the largest NPV.

At this juncture, it is essential to further explain about the term OCC. The term OCC comes from the fact that, investing in any project involves a particular type of opportunity cost, the return that one could have gotten if the money had been invested elsewhere. Note that, the discount rate is sometimes referred to as the required rate of return on the project. The logic remains the same, it is only a change in terminology. If the project investor states that, he requires the project to return a certain percentage in order to be worthwhile (this rate should be the OCC), then the NPV using that rate will tell the investor, if the project does meet the requirement. For the same reasons, another name for the discount rate is the hurdle rate. The project must provide a higher rate of return than the discount rate to be worthwhile undertaking. In order to be taken on by the project investor, the project's return must be higher than, or 'hurdle', the discount rate.

ii. Benefit Cost Ratio (BCR)

BCR of an investment is the ratio between PWB to PWC in a project during its life time. That is, BCR is obtained, when the present worth of the benefit-stream is divided by the present worth of the cost-stream. So, BCR measures the relative size of the benefits to the costs of a project. As mentioned earlier, BCR is a relative measure for selecting the projects, unlike NPV. This can be better understood from the following example (Table 10.3):

Table 10.3: Selection of Projects Based on NPV and BCR Measures

Projects	Discounted Benefits (Rs/-)	Discounted Costs (Rs/-)	Net Benefits (Rs/-)	BCR
1	8000	5000	3000	0.600
2	7420	4520	2900	0.642

A close perusal of the Table 10.3 reveals that, considering the NPV values, it will be recommended to select Project 1, as its NPV value is higher over Project 2. However, BCR indicates otherwise *i.e.* it guides to select Project 2 over Project 1, as the former yields higher rate of return from the investment compared to Project 2. Thus, for the selection of projects, BCR measure outweighs NPV, as the former being a relative measure. Of course, this is true, if initial investment in the projects is more or less same and are of the same duration and that too, if the projects are independent projects. The following is the formula employed to compute BCR:

$$BCR = [\sum_{t=1}^{n} B_t/(1+i)^t]/[\sum_{t=1}^{n} C_t/(1+i)^t]$$

$$BCR = \frac{\text{Sum of the PWB}}{\text{Sum of the PWC}}$$

Here, Bt: Discounted benefits or cash inflows or PWB

Ct: Discounted costs or cash outflows or PWC

i: Market rate of interest

t: Time period of project (1,2,3 — n years)

Criteria for Selection of Projects Based on BCR

☆ For a single project, BCR greater than 1 indicates its acceptability. If BCR > 1 then, NPV > 0. For multiple (competing) projects, the project with the highest BCR (greater than 1) should receive highest priority. Thus, BCR must be greater than one for suggesting the project investment (Table 10.4).

☆ Higher the BCR is desirable *i.e.*, selection of project should be based on the highest magnitude of BCR value. Note that, the value of BCR will vary depending on the discount (interest) rate chosen. If higher discount factor is considered, the smaller the resultant BCR and if the discount rate is further increased, it can even make BCR to one or even less than one. So, the BCR criterion suggest to accept all independent projects with a BCR of greater than one, when the cost and benefit streams are discounted at the OCC. In case of mutually exclusive projects, go with NPV rather than BCR in selecting the project.

☆ BCR is a relative measure and hence, we can compare one or more projects based on BCR values. This is because, BCR indicates the rate of return from each rupee invested in the project.

☆ BCR measure is widely used in economic analysis of social projects and not in private investment analysis.

Table 10.4: Decision about Project Based on BCR Value

BCR	Meaning	Decision
BCR > 1 or NBCR > 0	Investment would add value to the firm	Project may be accepted
BCR < 1 or NBCR < 0	Investment would subtract value from the firm	Project should be rejected
BCR = 1 or NBCR = 0	No gain-No loss to the firm	Project is break even and hence, the project manager will be indifferent in his decision, whether to accept or reject the project. This project adds no monetary value.

After computing the BCR, we can work out the Net BCR (NBCR) as follows: NBCR = BCR-1. For example, if the BCR of a project is 1.585 (Example 10.8), then the NBCR =1.585-1 = 0.585. This implies that, for every one rupee invested in the project, the gross returns derived are Rs.1.585 and net returns derived are Rs.0.585. If BCR is 1.585 and if it is to be declined to 1.000 (*i.e.,* to make the project break-even), then the benefits of the project could fall in terms of percentage is calculated by the following formula:

$$[1-(1/BCR)] \times 100$$

If BCR is declined from 1.585 to 1.000, then the percent fall in benefits to make the project break-even will be 36.925 percent. Note that, this value coincides with Switching Value (per cent) computed in the ensuing pages (Example 10.3).

Example 10.8

Assume a project with the following costs and benefits (Figures in Rs. Crores). Compute the BCR and NBCR of the investment, assuming discount factor: 10 per cent.

Year	Incremental Costs (Rs.)	Incremental Benefits (Rs.)	Discount Factor @ 10 per cent (1/(1+1.10)ʸ)	BCR	
				PWC	PWB
1	2.840	0.000	0.909	2.582	0.000
2	10.250	0.000	0.826	8.471	0.000
3	11.460	0.000	0.751	8.610	0.000
4	8.370	0.000	0.683	5.717	0.000
5	4.210	0.000	0.621	2.614	0.000
6	2.090	0.000	0.564	1.180	0.000
7	2.140	6.440	0.513	1.098	3.305
8	2.510	12.320	0.467	1.171	5.747
9	3.750	16.740	0.424	1.590	7.099
10	2.910	15.450	0.386	1.122	5.957
11	1.060	30.710	0.350	0.372	10.764
12	1.030	70.260	0.319	0.328	22.387
			TOTAL	34.855	55.259
			BCR	1.585	
			NBCR	0.585	

The above Examples 10.3 and 10.8 of NPV and BCR analyses clearly infer the following points:

☆ NPV measures totals, indicates the amount by which PWB exceed (or do not exceed) PWC.

☆ BCR measures the ratio (or rate) by which PWB do or do not exceed PWC.

☆ Both BCR and NPV are clearly similar, but not identical.

☆ It is essential to note that, in analyzing the NPV and BCR, year-by-year calculations is important to discount both cash outflows and cash inflows and not the total of discount factors to multiply it with the total of cash outflows and total of cash inflows.

Example 10.9

Assume the following data (Figures in Rs. Millions) regarding PWC and PWB of two mutually exclusive projects of different sizes. Select the project for investment.

Project A: PWC = Rs. 5.0,   PWB = Rs.7.0

Project B: PWC = Rs. 20.0,   PWB = Rs. 24.0

Solution

From the given data,

For Project A: NPV_A = Rs. 2.0 BCR_A = 7/5   = 1.4

For Project B: NPV_B = Rs. 4.0 BCR_B = 24/20 = 1.2

So, according to the BCR criterion, project A should be chosen over project B because, $BCR_A > BCR_B$. But, the NPV of project B is greater than the NPV of project A.

Since, the projects are mutually exclusive, project B should be chosen with higher NPV.

Limitations of BCR Analysis

The advantage of this measure is its simplicity. However, it suffers from some difficulties regarding its application. They include:

☆ It demands the analyst to assign monetary values to all benefits and costs. However, there are numerous benefits and costs that are intangible and therefore, difficult to value. Especially, for projects with an environmental impact, it can be difficult to place a rupee value on the benefits and also on costs. The value of a product can be easily estimated, but the exact value of social costs like environmental pollution cannot be easily estimated.

☆ The result of BCR is very sensitive to the choice of the discount rate.

☆ It is difficult to account for benefits and costs that can be realized from the project. In common, while most benefits and costs that arise in the present are known, many that arise in the future are unknown. So, the information will be limited to get the realistic BCR for the project. So, the concept of uncertainty plagues the exact measurement of BCR.

☆ Using the BCR to rank projects can lead to sub-optimal decisions. This is because, a project with a slightly higher BCR ratio will be selected over a project with a lower BCR even though, the latter project has the capacity to generate much greater economic benefits because, it involves greater scale.

☆ NPV measures in absolute or totals, indicates the amount by which PWB exceed (or do not exceed) PWC. But, BCR measures the ratio or rate by which, PWB do or do not exceed PWC. So, BCR measures the resource use in terms of efficiency.

☆ The BCR does not adjust for mutually exclusive projects of different sizes (Example 10.9).

☆ The BCR criterion is sensitive to the classification of project effect as a cost rather than a benefit or *vice versa*, unlike NPV criterion. This is because, BCR criterion will affect the magnitudes, which are entered as denominator and numerator. Let us look at this example: Assume the project's PWBs as: 10, 20 and 30 units and PWCs as: 10 and 20. So, the BCR= 60/30=2.0. But, if the PWC=10 units is treated as negative benefits, then the BCR becomes 50/25 =2.5. On the other hand, NPV remains same in both the cases *i.e.*, 30 units regardless of the transfer.

iii. IRR

It is the discount factor at which, NPV is equal to zero. We already know that, there exists inverse relationship between the NPV and discount factor. So, by increasing the discount factor, NPV gradually decreases and at one level of discount factor, NPV becomes zero. That particular discount factor at which NPV=0 is called IRR. So, at IRR discount factor, the project breaks even, as PWB equals to PWC or NPV=0 or BCR=1. As the name suggests, the IRR of an investment measures its rate of return, whereas NPV measures the size of the return. If a farmer invests Rs. 10000

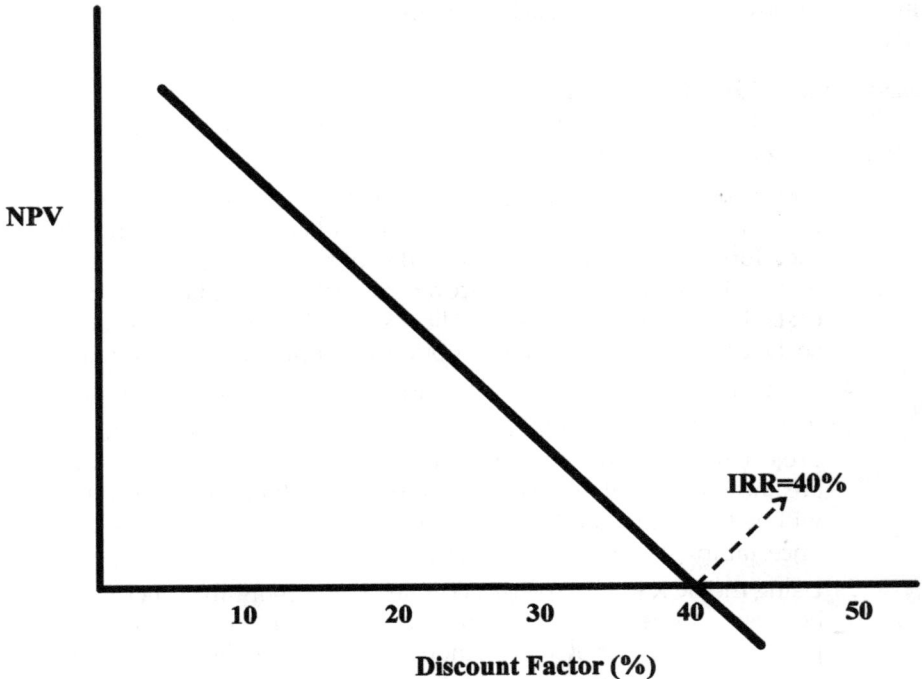

Figure 10.4: Inverse Relation between NPV and Discount Factor.

in a project with an IRR of 20 per cent is exactly equivalent to investing the same Rs. 10000 in an interest-earning bank account at an interest rate of 20 percent. Note that, IRR assumes re-investment of cash inflows at IRR.

It is shown through Figure 10.4, as the discount factor increases, NPV gradually decreases and at 40 per cent discount factor, NPV becomes zero. This discount factor (*i.e.*, 40 per cent) at which NPV=0 is called IRR. That is, at IRR discount factor (R), NPV=0 and this means that, at IRR, the PWB equals the PWC in a project indicating that, it is just break even at 40 per cent discount factor. This 40 per cent IRR implies that, for every one rupee investment in a project, it earns Rs.1.40 gross returns or Rs.0.40 net returns from the date of investment of the project. Having estimated the IRR to be 40 percent, the rule will be to ACCEPT the investment at any interest rate less than 40 percent per annum and to REJECT the investment at any interest rate that exceeds 40 per cent per annum. Thus, IRR indicates the earning capacity of the project right from the investment period. IRR is, otherwise, called as Marginal Efficiency of Capital (MEC). The students must note that, at IRR=40 per cent, even if the project earns net returns by Rs.0.40 from the date of initial investment of the project, the project finally breaks even by the end of the project period. This is because of the presence of gestation period during which the gross returns are nil or net returns are negative in the project. The negative net returns of the project during gestation period is compensated by the actual net returns of Rs.0.40 right from the initial investment of the project and this lead to break even of the project by the end of the project period.

We can write the formulae for IRR in terms of above formulae discussed under NPV and BCR as follows, by employing IRR discount factor (R).

$$NPV = \sum_{t=1}^{n}(B_t - C_t)/(1+R)^t = 0$$

$$BCR = [\sum_{t=1}^{n} B_t/(1+R)^t]/[\sum_{t=1}^{n} C_t/(1+R)^t] = 1$$

Procedure to Compute IRR

We already know, there exists inverse relationship between the NPV and discount factor. The IRR discount factor is computed by a trial and error procedure and it involves the following steps:

☆ First, an arbitrary discount factor is assumed and NPV is computed.

☆ If NPV is positive, it implies, the IRR is still higher and hence, a still higher discount factor will be considered to compute NPV again.

☆ If again NPV is positive, a still higher discount factor will be considered.

☆ This procedure is continued till NPV will become negative.

☆ So, between the last two successive NPVs *i.e.*, one positive NPV and one negative NPV, there is zero NPV. So, compute the discount factor at which the NPV=0, by interpolation method through employing the following formula:

$$IRR\ (R) = \text{Lower discount rate} + \text{Difference between two discount rates} \times \frac{\text{Present worth at lower discount rate}}{\text{Absolute difference between NPVs at two discount rates}}$$

The above trial and error procedure to compute IRR represent a mathematical method called 'Linear Interpolation' (Interpolation is simply finding the intermediate value between too discount rates we have chosen). As given in the formula, it is necessary to work out two NPV values. One of these calculations must give a positive NPV and the other calculation must give a negative NPV. The most difficult aspect of this trial and error procedure is making the initial estimates. If the estimate is too far from the final result, then several trials will have to be made to find two discount rates close enough together to permit accurate interpolation. In practice, it is better not to interpolate between intervals greater than about five percent because, the wider intervals can easily introduce an interpolation error. Note that, IRR is a mathematical concept, not an economic or financial criterion.

In practice, it is better not to try to interpolate between a spread wider than five percentage points. After calculating the IRR, it should always be rounded to the nearest whole percentage point. This rounding off the calculated IRR helps to minimize the error introduced by interpolation technique, where we move from one discount factor to another discount factor assuming a straight line fall in NPV, which was actually a concave curvilinear function.

Criteria to Use IRR

☆ For the project to earn profits, IRR must be greater than OCC of investment.

☆ The relationship between an NPV, IRR and OCC is given below:

❖ *Case 1:* If NPV >0 then, BCR>1 and IRR is greater than OCC. Then, it is advised to take up the project.

❖ *Case 2:* If NPV = 0, then BCR=1 and IRR is equal to OCC. This is the point of indecision.

❖ *Case 3:* if NPV < 0, then BCR<1 and IRR is less than OCC. Then, it is better to drop the project.

Example 10.10

Assume a project with the following costs and benefits (Figures in Crores) Compute the IRR of the investment, assuming discount factor: 10 per cent.

Year	Incr Costs (Rs.)	Incr Benefits (Rs.)	Discount Factor 10% (1/(1+1.10)ʸ	Net (Incre.) Benefits (NB)	PW of NB (or) NPV (Rs.)	15% df (1/(1+ 1.15)ʸ	NPV at 15% (Rs.)	20% df (1/(1+ 1.20)ʸ	NPV at 20% (Rs.)
1	2.840	0.000	0.909	−2.840	−2.582	0.870	−2.470	0.833	−2.367
2	10.250	0.000	0.826	−10.250	−8.471	0.756	−7.750	0.694	−7.118
3	11.460	0.000	0.751	−11.460	−8.610	0.658	−7.535	0.579	−6.632
4	8.370	0.000	0.683	−8.370	−5.717	0.572	−4.786	0.482	−4.036
5	4.210	0.000	0.621	−4.210	−2.614	0.497	−2.093	0.402	−1.692
6	2.090	0.000	0.564	−2.090	−1.180	0.432	−0.904	0.335	−0.700
7	2.140	6.440	0.513	4.300	2.207	0.376	1.617	0.279	1.200
8	2.510	12.320	0.467	9.810	4.576	0.327	3.207	0.233	2.281
9	3.750	16.740	0.424	12.990	5.509	0.284	3.693	0.194	2.518
10	2.910	15.450	0.386	12.540	4.835	0.247	3.100	0.162	2.025
11	1.060	30.710	0.350	29.650	10.392	0.215	6.373	0.135	3.991
12	1.030	70.260	0.319	69.230	22.059	0.187	12.940	0.112	7.765
			TOTAL	NPV	20.404	NPV	5.39092		−2.7655
						IRR (R)	18.3047		

Having estimated the IRR to be 18.31 percent, the rule will be to ACCEPT the investment at any interest rate less than 18.31 percent per annum and to REJECT the investment at any interest rate that exceeds 18.31 per cent per annum. This IRR also implies the maximum interest that a project could pay for the resources used, if the project is to recover its investment and operating costs and still break even. An IRR of 18.31 percent also means that, with a discount rate of 18.31 per cent, the project breaks even. This IRR approach is usually associated with a discount rate or OCC, against which the IRR is compared. If the IRR exceeds the OCC, the project is accepted (Table 10.5). In the above example, since IRR (18.31 per cent) is greater than the OCC (10 per cent), it is suggested to accept the project. Note that, although IRR of different projects will vary, a project manager cannot say with confidence that, the projects can be ranked on the basis of IRR. Only in a general way, the IRR will tell that, one project is better than another, in the sense that, it contributes more national income relative to resources used. For example, if the discount rate remains at 10 percent, then we cannot know with certainty that the project with 25 percent IRR contributes relatively more to national income than another project with 15 percent IRR and hence, we cannot say with confidence that, we should implement the former project with 25 percent IRR first. If the opportunity cost is raised to 18 percent, then the project with 15 percent IRR drops out of the investment and judgement will be easy to favour the investment of the project that yield 25 percent IRR.

Table 10.5: Decision about Project Based on IRR Value

IRR	Meaning	Decision
IRR > OCC	Investment would add value to the firm	Project may be accepted
IRR < OCC	Investment would subtract value from the firm	Project should be rejected
IRR = OCC	No gain-No loss to the firm.	Project is break even and hence, the project manager will be indifferent in his decision, whether to accept or reject the project. This project adds no monetary value.

There are some disadvantages associated with the IRR as a performance indicator. It is not suitable for the ranking of competing projects. It is possible for two projects to have the same IRR, but have different NPV values due to differences in the timing of costs and benefits. This implies, applying different appraisal techniques to the same basic data may yield contradictory conclusions.

Merits of IRR

Among the above three discounted measures, IRR is most widely used because of following reasons:

☆ It is a clear estimate indicating the rate of return from the initial period of investment.

☆ The estimate is unique in nature, as it cannot be compared with NPV and BCR.

☆ It has got wider applicability.

☆ The estimate is much consistent.

☆ This measure serves as the most important alternative to NPV.

☆ It is often used in practice and is intuitively appealing.

☆ It is based entirely on the estimated cash flows and is independent of interest rates found elsewhere.

☆ Results are expressed as a simple percentage and hence, are more easily understood than other measures.

☆ It indicates how sensitive investment decisions are to a change in interest rates.

☆ It is considered to be the most useful measure of project worth and used by almost all the institutions including World Bank in economic and financial analyses of the project.

☆ It represents the average earning power of the money used in the project over the project life. Hence, it is also sometimes called Yield of the investment.

☆ Projects are also ranked based on IRR and the project with highest IRR is ranked first for its investment. The lowest acceptable IRR for project investment is called cut-off rate and is generally set slightly above the OCC.

Limitations of IRR

However, there are many problems with IRR as a criterion for project evaluation (Cary and Dunn, 1997; Anonymous, 2004). Some of them are:

☆ Can produce multiple answers. That is, IRR is unreliable in the situation of non-conventional net cash flows (Net cash flow sign changes more than once *i.e.,* a negative net cash flow after a positive one). That is, in the case of positive net cash flows followed by negative ones and then by positive ones, the IRR may have multiple values. With reference to the cash outflow and cash inflow in a project given through Table 10.5.1, there are multiple IRRs, as NPV is zero at two discount factors *i.e.,* 25 and 400 per cent (Figure 10.4.1). Among these two IRRs, which is correct IRR? We can't say. So, there is no unambiguously correct answer. This implies, the occurrence of multiple IRRs for a project and in such case, the IRR rule breaks down.

Table 10.5.1: Project with Multiple IRRs

Year	Incremental Costs (Rs.)	Incremental Benefits (Rs.)	Net Incremental Benefits (Rs.)	25 per cent df	NPV at 25 per cent (Rs.)	400 per cent df	NPV at 400 per cent (Rs.)
1	160000	0	−160000	0.8	−128000	0.2	−32000
2		1000000	1000000	0.64	640000	0.04	40000
3	1000000	0	−1000000	0.512	−512000	0.008	−8000
				NPV	0		0

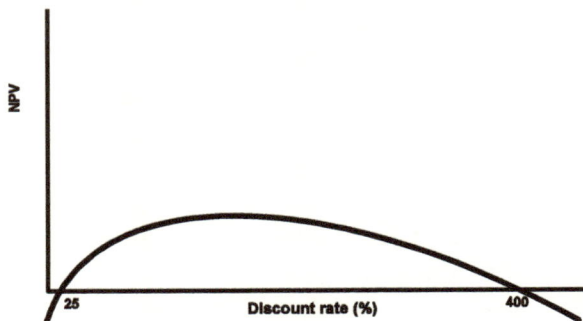

Table 10.4.1: Project with Multiple IRRs.

☆ IRR discount factor is misleading is case of mutually exclusive projects. For the data given through Table 10.5.2, Project A enjoys lower NPV, (Rs. 7015), but higher IRR (100 per cent) when compared to Project B with higher NPV (Rs. 15147) but lower IRR (50 per cent). Since, higher NPV contributes more to the value of the project, go with NPV rather than IRR in ranking mutually exclusive projects (*i.e.,* select Project B for investment), or we can say, IRR measure is misleading in case of mutually exclusive projects.

Table10.5.2: IRR is Misleading for Mutually Exclusive Projects

Year	Incr Costs (Rs.)	Incr Benefits (Rs.)	df 12%	Net Incremental Benefits (Rs.)	NPV (Rs.)	IRR	
						100% df	NPV at 100% df(Rs.)
Project A							
1	10000	0	0.893	−10000	−8929	0.50	−5000
2	0	20000	0.797	20000	15944	0.25	5000
				NPV	7015		NPV = 0

Year	Incr Costs (Rs.)	Incr Benefits (Rs.)	df 12%	Net Incremental Benefits (Rs.)	NPV (Rs.)	IRR	
						50% df	NPV at 50% df(Rs.)
Project B							
1	50000	0	0.893	−50000	−44643	0.67	−33333
2	0	75000	0.797	75000	59790	0.44	33333
				NPV	15147		NPV = 0

Table 10.5.3: IRR cannot Distinguish between Lending and Borrowing

Year	Incr Costs (Rs.)	Incr Benefits (Rs.)	df 10%	Net Incremental Benefits (Rs.)	NPV (Rs.)	IRR	
						50% df	NPV at 50% df(Rs.)
Project A							
1	4000	0	0.909	−4000	−3636.364	0.667	−2666.667
2		6000	0.826	6000	4958.678	0.444	2666.667
				NPV	1322.314		NPV= 0

Year	Incr Costs (Rs.)	Incr Benefits (Rs.)	df 10%	Net Incremental Benefits (Rs.)	NPV (Rs.)	IRR	
						75% df	NPV at 75% df(Rs.)
Project B							
1	0	4000	0.909	4000	3636.364	0.571	2285.714
2	7000	0	0.826	−7000	−5785.124	0.327	−2285.714
				NPV	−2148.760		NPV= 0

☆ Another important demerit of IRR is that, it cannot distinguish between lending and borrowing and hence, a higher IRR need not necessarily be a desirable thing. For the data given through Table 10.5.3, IRR is higher for Project B (75 per cent) compared to project A (50 per cent). But, project B is not an attractive project, as project A involves investment of Rs.4000 at a rate of return of 50 per cent, but project B involves borrowing Rs.4000 at a rate of return of 75 per cent. Even, if we go by NPV, Project A is more attractive over project B.

☆ IRR does not consider cost of capital and hence, it should not be used to compare projects of different duration. However, MIRR does consider cost of capital and provides a better indication of a project's efficiency in contributing to the firm's discounted cash flow.

☆ If cash flows are conventional and project is independent, then NPV and IRR lead to same accept and reject decisions. But, IRR measure can lead to erroneous rankings of mutually exclusive projects (taking one project means another is not taken), as the highest IRR may not have the highest NPV. For such mutually exclusive projects, IRR is inferior to NPV measure in ranking them. So, when projects are *mutually exclusive*, we cannot rank them by their IRRs. This is because, the IRR is independent of the size or scale of the project (*Scale-independence*) *i.e.,* a minute project could have a much larger IRR than a project ten times bigger. In such case, NPV should be used to choose between mutually exclusive projects.

☆ The IRR measure assumes that, the future cash flows will be reinvested and get the returns equal to IRR.

☆ IRR ignores differences in the life of the projects, the time span problem.

☆ The estimate of IRR is not unique, if the net cash flow into the project are non-conventional

☆ It is tedious to calculate.

☆ It says nothing about the size of the project because, one may prefer bigger project with higher NPV than a small project with low NPV, but higher IRR.

☆ The IRR of individual projects cannot be added or averaged to derive the IRR of a combination of projects.

Comparison between NPV and IRR

☆ NPV measure takes the interest rate as a known factor, where as IRR takes it as an unknown factor.

☆ NPV measure seeks to find out the cumulative net present cash flows (PWB - PWC) of an investment at a given market rate of interest. On the other hand, IRR seeks to find out the discount factor at which the project breaks even (PWB = PWC).

☆ Both NPV and IRR measures proceed with the presumption that, cash inflow can be re-invested in the new project. However, NPV assume re-investment at discount rate (OCC), but IRR measure assumes the re-investment at IRR discount factor. However, re-investment of funds at the NPV discount rate (OCC or cut off rate) is more feasible than at the IRR. This makes the NPV more reliable compared to IRR in ranking two or more capital investment projects.

☆ NPV measures in absolute or totals, indicates the amount by which PWB exceed (or do not exceed) PWC. But, IRR measures the rate of return in the project in terms of percentage. Thus, IRR is a rate quantity and is an indicator of the efficiency, quality, or yield of an investment, whereas NPV is an indicator of the value or magnitude of an investment.

☆ The condition for the accepting the project is when NPV > 0. The same with reference to IRR measure is, when the IRR discount rate is more than NPV discount rate.

Similarities in Results of NPV and IRR

Both NPV and IRR measures gives the same result regarding acceptance or rejection of project investments in the following cases

☆ If the project involves conventional cash flows *i.e.*, when an initial cash outflow is followed by a series of cash inflows

☆ When the projects are independent and not mutually exclusive (Independent projects are the projects, where the proposal of one project investment does not preclude the acceptance of other projects).

Conflict between NPV and IRR in Selecting Project Investment

As mentioned earlier, in case of mutually exclusive projects, there arises the conflict between NPV and IRR *i.e.*, regarding which measure should be taken into consideration for selection of mutually exclusive projects. In general, the conflicts between these two measures will arise, because of one or more of the following reasons:

☆ If the projects differ in their cash outlays

☆ If the projects differ in their duration

☆ If the projects have different pattern of cash flows

Regarding conflicts that may arise in the selection of mutually exclusive projects, the selection of project investment should be based on NPV criterion and not on IRR. This is because, NPV measure directly indicates the wealth maximization of the investments, whereas IRR indicates only the rate of return on the investment rather than total wealth maximization of the investment. Hence, NPV is the best measure to rank mutually exclusive projects and the project with highest NPV is desirable for investment.

Applicability of NPV, BCR and IRR

Though several measures were available for project appraisal under discounting technique as discussed earlier, the most commonly used measures include NPV, BCR and IRR for social cost-benefit analysis.

☆ World Bank employs discounted measures to evaluate agricultural projects.

☆ Among the three discounted measures, BCR and IRR indicate the rate of return in the project investment, unlike NPV.

☆ NPV and BCR will be used for *ex-ante* evaluation studies, while IRR will be **used** for *ex-post* evaluation studies.

☆ NPV and IRR are the most commonly used primary investment criteria whereas, PBP is a commonly used secondary investment criteria, only because of its ease of use.

☆ Neither IRR nor BCR can be adequately used to choose between two mutually exclusive projects. In such case, NPV is the best measure.

☆ With regard to the implementation of single project or two or more projects with the same cost structure, NPV criterion is adequate. However, when there are several competing projects with different cost structures, NPV criteria being an absolute measure is not a correct choice.

☆ Unlike NPV, for competing projects with different cost structures, BCR criterion is the correct choice, being a relative measure. This criterion states that:

❖ In case of single project, choose it, if the BCR is >1.

❖ In case of competing projects with different cost structures, choose the project with highest BCR and rank the projects in the descending order of their BCR estimates. Choose the number of projects in such a way that the given investment fund is exhausted.

❖ In case of mutually exclusive projects, still NPV criterion is meritorious over BCR. Assume two projects A and B with the following values: PWC_A: 100 units; PWB_A: 130 units; PWC_B= 40 units and PWB_B= 60 units. So, NPV_A=30, BCR_A=1.3, NPV_B=20 and BCR_B=1.5. Since NPV_A is higher, go with Project A, as the two projects are mutually exclusive.

☆ The demerit of NPV and BCR measures is that, they depend on an externally given SRD. However, IRR enjoy the advantage of not depending on SRD at least in the initial stages of its computation. IRR criterion states that:

❖ For a single project, select it, if the R>i

❖ In case of competing projects, rank them in descending order their R values and choose that set of projects from the top for which R>i, until the given investment fund is exhausted.

❖ Note that, 'R' can be calculated purely from the project data, whereas computation of NPV and BCR require external SRD.

❖ In case of mutually exclusive projects, still NPV is preferred over IRR in selecting the project.

☆ In case of single project, NPV or IRR criteria holds good. But, in case of mutually exclusive projects, NPV is used as decision criterion over BCR and IRR. However, in case of rationing a given investment, BCRs of projects will be the decision criterion for ranking the projects.

Note that, whenever there is a conflict between NPV and another decision rule, always use NPV. Please see the following examples:

Example 10.11

Assume the following data for two projects (Figures in Rs. Millions), which are mutually exclusive. Which project is to be selected for investment?

Period	Project A	Project B
0	−500	−400
1	325	325
2	325	200
IRR	19.43 per cent	22.17 per cent
NPV	64.05	60.74

Solution

Since the two projects are mutually exclusive, Project A should be preferred over Project B, as Project A enjoys higher NPV (Rs.64.05 millions).

Example 10.12

From the following table, draw the conclusion, whether to accept or reject the project?

Year 0	−90,000
Year 1	132,000
Year 2	100,000
Year 3	−150,000
IRR	10.11 per cent
NPV at 15 per cent discount factor	1,770

Solution

In the above table, IRR says to reject, but NPV says to accept. So, go with NPV and select the project for investment.

In computing the discounting technique, it is interesting to note that, the depreciation of capital investment is automatically taken care off in the computation process i.e., depreciation need not be included as a separate cost in computing total costs of the project. Please look at the following example: Assume a project of five years duration with a total cash outlay of Rs.10 lakhs and total cash inflow of Rs.10 lakhs spread in five years. Assume the discount factor as zero per cent. Then, after computation, NPV=0, BCR=1 and IRR=0%. This implies, even after five years, the project has not earned anything (no economic returns) and even there are no losses. This further implies, the return on capital is realized in the project (even depreciation is covered) when the project earns zero NPV or more at zero discount factor, IRR equal to zero or more and BCR equal to one at a zero or greater rate of interest. So, depreciation need not be shown as a separate cost in the computation process and is automatically taken care off in the analysis.

iv. Modified IRR (MIRR)

Despite the deficiencies of IRR (*i.e.*, may lead to multiple rates of return in case of projects with non-conventional cash flows, may lead to incorrect decisions in comparing mutually exclusive projects etc), it is still popular in practice even more than NPV as the former appraise the project in terms of rate of return (per cent) rather than on absolute terms. Further note that, without knowing the discount rate, we cannot estimate the NPV, but still we can calculate the IRR. Say, for example, if the IRR of the project is 40 percent, then the project manager may go for implementing the project, with the presumption that, the discount rate would be still less than IRR. Though IRR enjoys superiority over NPV, it too suffers from short comings as mentioned above. This calls for a percentage measure that overcomes the shortcomings of the IRR and this is nothing but, MIRR. NPV assumes that, periodic cash ows can and will be reinvested at the NPV discount rate, either at the cost of capital or another risk adjusted discount rate; IRR assumes reinvestment at the IRR. Neither assumption is usually realistic. In addition, when evaluating projects in terms of their nancial attractiveness, the two measures may rank projects differently. This becomes important when capital budgets are limited. Finally, a project may have several IRRs, if net cash flows go from negative to positive more than once. The MIRR, discovered in the 18th century, does account for these cash ows. While the IRR assumes that, the cash flows from a project are reinvested at the IRR, the MIRR assumes that, all cash flows are reinvested at the firm's OCC. Therefore, MIRR more accurately reflects the profitability of a project.

Procedure

The procedure to compute MIRR is discussed here under.

Step 1

Compute the PWC of cash outflows using the OCC or market rate of interest as discount factor:

$$\sum PWC = \sum_{t=1}^{n} C_t/(1+i)^t$$

where, Ct is the cash outflows, 'i' = market rate of interest, t = time period of project cash outflows

Step 2

Compute the Terminal Values (TV) of the cash inflows expected from the project by employing the discount factor 'i'. This is where, MIRR differs from IRR, as the modified MIRR assumes that, all cash flows are reinvested at the firm's cost of capital whereas, the IRR assumes that, the cash flows from a project are reinvested at the IRR. The formula used for computing TV is given by:

$$\sum TV = \sum_{t=1}^{n} B_t/(1+i)^{n-t}$$

where, Bt is the cash inflows, 'i' = market rate of interest, n = total duration of the project

Step 3

Compute MIRR by employing the following formula:

$\Sigma PWC = \Sigma TV / (1 + MIRR)^n$

Example 10.12.1

Table 10.5.4: Computation of MIRR

Year	Incr Costs	Incr Benefits	df @ 12%	PWC	NB	NPV@ 12% df	df @ 25%	NPV@ 25% df	TV @ 12% df
0	195		1.000	195.00	−195.000	−195.000	1.000	−195.000	
1		121	0.893		121.000	108.036	0.800	96.800	$121*(1.12)^1 =$ 135.520
2		131	0.797		131.000	104.432	0.640	83.840	$131*(1.12)^0 =$ 131.00
				ΣPWC = 195.00		NPV= 17.468		NPV= (-14.360)	ΣTV = 266.520
						IRR = 18.66 per cent			

For the data given through the Table 10.5.4, MIRR is given by:

$$\Sigma PWC = \Sigma TV/(1+MIRR)^n$$
$$195 = 266.520/(1+MIRR)^2$$
$$(1+MIRR)^2 = 266.520/195$$
$$(1+MIRR)^2 = 1.367$$
$$(1+MIRR) = (1.367)^{1/2} = 1.169$$
$$So, MIRR = 0.169 = 16.9 \text{ per cent.}$$

Example 10.12.2

Table 10.5.5: Computation of MIRR

Year	Incr Costs	Incr Benefits	df @ 15%	PWC	NB	NPV@ 12% df	df @ 25%	NPV@ 25% df	TV @ 15% df
0	120		1.000	120.000	−120.00	−120.000	1.000	−120.000	
1	80		0.870	69.565	−80.00	−69.565	0.833	−66.667	
2		20	0.756		20.00	15.123	0.694	13.889	$20*(1.15)^4 =$ 34.980
3		60	0.658		60.00	39.451	0.579	34.722	$60*(1.15)^3 =$ 91.253
4		80	0.572		80.00	45.740	0.482	38.580	$80*(1.15)^2 =$ 105.800
5		100	0.497		100.00	49.718	0.402	40.188	$100*(1.15)^1 =$ 115.000
6		120	0.432		120.00	51.879	0.335	40.188	$120*(1.15)^0 =$ 120.000
				ΣPWC = 189.565		NPV= 12.346		NPV= (-19.100)	ΣTV = 467.033
						IRR=16.96 per cent			

For the data given through the Table 10.5.5, MIRR is given by:

$$\Sigma PWC \qquad = \Sigma TV / (1 + MIRR)^n$$

$$189.565 \qquad = 467.033 / (1 + MIRR)^6$$

$$(1 + MIRR)^6 \qquad = 467.033 / 189.565$$

$$(1 + MIRR)^6 \qquad = 2.464$$

$$(1 + MIRR) \qquad = (2.464)^{1/6} = 1.162$$

$$So, MIRR \qquad = 0.162 = 16.2 \text{ per cent.}$$

It can be inferred that (in Example 10.12.1), the 16.9 per cent MIRR is materially lower than the IRR of 18.66 per cent. In this case, the IRR gives a too optimistic picture of the potential of the project, while the MIRR gives a more realistic evaluation of the project. Let us look at another Example 10.12.2 shown in Table 10.5.5. Again, MIRR (16.2 per cent) is lower than the IRR (16.96 per cent) and this MIRR gives a more realistic evaluation of the project. Note that, MIRR is superior than IRR in measuring the true rate of return. Superior in the sense that, MIRR assumes the project cash flows are re-invested at the OCC or market rate of interest, whereas the IRR assumes that, the project cash flows are re-invested at the IRR discount factor. We know, the re-investment of cash flows of a project at OCC is more realistic and this makes MIRR more superior to IRR. Further, MIRR does not lead to multiple rates of return, unlike IRR. So, we can infer that, in ranking mutually exclusive projects of the same duration and size, NPV and MIRR leads to the same decision. However, if the mutually exclusive projects are of different duration and size, then NPV measure still outweighs MIRR. Most financial analysts consider the MIRR to be a more prudent method of evaluating the future returns for a given investment opportunity. MIRR calculations are also helpful, if the cash flows of the project go from negative to positive and back again. For example, if you run IRR on a series of numbers that have more than one change in the signs, say -500, 150, 450, -100, 575 etc., you will have two unique IRRs. The rule is that, we will have as many unique IRRs as there are changes in signs. MIRR solves this problem, as negative and positive numbers are treated separately. MIRR is considered as a more accurate measure of the attractiveness of an investment alternative because, attractiveness depends not only on the return on the investment itself, but also on the return expected from cash flows it generates.

Note that, there is some confusion in choosing the year for discounting *i.e.,* Year 0 or Year 1. World Bank believes that, since investment is made and some returns may accrue from the first year, then discounting should start from 0 to first year. In this case, the initial year is Year 1. But, other international organizations use Year 0. Their argument is that, investment must take place before benefits accrue. Thus, discounting should start from the second year. So, the students can choose any convention, but be consistent. However, in the above explanation, both the cases have been exemplified, so as to make the students familiar with the analysis.

v. Net Benefit-Investment Ratio (NBIR)

This is otherwise called as N/K ratio. It is simply the present worth of net benefits divided by the present worth of investment. NBIR serves as the suitable and more convenient selection criterion for the project implementation. To calculate this measure, simply divide the sum of the present worth after the incremental net benefits-stream has turned positive by the sum of the present worth of the negative incremental net benefits in the early years (during gestation period) of the project. The reason for calculating the NBIR in this manner is that, we are interested in an investment measure that selects projects on the basis of return to investment during the initial phases of a project. If the NBIR is one or greater than one, when we are discounting at the OCC, choose the project beginning with the largest ratio value and proceed until available investment funds are exhausted. This NBIR also helps to rank projects, especially when sufficient funds are not available to implement all the projects. At any given discount rate, it is difficult to rank the project based on considering NPV, BCR and IRR ranking measures, as selection criterion vary across all these three measures. In this context, the NBIR is the only measure that can be used with confidence to rank the projects directly. This ratio is computed by employing the following formula:

NBIR or N/K ratio = (Σ Present Worth of Positive NB)/(Σ Present Worth of Negative NB)

The selection criterion for the project in using N/K ratio measure must be greater than 1. Generally, for the project net incremental benefits will be negative during the gestation period because, gross returns are zero and only costs are incurred. Net incremental benefits will turn positive only after gestation period *i.e.,* when there is cash inflow into the project. This measure is often used for ranking projects especially, if rationing is in place.

Methods to make N/K Ratio = 1

If N/K ratio is more than, then it can be made equal to 1 by employing the following methods:

☆ *Increasing the project investment:* The percent by which the project investment should be increased in order to make N/K ratio = 1 is given by the following formula:

$$I(\%) = \frac{P - N}{N} * 100$$

Where, I – Increase in project investment (per cent)

P: Sum of present worth of positive net incremental benefits

N: Sum of present worth of negative net incremental benefits

☆ *By decreasing net benefits:* The percent by which the net incremental benefits should be reduced in order to make N/K ratio = 1 is given by the following formula:

$$B(\%) = 1 - \frac{1}{N/K} * 100$$

Example 10.12

Assume a project with the following costs and benefits (Figures in Rs. Crores). Compute the NBIR or N/K of the investment, assuming discount factor: 10 per cent.

Year	Incremental Costs (Rs.)	Incremental Benefits (Rs.)	df 10% (1/(1+1.1))	N/K Ratio	
				Net (Incremental) Benefits (NB) (Rs.)	Present Worth of NB or NPV (Rs.)
1	2.84	0	0.909	−2.84	−2.582
2	10.25	0	0.826	−10.25	−8.471
3	11.46	0	0.751	−11.46	−8.61
4	8.37	0	0.683	−8.37	−5.717
5	4.21	0	0.621	−4.21	−2.614
6	2.09	0	0.564	−2.09	−1.18
7	2.14	6.44	0.513	4.3	2.207
8	2.51	12.32	0.467	9.81	4.576
9	3.75	16.74	0.424	12.99	5.509
10	2.91	15.45	0.386	12.54	4.835
11	1.06	30.71	0.35	29.65	10.392
12	1.03	70.26	0.319	69.23	22.059
				Sum of present worth of +ve NB	49.578
				Sum of present worth of -ve NB	−29.174
				N/K	1.699
				To make N/K equal to 1	
				Per cent Cost should be increased	69.939
				Per cent Benefits should be decreased	41.155

vi. Profitability Index

This measure allows a comparison of the costs and benefits of different projects to be assessed and thus, allow decision making to be carried out. This PI is given by:

PI = Total Present Value of Cash Inflows/Initial Capital Investment

Year	Cost (Rs.)	Cash Inflow (Rs.)	df (10 per cent)	PWB (Rs.)
0	100000		1.000	
1		30000	0.909	27270
2		50000	0.826	41300
3		60000	0.751	45060
				Total = 113630

P.I. = 113630/100000 = 1.1363 (So, accept the project)

The PI can also be computed as follows:

PI = 1+ [NPV/Initial capital investment]

PI = 1+[13630/100000] = 1.1363

This measure is often used for government or other non-for-profit investments. It measures the benefit per unit cost, based on the time value of money. In the given example, a PI of 1.1363 suggests that, for every Rs.1 of initial investment, the project yields an additional Rs.0.1363 in value. Since, the PI is > 1, we accept the project. For mutually exclusive projects, practitioners sometimes choose the project with the highest PI. However, this approach is problematic. If there is no capital constraint, one should choose the project with the highest NPV from the mutually exclusive pool.

Merits of PI
They include:

☆ Investment decisions based on PI will be same as decisions made using NPV. All projects having positive NPV have PI larger than 1.0 and therefore, are acceptable.

☆ Since this measure is related to NPV, it generally leading to identical decisions.

☆ Easy to understand and communicate.

☆ The PI is most useful when a firm is facing capital rationing.

Demerit
However, this measure should not be used for making mutually exclusive decisions. But, between two or more mutually exclusive projects having different costs, choose project with highest PI.

VII. Differences between Discounted and Undiscounted Techniques

The following Table 10.6 highlights the differences between discounted and undiscounted techniques:

Table 10.6: Differences between Discounted and Undiscounted Techniques

Discounting Technique	Undiscounting Technique
1. Time value of money is taken into consideration.	1. Time value of money is not taken into consideration.
2. OCC is taken into consideration.	2. It is not taken into consideration.
3. Projects are appraised based on discounted benefits and discounted costs.	3. Projects are appraised based on the absolute benefits and absolute costs.
4. Discounting techniques are more realistic to appraise the project for its implementation.	4. These techniques are relatively less realistic to appraise the project for its implementation.
Examples: NPV, BCR, IRR.	Examples: Ranking by inspection, PBP.

Merits of Discounting Technique
They include

☆ Takes time value of money into consideration

☆ Takes into account directly the amount of cash outflows and cash inflows over the entire project's life, unlike undiscounted measure, where simply their averages are taken.

☆ Gives more weight to the money values which are nearer to the present period than those which are farther from it. In case of undiscounted measures, all money units are given the same weightage, which is not realistic.

☆ Since discounting technique considers time value of money, it will enable to rank projects of different duration, different cash outflows and inflows etc, unlike undiscounted measures.

However, the discounting technique suffers from the limitation that, it is based on the presumption that, the cash inflows in the project can be re-invested at the discounting rate in the new investment opportunities. However, this presumption does depend upon the availability of new attractive investment opportunities.

VIII. Sensitivity Analysis

In a project cycle, appraisal or analysis of the project will be done before implementation of project taking into consideration the proposed costs and benefits by employing discounted measures like NPV, BCR, IRR, MIRR, NBIR and PI and we will study the worthiness of implementing the project. If all discounted measures are found desirable as per their criteria for economic viability of the project, then the project will be selected for its implementation. But, after implementation of the project, in due course of time, both input costs and output prices, discount factor etc., may fluctuate. So, accordingly the PWC and PWB of the project will change due to these variations. So, the discounted measures computed earlier before project implementation taking into consideration proposed costs and proposed benefits and the given discount factor may not give a true or realistic picture. The variations in cost and benefits and discount factor should be frequently incorporated and project data should be updated after the implementation of project and again discounted measures should be computed, so as to derive the realistic picture about the project performance for the completed period or duration and for the future period. This procedure of working out discounted measures for the project taking into consideration due changes in the costs and benefits, discount factor etc., frequently after project implementation is called Sensitivity analysis. As the costs and benefits data and changes in discount factor are frequently updated in sensitivity analysis and if the results of discounted measures are still found congenial, then it is worth for continuing the project. Thus, sensitivity analysis of project will be done considering the following aspects:

☆ Changes in input cost.
☆ Changes in output prices.
☆ Changes in discount factor.
☆ Change in the length or duration of project.
☆ Changes in the gestation period of project.

Besides above factors, risk and uncertainty factors should also be considered to get the realistic picture about the performance of the project. One important method of analyzing the sensitivity analysis of the project is Switching value percentage method.

i. Switching Value Percentage Method

This method estimates the extent to which the percent fall in incremental benefits would make NPV = 0 at the given discount factor or OCC. This method is similar to the methodology employed in computing IRR, but here we make NPV = 0 by decreasing the incremental benefits without changing the discount factor. The procedure in this method is outlined here under.

☆ First, we assume a certain fall in incremental benefits of the project and we will work out present worth of net incremental benefits (*i.e.,* NPV).

☆ If NPV is positive, still higher percent decline in incremental benefits will be considered to estimate NPV.

☆ If NPV is still positive, this procedure is continued till NPV become negative.

☆ Between the last two successive NPVs *i.e.*, one positive NPV and one negative NPV, there is zero NPV. So, compute the percent of incremental benefits at which the NPV=0, by interpolation method through employing the following formula:

$$\text{SW per cent} = \begin{array}{c} \text{Lower per cent} \\ \text{fall in benefits} \end{array} + \begin{array}{c} \text{Difference between} \\ \text{two per cent fall} \\ \text{in benefits} \end{array} \times \dfrac{\begin{array}{c} \text{NPV at lower per cent fall} \\ \text{in benefits} \end{array}}{\begin{array}{c} \text{Absolute difference between} \\ \text{NPVs at two per cent} \\ \text{fall in benefits} \end{array}}$$

Example 10.13

Assume a project with the following costs and benefits (Figures in Rs. Crores). Compute the Switching Value percentage to make the project break even, assuming discount factor: 10 per cent.

Year	Incr Costs (Rs.)	Incr Benefits (Rs.)	df 10%	NB (Rs.)	PW of NB at 10% (or) NPV (Rs.)	Benefits after 30% Fallin NB	NB (Rs.)	PW of NB at 10% df (Rs.)	Benefits after 45% Fallin NB	NB (Rs.)	PW of NB at 10% df (Rs.)
						30% Fall in Benefits			**45% Fall in Benefits**		
1	2.840	0	0.909	−2.840	−2.582	0	−2.84	−2.582	0	−2.840	−2.582
2	10.250	0	0.826	−10.250	−8.471	0	−10.25	−8.471	0	−10.250	−8.471
3	11.460	0	0.751	−11.460	−8.610	0	−11.46	−8.610	0	−11.460	−8.610
4	8.370	0	0.683	−8.370	−5.717	0	−8.37	−5.717	0	−8.370	−5.717
5	4.210	0	0.621	−4.210	−2.614	0	−4.21	−2.614	0	−4.210	−2.614
6	2.090	0	0.564	−2.090	−1.180	0	−2.09	−1.180	0	−2.090	−1.180
7	2.140	6.440	0.513	4.300	2.207	4.508	2.368	1.215	3.542	1.402	0.719
8	2.510	12.320	0.467	9.810	4.576	8.624	6.114	2.852	6.776	4.266	1.990
9	3.750	16.740	0.424	12.990	5.509	11.718	7.968	3.379	9.207	5.457	2.314
10	2.910	15.450	0.386	12.540	4.835	10.815	7.905	3.048	8.4975	5.588	2.154
11	1.060	30.710	0.350	29.650	10.392	21.497	20.437	7.163	16.8905	15.831	5.548
12	1.030	70.260	0.319	69.230	22.059	49.182	48.152	15.343	38.643	37.613	11.985
				NPV	**20.404**		**NPV**	**3.826**		**NPV**	**−4.462**
					Switching value %			36.925			

The switching value of 36.925 percent implies that, if benefits fall by such percentage in the project, the project will become break even. Note that, this switching value (per cent) coincides with the value of percent fall in benefits to make the project break even worked out under BCR. Likewise, the sensitivity analysis can be worked out in the project by assuming different possible changes in the project like:

☆ 10 per cent fall in factor prices and 10 per cent rise in output prices

☆ 10 per cent rise in factor prices and 10 per cent fall in output prices

☆ 10 per cent fall both in factor and output prices

☆ 10 per cent rise both in factor and output prices

☆ 5 per cent rise in factor prices and 10 per cent rise in output prices

☆ 10 per cent rise in factor prices and 5 per cent rise in output prices

IX. Shadow Price

In an economic appraisal of project, the appraiser must necessarily estimate both cash outflows and inflows. In doing this analysis, he seeks to estimate the magnitudes of both benefits and costs of a project in order to establish, whether or not going ahead with the project would increase social welfare. That is, he analyze about NPV, BCR, IRR etc., and in accordance with their bench mark criteria, he decide to accept or reject the project investment. However, not all components of costs and benefits can be quantified in the economic appraisal. For instance, regarding benefits from the project like time saving, lives saved, additional numbers of farm family children educated to particular benchmark standards etc. But to convert such flows into value forms, prices are needed. A question then arises as to which price (or prices) should be used in economic appraisal exercises. In this context, shadow pricing is often used, where the whole purpose is to capture all the variables involved in economic appraisal, and not merely those for which market prices exist. Thus, shadow prices are calculated for those items (goods and services) that do not have a market price, perhaps because, they are set by the Government. The name shadow price was so coined because, this price cannot be observed in a market economy. Dreze and Stern (1990, page 4) defined ' *shadow price of a commodity is its social opportunity cost, i.e. the net loss (gain) associated with having one unit less (more) of it. The losses and gains have to be assessed in terms of a well-defined criterion or objective, which is referred to as 'social welfare'.* For example, the shadow price (the opportunity cost in this case) of one labour employed on a project is given by the reduction in social welfare that would result from his or her employment in the project. Of course, the opportunity cost would vary depending on whether the labour employed in the project was drawn from employment elsewhere or would otherwise have been unemployed. Again assume that, a project has generated one additional unit of education. The value of that additional unit of education to the recipient country is given by the increase in welfare that the society in question would obtain from that additional unit. Thus, shadow price of a commodity or resource is always expressed in terms of its social opportunity cost. Shadow price is otherwise called as Accounting price, because this price will be employed in economic analysis of the project. In general, shadow prices are considered fot three main items in a project's economic appraisal *viz.,*

   i. Determining labour wage rate.

  ii. Determining foreign exchange rate of currency.

 iii. Determining the price of project output traded internationally.

i. Determining Shadow Wage Rate of Labour

For more populous countries like India, the labour are characterized by disguised unemployment *i.e.*, MPP_L is zero or almost equal to zero. In agricultural sector, since production is season bound, the MPP_L is zero during lean season of production and during peak season of production, slowly the marginal value product of labour will increase in the direction of prevailing market wage rate. We know, generally labour can be categorized into two types *viz.*, Unskilled labour and Skilled labour.

    ☆ For unskilled labour, the prevailing market wage rate is taken as shadow ware rate.

    ☆ In case of skilled labour, private sector wage rate is generally taken as shadow wage rate, when compared to Government sector wage rate. This is because, in private sector, the amount of wage rate received by skilled labour is in proportionate with the amount of work turned out, unlike in Government sector. Hence, private sector wage rate is taken as shadow wage rate for skilled labour.

ii. Exchange Rate of a Country's Currency

The true value of a country's currency is the price it fetches, when exchanged with other country's currency. In general, there are fixed exchange rates for exchanging one country currency with other countries currencies. However, the Government may announce official exchange rate favouring certain segments of the population in the country. Following are the examples regarding export and import scenarios of commodities:

    ☆ Indian Government will favour exporters of the country for exporting the commodities to different countries in the international market because, they are the foreign exchange earners for the country. Let us assume, the fixed exchange rate of 1$ = Rs.45. To favour the Indian exporters, Indian Government will announce the official exchange rate for exporters as 1$=Rs.50. So, the value of Indian currency is devalued and this promotes exports from the country.

    ☆ Black market rate of foreign exchange is generally lowered when compared to fixed exchange rate thereby, the Indian rupee is overvalued.

    ☆ To protect the domestic producers from large scale imports, the Government will impose import duties on imported goods. As a result, the market price of imported good will be higher than the domestically produced good and this protects the domestic producers from large scale imports.

Due to these imperfections both in import and export scenarios of commodities, it is very difficult to estimate the shadow price for foreign exchange. Hence, Gittinger opined that, the project analyst should use the shadow price of foreign exchange as suggested by the Central Planning Unit of the country.

iii. Determining of Price of Project Output Traded Internationally

Regarding project output, domestic market price is not taken as a shadow price, because of large scale imperfections in the form of Minimum Support Prices, Government subsidies to various inputs like seeds, fertilizers, electricity, water etc. Hence, international price of the project output will be generally taken as a shadow price, because of the prevalence of perfect market competition.

X. Differences between Financial Analysis and Economic Analysis of Project

There are important differences between financial and economic analyses of project investment. Gittinger describes these differences: '*The point of view taken in the economic analysis is that of society as a whole. the financial analysis takes the viewpoint of the individual participants. The methodology of comparing costs and benefits. is the same for either an economic or financial measurement of project worth, but what is defined as a cost and what is considered a benefit are different*'. No doubt, both financial and economic analyses appraise the outcome or profit of project investment. But, the concept of financial analysis is not the same as economical analysis of project and it is discussed through the following Table 10.7:

Table 10.7: Financial Analysis vis-à-vis Economic Analysis of a Project

Financial Analysis	*Economic Analysis*
1. Financial analysis of project studies the increase in income and employment opportunities at the beneficiary level. So, financial analysis is micro in its scope,	1. Economic analysis of project indicate, how the National Income of country is increased, what extra employment is generated in the country, how best the resources are utilized in the country, what is the effect of project on foreign exchange earning of the country etc. So, economic analysis is macro in its scope.
2. Financial analysis compares benefits and costs to the project investment. That is, financial analysis studies the viability of project from the view point of beneficiaries under prevailing marketing conditions.	2. Economic appraisal is a more comprehensive method of analyzing project costs and benefits than financial appraisal. Economic analysis compares the benefits and costs to the whole economy. That is, economic analysis studies the viability of project from the view point of region or state or nation as a whole.
3. Revenue and Expenditure Statement, Balance Sheet, Source and Application of Fund Statement etc., are prepared to provide most of the information needed for financial analysis.	3. No such statements are prepared in economic analysis.
4. Project costs and benefits are estimated at constant market prices to overcome the effects of inflation. These prices are called as Financial prices.	4. Project costs and benefits are estimated at economic prices or shadow prices by properly adjusting the financial prices with appropriate weightage.
5. No such information is available for financial analysis.	5. Economic analysis provides information on key economic variables like foreign exchange earnings, taxation revenue, employment generation in the country etc.

Contd...

Table 10.7 *–Contd...*

Financial Analysis	Economic Analysis
6. Project appraisal techniques like BCR, IRR, N/K ratio will be studied for discounting costs and benefits at constant market prices. Break even analysis and PBP are the undiscounted measures employed.	6. Project appraisal techniques will be studied by using economic prices or shadow prices. Nominal and Effective rate of protection are the undiscounted measures employed.
7. No such detailed information is needed in financial analysis.	7. Economic analysis deals with all types of investments and costs on infrastructure development, staff housing and transport facilities, construction of schools, hospitals etc. Social cost will be taken into consideration and quantified, if possible.
8. No shadow prices will be used in financial analysis.	8. Shadow price will be used to determine labour wage rate, foreign exchange rate and project output traded internationally.
9. Taxes, custom duties, subsidies, welfare contributions, charitable contributions etc., were included in financial analysis. Taxes in the form of excise duties, customs duties and sales taxes are considered cost, while subsidies and loan receipts are considered as benefits and are fully accounted for in the analysis. Interest payments on borrowed capital and repayment of loans are not included.	9. Taxes (Direct and Indirect), Subsidies, Credit Transactions and Interest are four kinds of transfer payments and they are not included in economic analysis.
10. In financial analysis, interest paid to external suppliers of money may be deducted to derive the benefit stream available to the owners of capital. But, interest imputed or 'paid' to the entity from whose point of view the financial analysis is being done is not treated as a cost because, the interest is part of the total return to the equity capital contributed by the entity. Hence, it is a part of the financial return that entity receives (Gittinger, 1982).	10. In economic analysis, interest on capital is never separated and deducted from the gross returns because it is part of the total return to the capital available to the society as a whole and because it is that total return, including interest, that economic analysis is designed to estimate.

The purpose and objectives of financial and economic appraisals are quite different, so it will not always be the case that a project that is financially viable will be economically viable or a project that is economically viable will be financially viable. Despite these differences, both financial and economic analyses have similar features. Both estimate the net-benefits of a project investment based on the difference between the with-project and the without-project situations. However, it is to be noted that, economic and financial analyses are also complementary. For a project to be economically viable, it must be financially sustainable. If a project is not financially sustainable, there will be no adequate funds to properly operate, maintain and replace assets. As long as the project is economically viable, financial viability is not a concern, as it can be supported through government subsidies.

Project Scheduling or Project Management Techniques

Project scheduling or management involves decision making process regarding planning, organizing, control, direction and co-ordination of various activities that are performed in a project. Project manager, therefore, depends on various tools and techniques that are effective not only for acting on the desired plan, but also capable of identifying the constraints and in controlling or correcting the same. We know, a project consists of several activities that have to be completed and some of them are interdependent *i.e.,* they cannot start before the completion of some other activities. In many situations, project managers face several managerial problems in executing the project, so as to complete it on time and within the allocated budget. In this context, project management provides a number of approaches to cope up with these challenges and among them, two important approaches are Bar Charts and Net works. Bar charts are of two types *viz.,* Gantt Chart and Milestone Chart and Net works include two important techniques *viz.,* Programme Evaluation and Review Technique (PERT) and Critical Path Method (CPM). Let us discuss about these two approaches in-detail here under.

1. Bar Charts

It is a pictorial representation of various tasks or events to be performed for accomplishment of project objectives in the form of bar diagrams. Bar charts are of two types:

i. Gantt Chart

This was developed by Henry L. Gantt in 1917. It is a system of bar charts specifying the starting time and finishing time of an event to be performed in a project. First the project is broken down into a physically identifiable and control units called 'Tasks or Events' represented by bars. These bars are spaced preferably at equi-distance on Y-axis and time element is taken on X-axis. Hence, these charts help the project manager in planning the schedule, progress and completion of events. Here, the length of the bar denotes the required time to complete the task or event and width of the bar do not have any significance.

From the Figure 10.5, it is clear that, Task A should be completed in 4 days *i.e.,* from October 1st to October 4th and another task *i.e.,* procurement of inputs will be performed simultaneously along with Task A and it should get completed from October 2nd to October 4th *i.e.,* in 3 days.

Limitations

☆ Difficult to handle, when more number of tasks are there in the project.

☆ It won't indicate the inter relationships between the tasks.

☆ It won't indicate the time taken for different activities within the same task. If any task is delayed or over runs time, it won't indicate, what is the impact on the project completion date.

ii. Milestone Chart

This chart is an improvement over Gantt chart by introducing different milestones or activities for every task or event. This is because, from Gantt chart, it is very difficult to monitor the progress of every activity in each task. The milestones are represented

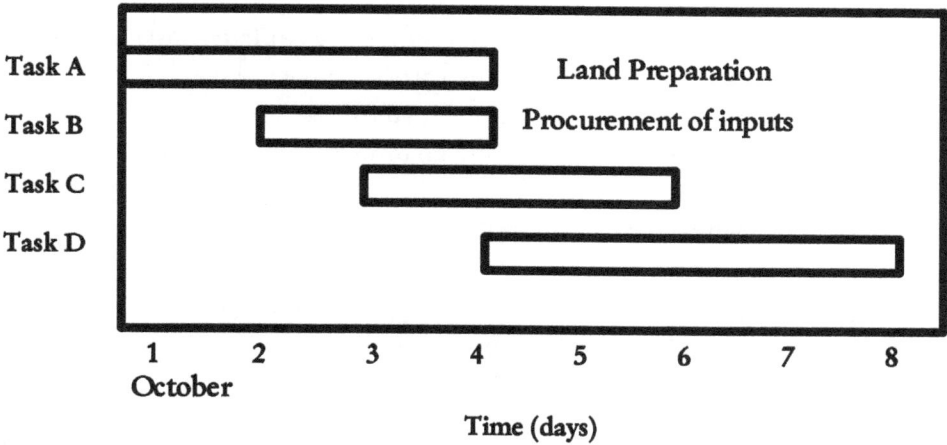

Figure 10.5: Gantt Chart showing schedule of Tasks or Events.

by a circle in the task (Figure 10.6) indicating the completion of a specific activity or milestone of the task by that time. That means, in a milestone chart, a task bar is divided into different milestones or activities and only, if these activities are fulfilled, we can say an event or task is fulfilled.

From the Figure 10.6 it is clear that, in Task A *i.e.* land preparation, there are 2 milestones or activities which are, ploughing and leveling. Indicating a milestone on the day 3 on task bar A indicates that, ploughing activity must complete by 3rd October and leveling by 5th October.

Merits

☆ It helps the project manager to plan the activities accurately within a task or event so that, the entire task can be fulfilled or completed in time.

☆ It also helps to draw the relationship between different activities in an event.

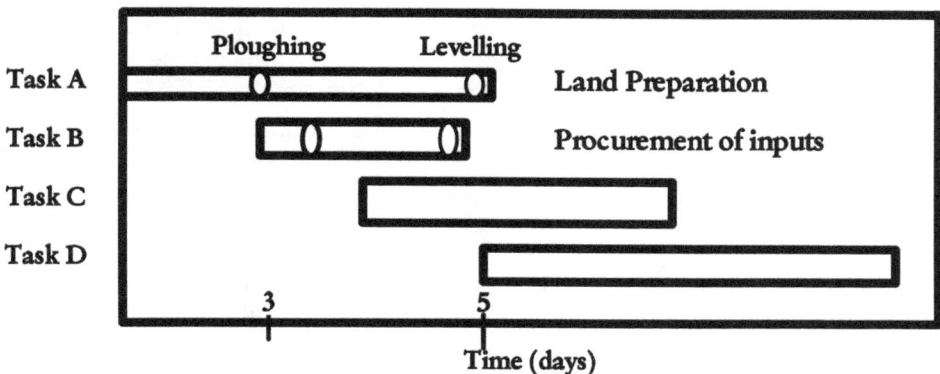

Figure 10.6: Milestone Chart showing Schedule of Tasks or Events and Activities.

Demerits

☆ It does not show any inter-dependence between different tasks or events.

☆ It won't indicate the interdependency of different tasks.

☆ It does not indicate critical activities of the project.

☆ If one activity is delayed, it is difficult to analyze the impact on the project duration

☆ It is very cumbersome to draw this chart for large projects.

2. Net Works

The network is a logical extension of Gantt and Milestone charts incorporating the modifications, so as to illustrate inter-relationship between different tasks and among all the milestones in an entire project. There are two important techniques of network analysis *viz.*, PERT and CPM. Both the techniques are almost similar and developed almost simultaneously during 1956-58. Both CPM and PERT provide the user with project management tools to plan, monitor, and update their project as it progresses. There are many similarities and differences between the two, however.

Similarities between PERT and CPM

These two techniques enjoy the following similarities:

☆ Both follow the same steps and use network diagrams to display the relationships between project activities and to help managers to address questions such as:

❖ What is the total time required to complete the project (the expected total time for PERT)?

❖ What are the start and the completion times for individual activities?

❖ Which critical activities must be completed as scheduled to meet the estimated project completion time?

❖ How much delay can be tolerated for non-critical activities without incurring a delay in the estimated project completion time?

❖ What is the least expensive way to speed up a project to meet a targeted completion time?

❖ PERT also provides answers to the additional questions like what is the probability of completing a project within a given time frame?, what is the variability in the project completion time?

☆ Both are used to plan the scheduling of individual activities that make up a project

☆ They can be used to determine the earliest/latest start and finish times for each activity.

While both techniques serve the same purpose, regarding the fast and effective completion of a project, they are different in many aspects (Table 10.8)

However, now-a-days the two techniques are used synonymously in network analysis and the differences are considered to be historical.

Basic Terms and Concepts Used in Network Analysis

i. Network analysis : This helps to indicate various events and activities to be performed in the project. In this analysis, both CPM and PERT describe the work plan of project. This analysis includes arrows and circles, which indicate the activities and events respectively in the project. The activities and events are laid in a planned sequence of their accomplishments. These activities should get completed to achieve the project objectives in time. In general, there are two types of notations used in the network diagram:

a. Activity-on-Arrow (AoA): In AoA notation, the arrow represents the work to be done and the circle represents an event. AoA network diagram are usually associated with the PERT diagram

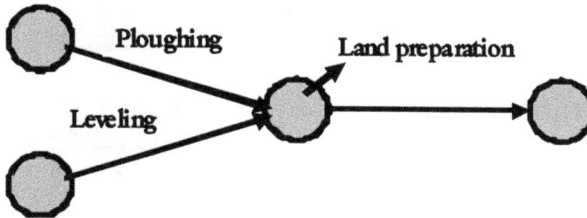

b. Activity-on-Node (AoN): In AoN notation, a box (or node) is used to show the activity to be done and the arrow simply show the sequence in which work is done. Most project management softwares usually uses AON diagram

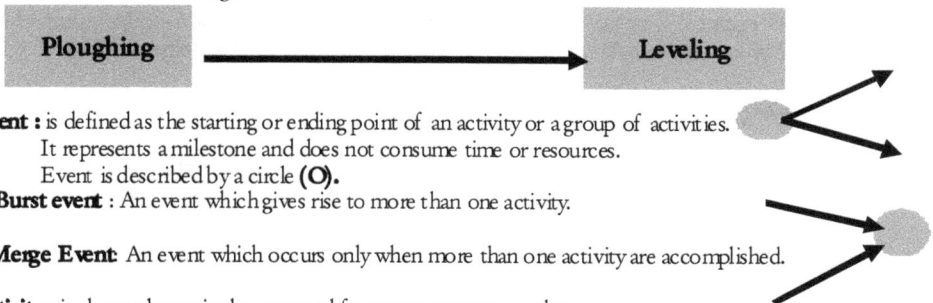

- **Event :** is defined as the starting or ending point of an activity or a group of activities. It represents a milestone and does not consume time or resources. Event is described by a circle **(O).**
  a. Burst event : An event which gives rise to more than one activity.

  b. Merge Event: An event which occurs only when more than one activity are accomplished.

- **Activity :** is the work required to proceed from one event to another. It, therefore, needs both time and resources for its execution and completion. It is represented by an arrow(-----→). Tail represents the start and head the end of activity

- **Path :** An unbroken chain of activity indicated by arrows connecting initial event to other event

- **Critical Path:** The longest time path connecting the critical activities in the project network. The total time on this path is the longest duration of project.

- **Critical Activity:** Activities on the critical path having zero slack/float time. Also called Bottleneck activities. These activities must be started on right time and must be completed in the right time. Otherwise, project completion gets delayed.

- **Earliest Start Time (EST):** EST is the time at which the activity cannot be started earlier than this time. That means it is a waiting time to start next activity i.e., the earliest possible time at which the event can occur. The EST of an activity is the time before which it cannot commence and will not affect the immediate preceding activity.

- **Latest Start Time (LST):** LST is the time, at which the starting of an activity cannot be delayed beyond this time. In other words, it includes non-waiting time. A further delay beyond this time will adversely affect the project duration. The path with shortest time among the path is considered for LST.

- **Earliest Finishing Time (EFT) :** is the minimum time required to complete/finish the activity or is the time at which the activity cannot be finished before this time.

- **Latest Finishing Time (LFT) :** is the time at which the activity must be finished or cannot be extended beyond this time, so as to complete the project in time.

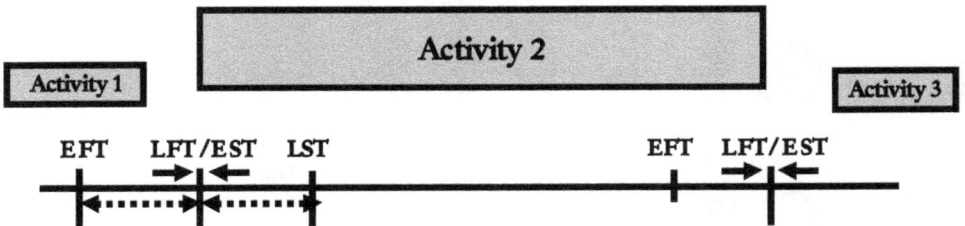

- ***Predecessor event:*** It is an event (or events) that immediately precedes some other event without any other events intervening. It may be the consequence of more than one activity.

- ***Successor event:*** It is an event (or events) that immediately follows some other event without any other events intervening. It may be the consequence of more than one activity.

- ***Fast tracking:*** Refers to performing more critical activities in parallel

- ***Crashing critical path:*** Refers to shortening the duration of critical activities

- ***Slack/Float:*** The amount of spare time available between completion of an activity and beginning of next activity or is the amount of time that a task in a project network can be delayed without causing a delay to project
  Slack/Float = LST – EST = LFT – EFT

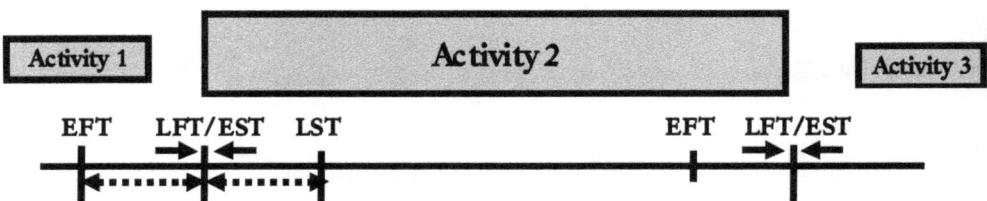

Table 10.8: Differences between CPM and PERT

CPM	PERT
Developed by J. E. Kelly of Remington Raud and M.R. Walker of Dupont Company, as an application to construction project.	Developed by the US Navy Special Project Office for scheduling the R&D activities for Polaris missiles programme.
The time estimates for activities is assumed deterministic in CPM. There is only one estimate of duration. Hence, CPM is a deterministic tool, as it requires one time estimate.	The time estimates for activities are assumed probabilistic in PERT. Three time estimates are used to form a weighted average to estimate expected time based on probabilistic distribution of completion times. Hence, PERT is a probabilistic tool, as it requires three time estimates.
CPM is used where emphasis is on optimizing resource allocation. It can be used to control both time and cost of the project.	PERT is used basically for planning and control of time in the project.
It is activity oriented because, it is built on the basis of activities and the analysis indicates the progress of activities.	It is event oriented because, it is built on the basis of events and the analysis indicates progress of events.
It allows the project manager to crash the activities, in such a way that, the project duration can be shortened at optimal cost.	It allows the project manager to schedule and coordinate various activities so that, the project can be completed in scheduled time.
The activities involved in a construction project are much more predictable, and may not need three estimated completion times. In this case, CPM may be more appropriate, since unlike PERT, CPM also allows for planners to make trade-offs between the cost of the project and the amount of time needed to complete it. So, CPM requires a single deterministic time value for each activity.	PERT is used for projects in which activity times are unknown. For example, take a R&D project, where the amount of time to complete a given task is unpredictable. In such a case, PERT is the best choice, since it allows planners to allocate three estimates for completion times — the most likely, the most optimistic and the most pessimistic. So, PERT treats activity time as a random variable.
CPM is a manual technique.	PERT requires computer solutions.
CPM includes the analysis of the Time-Cost Trade-off.	PERT focuses exclusively on the time variable

Time of Completion of Activity in the Project

PERT technique has the ability to deal with uncertainty in activity completion times. For each activity, this technique usually includes three time estimates:

☆ *Optimistic time (O):* It is the minimum possible time required to accomplish an activity, assuming everything proceeds better than is normally expected. This situation may occur approximately 1 percent of time.

☆ *Most likely or Normal time (M):* It is the model time/normal time required to perform an activity under normal circumstances or the time required to accomplish an activity, assuming everything proceeds as normal.

☆ *Most pessimistic time (P):* It is the maximum possible time required to accomplish an activity assuming everything goes wrong (but excluding major catastrophes). This situation may occur approximately one percent of time.

☆ **Expected/Estimated time (T_E):** It is the best estimate of time required to accomplish an activity, assuming everything proceeds as normal. That is, it is the average time the activity would require, if it is repeated on a number of occasions in a project or the weighted average of the estimated optimistic, most likely and pessimistic time duration of a project activity.

$$T_E = (O + 4M + P)/6$$
$$Variance(T_E) = [(P-O)/6]^2$$

Three time estimates, optimistic, pessimistic and most likely, could the decided on past experiences in execution of similar activities or from the feedback from individuals with relevant experience.

Assuming all the activities following normal distribution, the probability of completion of activity taking the 3 time periods i.e; O, M and P and the variance of computed T_E is shown through the following Figure 10.7:

☆ *Crashing:* It implies shifting resources to reduce slack time so the critical path is as short as possible. Crashing always raises project costs and is typically disruptive – a project should be crashed with caution. The goal of crashing a project is to reduce the duration as much as possible regardless of cost. It is the opposite of relaxing a project.

☆ *Relaxation:* The method that is the opposite of crashing a project. Relaxation is used to lower costs while extending the duration of the project. A typical use of this method is when a project may be relaxed if its resources are needed on higher priority projects. This method involves deliberately lengthening the duration of the project with the specific aim of lowering costs as much as possible.

ii. Network Construction or Drawing a Network Diagram

☆ To draw the network diagram, first the project should be divided into different possible events and activities.

☆ In a project, we have to identify which is the starting event and ending event. (Cont'd Page 773)

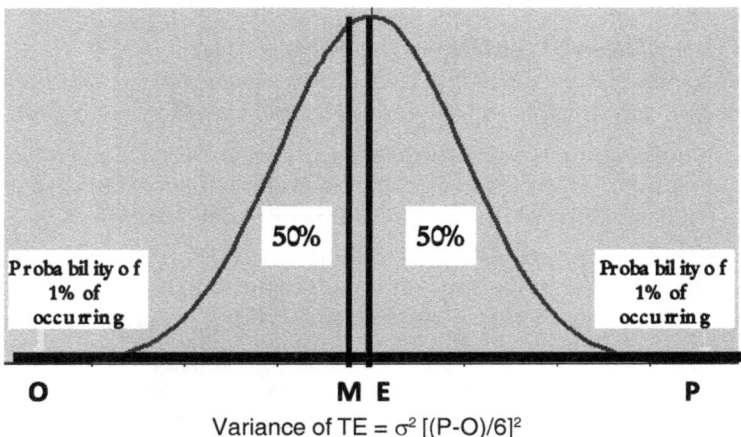

Variance of TE = $\sigma^2 [(P-O)/6]^2$

Figure 10.7: Dispersion of variance of Expected Time estimate (TE).

- **Network :** is a graphical representation of logically **and** sequentially connected events through arrows representing activities of a project. Also called as Arrow diagram
- **Network construction:** First the project is split into activities.
  Starting & Finishing events are then decided
  Then analyze the logical sequence
    - What activities must be completed before a particular activity starts (Predecessor activities)?
    - What activities follow the particular activity (Successor activities)?
    - What activities must be performed concurrently with this activity?
    - Estimate the time for the completion of each activity. (O, M, P)

Network Rules

- Each activity must be represented by one and only arrow
- Arrow and time move from left to right.
- Arrows pointing in opposite direction must be avoided
- Arrows should be kept straight and not curved or bent
- Arrows should not cross each other. If inevitable, the following methods should be followed

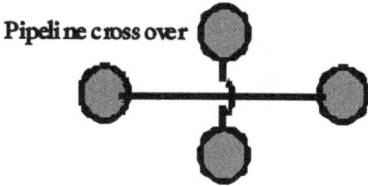

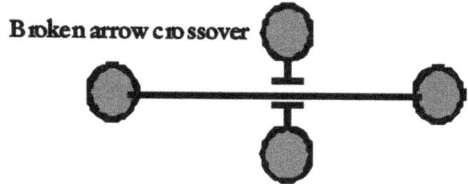

Pipeline cross over

Broken arrow crossover

- Each event should have a distinct (unique) number. The event number should not get replicated. An event can't occur until all the incoming activities are completed
- There should not be any loop in the project network as shown below:

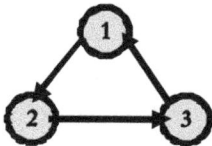

- Not more than one activity can have the same preceding and succeeding event. No two activities can be identified by the same head and tail event

Every activity, except the first and the last, must have at least one preceding and one succeeding activity
- Any number of activities may merge with an event.

- Each activity must have a preceding and a succeeding event

Dummy : An activity which only determines the dependency of one activity over the other, but does not consume any time refers to dummy activity. Dummies are represented by broken/dotted arrow

Assume that, start of C activity depends upon the completion of A and B activities and the start of E activity depends only on the completion of activity B. Figure A shows the wrong presentation and Figure B is the right method through introduction of dummy. No two activities have the same starting and ending event. Among Figures C and D, Figure D representation is correct.

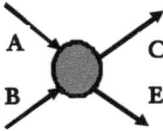

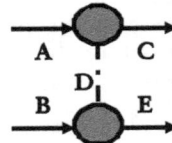

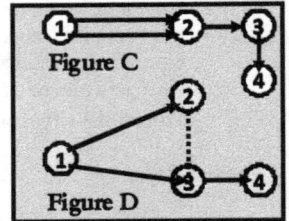

Figure A   **Figure B**

Dangling : It is the situation where events other than initial and final events do not have any successor activity. This is because, all the events except first and last of the whole project must have at least one entering and one leaving activity. By performing this dangling, it costs both time and resource on the part of project because by performing that event, it won't meet the end event. Hence, doing dangling event is merely waste of time & resources

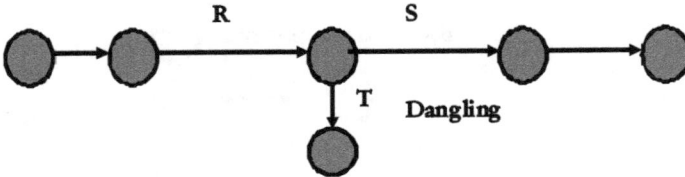

Partial dependency: In certain situations, the starting of an activity depends upon the partial completion of a predessor activity. In such cases, the predessor activity is further broken into two parts and dummy is used to make the connection. Ex: In a pipe line laying project, there are 3 activities ie., digging of 20 metres long trench, laying of 20 metre pipe and filling of the trench. Here, laying of the pipe can be started after 8 metre of trench digging and similarly after 8 metre of pipe laying, filling can be started. This is shown below:

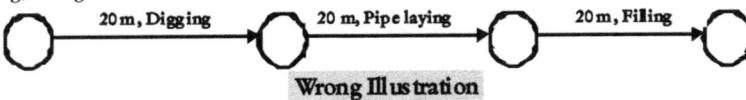

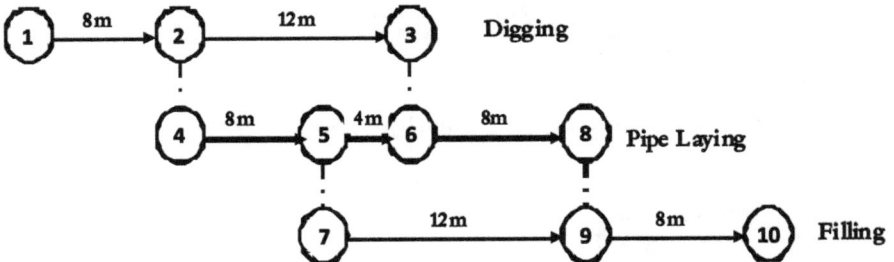

Correct Illustration

☆ Deciding starting and ending event will help the project manager to analyze the logical sequence of different activities. Logical sequence in the sense that, we have to identify three types of activities.

❖ *Predecessor activity:* It is an activity, which should get completed before starting another activity.

❖ *Successor Activity:* It is an activity, which should be started after completing an activity.

❖ *Concurrent Activity:* These are the activities, which should be executed simultaneously in the project. A project with more number of concurrent activities will have less duration for its completion. That is, concurrent activities are accomplished simultaneously. Note that, an activity may be a predecessor or successor to another activity or it may be concurrent with one or more activities.

☆ After identifying different activities, then assume the time duration for completion of each activity.

☆ In case of CPM method, we will give a single value for time period implying that it is a deterministic tool or approach.

☆ In case of PERT technique, we will assume 3 different time periods *i.e.*, O, M, and P for completing an activity based on weighted average and we estimate T_E values. Hence, we can say PERT technique is probabilistic tool/ approach.

iii. Steps involved in Network Analysis include:

1. To prepare the list of activities
2. Define the inter-relationship among the activities
3. Estimate the activity duration
4. Assemble the activities in the form of a flow diagram
5. Draw the network diagram
6. Analyze the network *i.e.* compute EST and LST; EFT and LFT, float, identify critical activities and critical path.

Step 1- Prepare the List of Activities

The project may involve a number of activities (Table 10.9) to be performed and each activity represents the work to be performed in the project, which will consume both time and resources. Once an activity is completed, an event will occur in the project. An activity in a project characterized by:

☆ It should be cost effective *i.e.* should consume less amount of money for its execution.

☆ It should have specific time period for its completion. That means, it should have a specific starting point and a specific ending point.

☆ The activity should be measurable (costable) or quantifiable.

Table 10.9: List of Activities in the Project with their Codes

Sl.No	Activity	Code/Symbol
1.	Land surveying	A
2.	Plan preparation	B
3.	Rock blasting	C
4.	Land leveling	D
5.	Drainage channel digging	E
6.	Stone pitching of drainage channel	F
7.	Digging wells	G
8.	Laying of irrigation lines	H
9.	Construction of pump house	I
10.	Procurement of pumps	J
11.	Installation of pumps	K

☆ For convenient execution of the project, an event is sub-divided into various activities and each activity is given an alphabetical symbol/code.

☆ When the number of activities is more, alphanumeric/multi-alphabet codes can be used.

☆ In a simple project, it may be easier to identify the activities. In complex projects, activities are identified and they can be split into different sub-projects. For example, the activities of a watershed project could be broken down into sub-projects such as agricultural subprojects, soil and water conservation sub-projects, afforestation sub-project etc. For each sub-project, again the activities will be identified. Depending on the size and nature of sub-project, they can be further divided into sub-sub projects.

Step 2 - Define the Inter-Relationship among the Activities

After identifying the activities in a project, analyze the inter-relationship between the activities. Generally, three types of relationships will occur among the activities:

☆ *Preceding activity:* Preceding activity for an activity is its immediate predecessor. That means, a preceding activity must be completed before starting a succeeding activity or new activity. In the Table 10.10, land surveying is the preceding activity for rock blasting. That means, rock blasting is done after completing land surveying. Only terminating activity in the project will not be considered as a preceding activity and all other activities must appear at least once as a preceding activity in the project.

☆ *Succeeding activity:* Succeeding activity is one that immediately starts after the completion of preceding activity. In the Table 10.10, rock blasting is the succeeding activity for land surveying. That means, after completion of land surveying only rock blasting starts.

☆ *Concurrent or Competing activities:* These are the activities, which are performed simultaneously in a project.

The table that shows the relationship between the activities along with their preceding activities is called Precedence table (Table 10.10).

Table 10.10: Precedence Table of Activities

Sl.No.	Activity	Code	Preceding Activity
1.	Land surveying	A	—-
2.	Plan preparation	B	—-
3.	Rock blasting	C	A
4.	Land leveling	D	A
5.	Drainage channel digging	E	A
6.	Stone pitching of drainage channel	F	B,C
7.	Digging wells	G	B,C
8.	Laying of irrigation lines	H	E,F
9.	Construction of pump house	I	E,F
10.	Procurement of pumps	J	D,H
11.	Installation of pumps	K	G,I

Step 3: Estimate the Activity Duration

In PERT technique, we generally use three different time periods for activity completion *i.e.*, Optimistic, Most likely and Pessimistic and based on probabilities, we estimate the expected time T_E (Table 10.11). However, in case of CPM, we consider only one time period. Hence, we can say PERT is a probabilistic tool (Table 10.11) and CPM method is a deterministic tool.

Ex: Estimation of Expected Time for the Activity 'Land Surveying'

For this activity, the assumed three time estimates *i.e.*, Optimistic, Most likely and Pessimistic times are 4, 6 and 8 days respectively *i.e.*, O = 4, M = 6, and P = 8. The T_E is given by:

$$T_E = [(O+4M+P)/6] = (4 + 4*6 + 8)/6 = (4+24+8)/6 = (36)/6 = 6 \text{ days}$$

Table 10.11: Computation of T_E of Activities

Activity	Preceding Activity	Optimistic Time (O)	Most likely Time (M)	Pessimistic Time (P)	Expected Time (T_E) (O+4M+P)/6
A (Land surveying)	—	4	6	8	6
B	—	1	4.5	5	4
C	A	3	3	3	3
D	A	4	5	6	5
E	A	0.5	1	1.5	1
F	B,C	3	4	5	4
G	B,C	1	1.5	5	2
H	E,F	5	6	7	6
I	E,F	2	5	8	5
J	D,H	2.5	2.75	4.5	3
K	G,I	3	5	7	5

Step 4 - Assemble the Activities in the Form of a Flow Diagram

Having decided on activities, their inter-relationship and duration (expected time of each activity), the next step is to draw the flow diagram (Figure 10.8) of the project based on preceding and succeeding activities.

☆ In a flow chart, the activity and its duration is shown in a box.

☆ The boxes are connected with lines based on preceding and succeeding activity relationship.

☆ However, the critical path for the project can be identified by comparing the various path lengths (sum of activity time from start to finish, on any path from start to end).

☆ The longest path in the chart is the critical path.

☆ The flow charts do not give details like start and completion time of each activity unless it is super imposed on a calendar. If it is not superimposed on calendar, it does not facilitate computation of slacks.

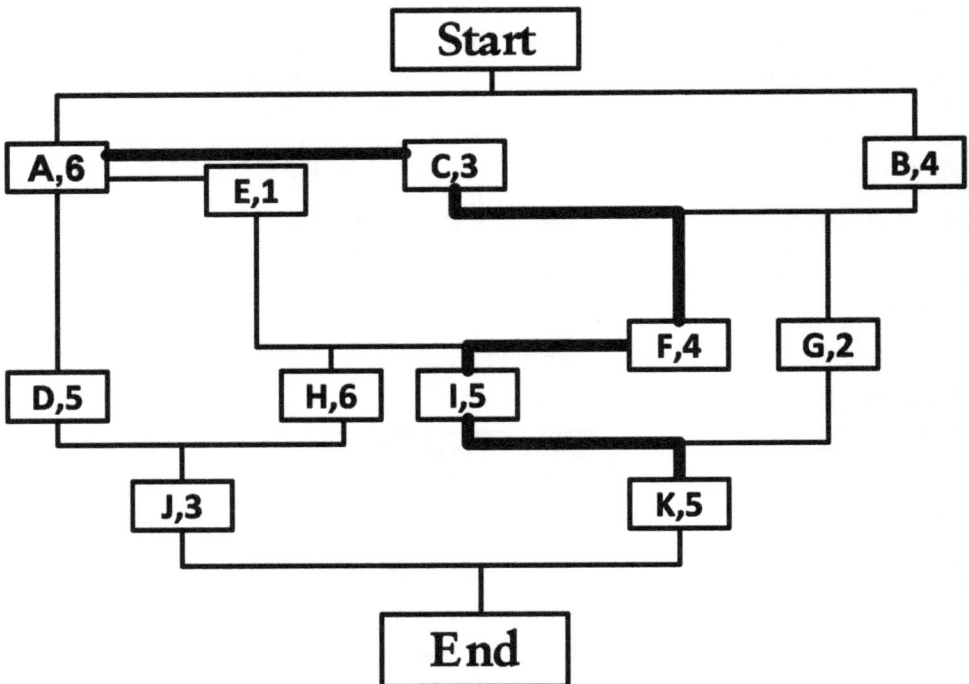

Figure 10.8: Flow Diagram.

Step 5 - Draw the network diagram

- Shows the precedence and successor relationship among the activities.
- An arrow generally represents activity in the diagram, while a circle represents event.
- Each activity starts with an event and end in an event. Number indicates an event and alphabet indicates an activity.
- Activities in a project are performed either sequentially one after another or they are undertaken concurrently i.e. simultaneously.
- To draw the network, it requires the knowledge of specifying which activities must be completed before other activities can be started, which activities immediately succeed other activities and which activities can be performed in parallel.

Possible combinations of activities

	Activity "A" is preceding activity of "B". i.e activity "A" need to be completed before start of activity "B". In other words "B" starts after "A" is finished.
	Activity "A" and "B" are concurrent. Activity "C" cannot start until both the activities "A" and "B" are completed.

	Activity "B" and "C" are concurrent activities. Any one of these cannot start until activity "A" is completed.
	Neither activity C nor D can start until both the activities A and B are completed. But, C and D can start independently.
	Activity D cannot begin until both A and C are completed. But B can start after A is complete. The activity Z, represented by dashed arrow, is a dummy activity. This does not consume any resource i.e., have zero time and zero cost. This only represents the logical relation among the activities.

Step 6 - Analyze Net Work

Network analysis helps the manager to calculate start time, finishing time, slack and identify critical activities in a project and thereby, critical path of the project. The starting and finishing time for each individual activity is calculated through the network analysis. The duration of project is not necessarily the simple arithmetical sum of the individual activity durations. This is so because, several activities occur concurrently in the project. Project duration would be equal to the sum of all individual activity durations only when all the activities in the project are sequential.

i. Components of Net Work Analysis

From the network diagram (Figure 10.9) the following are the important components we can analyze:

- a. Event numbering
- b. Computation of the EST, EFT, LST and LFT to identify critical path
- c. Computation of Slack or Float
- d. Identification of critical activities
- e. Identification of Critical Path and duration
- f. Estimation of variance of critical activities
- g. Estimation of the probability for completion of the project in right time

a. Event Numbering

It is very important to assign a number for every event because, they should not get repeated in the project. There are two ways of numbering the events:

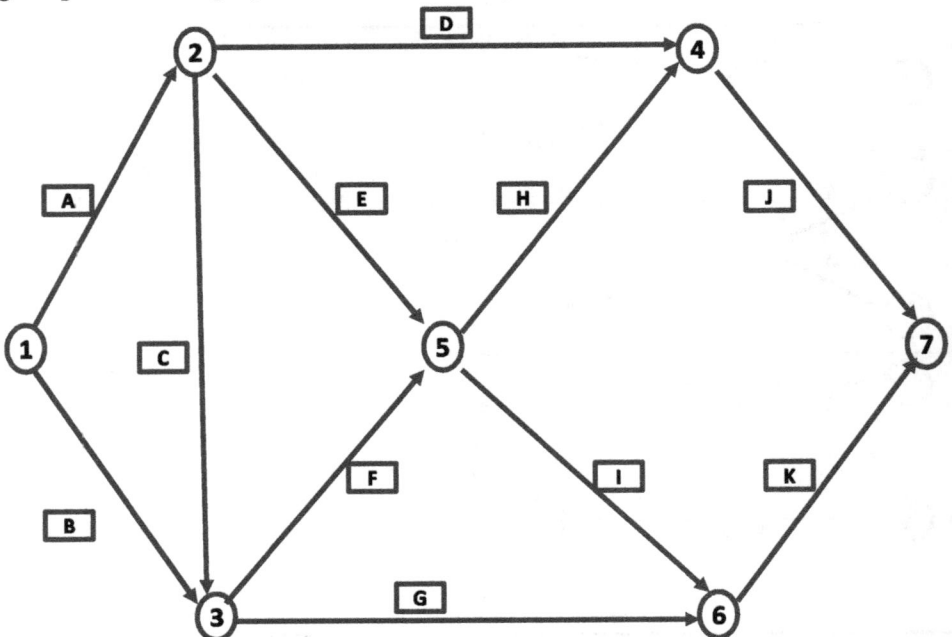

Figure 10.9: Network Diagram.

☆ *Sequential numbering system:* This is suitable for small projects, where the number of events is low. In this system, the activities are sequentially numbered such that, the head event/succeeding event will bear a higher number than the tail/preceding event.

☆ *Random/Skip numbering method:* This is suitable in case of large projects or complex projects, where more number of events are involved. This system facilitates to number extra events, if they are introduced during the course of project implementation and this is not possible in case of sequential numbering system.

In sequential numbering system, if any new or event is to be introduced in the project during its implementation, the events succeeding after the newly introduced event should again renumbered. So, to avoid this difficulty generally Skip numbering (Figure 10.10) or Random numbering system is followed in case of large projects.

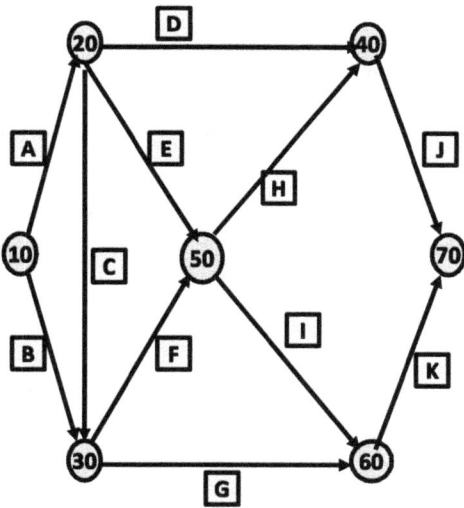

Figure 10.10: Skip Numbering.

Fulkerson's Rule

☆ First identify the initial event and number it as '1' (Figure 10.11). An initial event is an event, which has arrows emerging out of it and none entering into it.

☆ Now delete all the arrows emerging out of that event already numbered and this will create at least one new initial event with no other arrows entering into it. If more than one initial events are created, then according to the priority assign the number.

☆ This procedure is continued till a final event is identified and numbered. Final event is an event, which has no arrows emerging out of it.

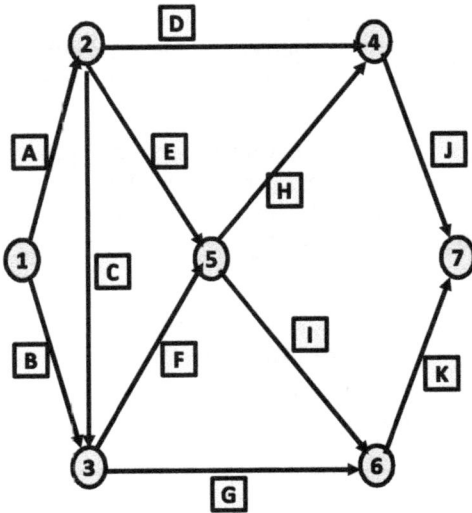

Initial event 1 is identified, as there are no incoming arrows into it.

•Delete the arrows A and B. This will create one more initial event 2.

• Again delete the arrows from 2 *i.e.*, C, D and E from event 2, and this will create new event 3.

• Again delete the arrows from event 3 *i.e.*, G and F and this will create new initial event 5.

• From event 5, delete H & I arrows, this will create two new initial events 4 & 6.

• Again delete J & K arrows from 4 and 6 events, and it leads to new initial event 7, which is the terminating/end event, because no arrows emerge out of it.

This sequential numbering system is convenient when project is simple & small with less number of activities.

Figure 10.11: Fulkerson's Rule.

b. *Computation of EST and EFT; LST and LFT to Identify Critical Path*

☆ The EST is calculated first in the forward pass beginning from the start event (Table 10.12).

☆ For the start event, the EST is always set to zero because, there is no preceding event.

☆ The EST at the last event is generally considered to be the project duration *i.e.*, the minimum time required for project completion (longest duration equal to critical path duration).

☆ EST and LST are equal at the end event.

☆ LST for events is calculated through backward pass starting from the end event.

Table 10.12: Steps Involved in Computation EST and LST

EST	LST
Through forward pass *i.e.*, from first event	Through backward pass, *i.e.*, from last event
Calculation begins from start event	Calculation stars from end event
Proceeds from left to right	Proceeds from right to left
At start event, EST is Zero	At end event, LST equals to EST
Adding the activity time to EST	Subtracting the activity time from LST
At a merge event, take maximum value	At a burst event, take minimum value

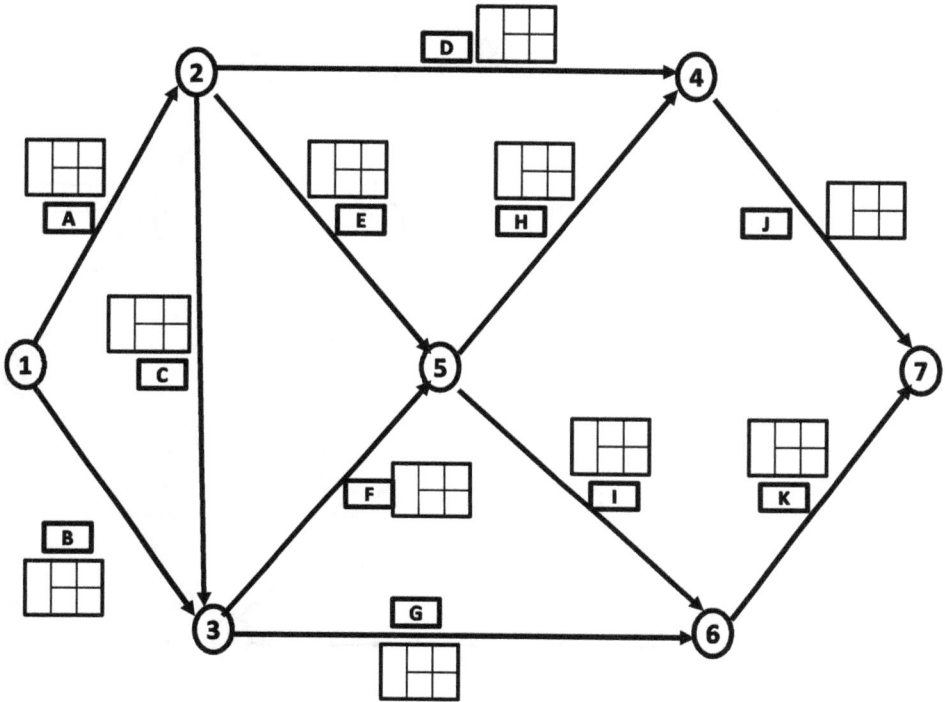

Figure 10.12: Outline of a Network Diagram.

Table 10.13: Computation of T_E for different Activities (PERT)

Activity	Preceding Activity	Optimistic Time (O)	Most Likely Time (M)	Pessimistic Time (P)	Estimated Time (T_E) (O+4M+P)/6
A	—-	4	6	8	6
B	—-	1	4.5	5	4
C	A	3	3	3	3
D	A	4	5	6	5
E	A	0.5	1	1.5	1
F	B,C	3	4	5	4
G	B,C	1	1.5	5	2
H	E,F	5	6	7	6
I	E,F	2	5	8	5
J	D,H	2.5	2.75	4.5	3
K	G,I	3	5	7	5

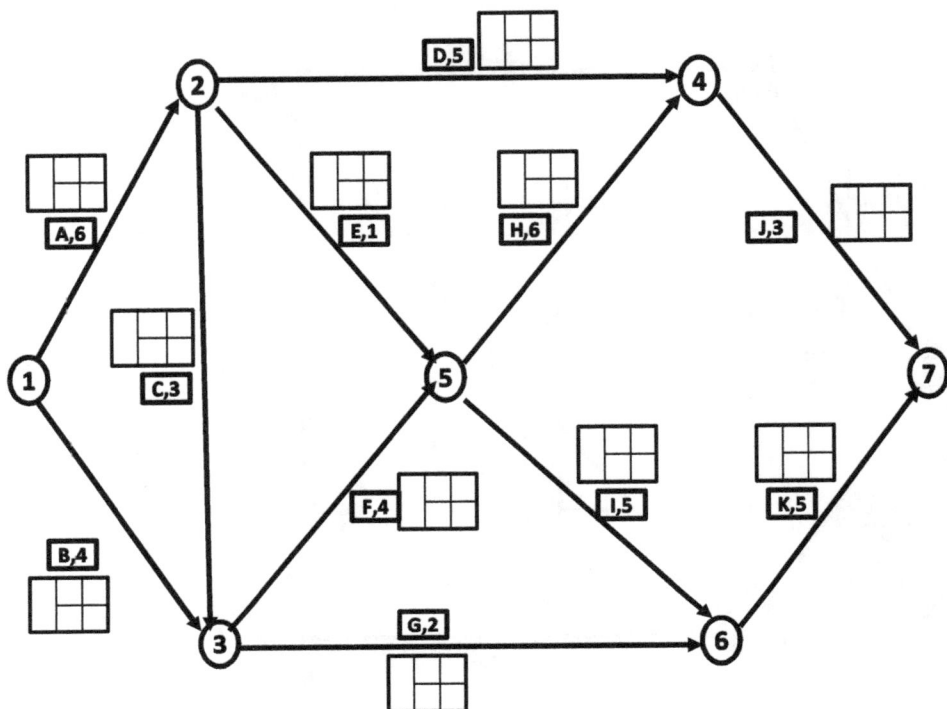

Figure 10.13: Network Diagram Showing Activities with their Respective TE.

Computation of EST and EFT

EST of an event = EST of preceding event + Activity duration

EFT of an event = EFT of preceding event + Activity duration

☆ EST at start activity is zero (Table 10.14 and Figure 10.14), because it is arising from the starting event and there is no preceding activity.

☆ To compute EFT at event number 2, add 6 to zero *i.e.*, the duration of activity A to zero. So, EST of activity A is 0 and EFT is 6. This 6 is the EST for activities C,D,E, because they arise from event 2.

☆ Compute EFT at event number 3, (merge event of B and C). Since, event 3 is a merge event of activities B and C, there are two EFT values *i.e.*, 4 and 9, (0+4 of Activity B and 6+3 of Activity C) and select MAXIMUM, *i.e.* 9. This is the EST value for activities F and G, because they arise from event 3.

☆ Since, event 5 is also a merge event of activities E and F, there are two EFT values *i.e.*, 7 and 13, of E and F respectively and select MAXIMUM, *i.e.*, 13. This is the EST value for activities H and I because, they arise from event 5.

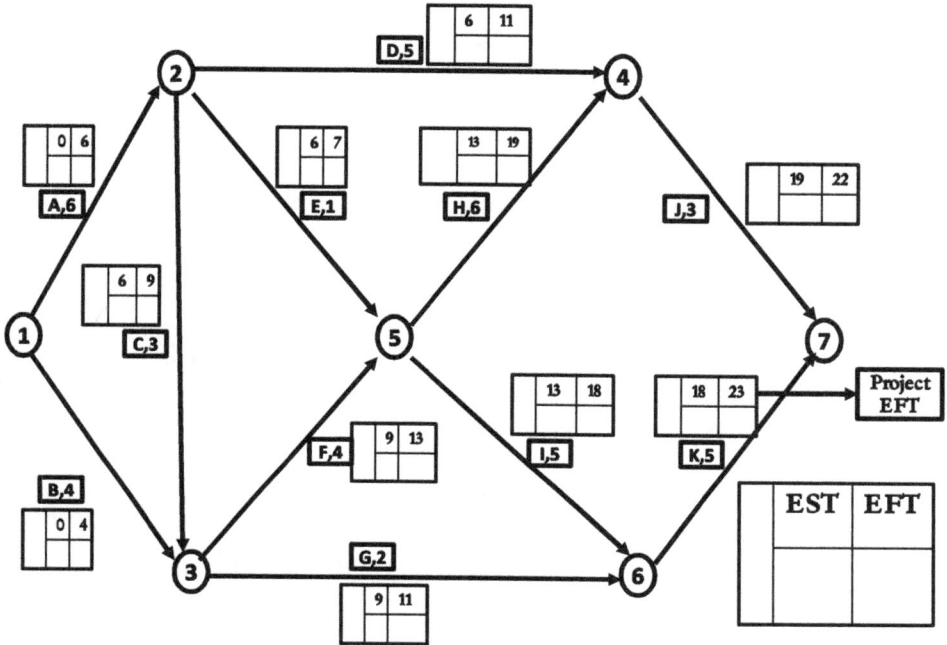

Figure 10.14: Network Diagram Showing Activities with their Respective TE , EST and EFT.

Table 10.14: Computation of EST and EFT

Activity No.	Activity duration	EST	EFT
A	6	0	6
B	4	0	4
C	3	6	9
D	5	6	11
E	1	6	7
F	4	9	13
G	2	9	11
H	6	13	19
I	5	13	18
J	3	19	22
K	5	18	23

☆ Since, event 4 is also a merge event of activities D and H, there are two EFT values *i.e.*, 11 and 19, of D and H respectively and select MAXIMUM, *i.e.*, 19. This is the EST value for activity J because, it arise from event 4.

☆ Event 6 is also a merge event of activities G and I, there are two EFT values *i.e.*, 11 and 18, and select MAXIMUM, *i.e.*, 18. This is the EST value for activity K because, it arise from event 6.

☆ Event 7 is also a merge event of activities J and K, there are two EFT values *i.e.*, 22 and 23, and select MAXIMUM, *i.e.*, 23. Since event 7 is the end event of project, this EFT 23 is project's EFT.

Computation of LST and LFT

LST of an event = LFT of succeeding event - Activity duration

(LST = LFT of 7th event – Activity duration)

LFT of an event = LST preceding activity + Activity duration

(LFT = LST of 6th event + Activity duration)

☆ To compute LST and LFT proceed from backward *i.e.* from end event 7 (Table 10.15 and Figure 10.15). EFT of project is always equal to LFT because, project should get completed without any delay. *i.e.*, at the end event EFT = LFT.

☆ For activities J and K, LFT is same because they leave the same event 7. LST = LFT – Activity duration *i.e.*, 20 and 18 for J and K respectively.

❖ LST_J= 23-3=20, LST_K=23-5=18

☆ This LST 18 of K activity is the LFT for I and G activities, as they leave the same event 6.

❖ LST_I= 18-5=13, LST_G=18-2=16

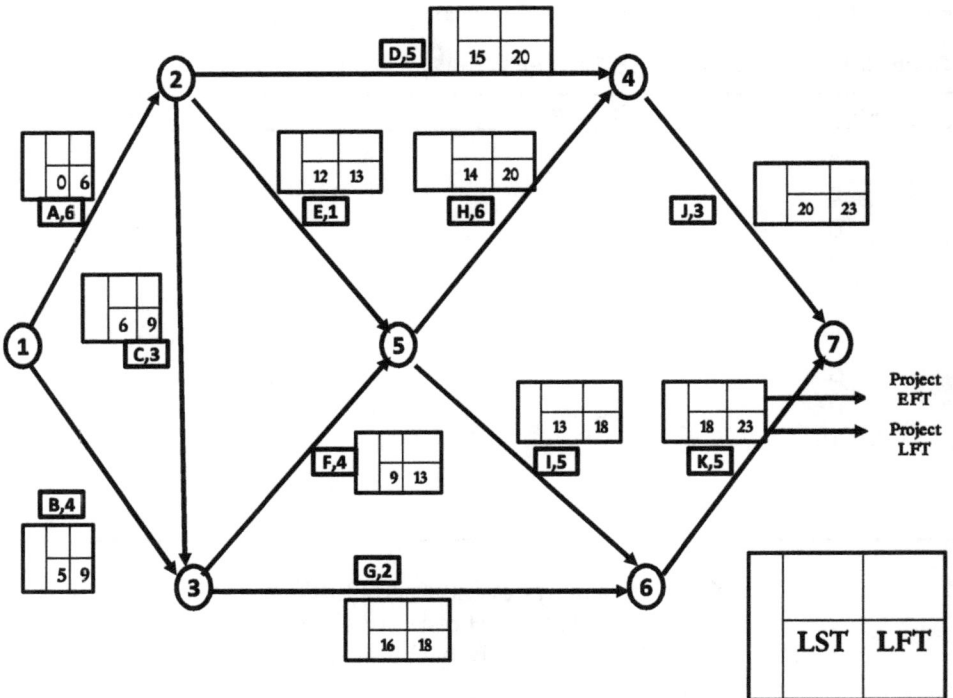

Figure 10.15: Network Diagram Showing Activities with their Respective TE , LST and LFT.

☆ The LST 20 of J activity is the LFT for D and H activities, as they leave the same event 4.

❖ $LST_D=20-5=15$, $LST_H=20-6=14$

☆ Since event 5 is the burst event with respect to H and I activities, there will be two LST values *i.e.* 14 and 13 for H and I activities respectively and select MINIMUM *i.e.* 13. This forms the LFT for F and E activities leaving event 5.

☆ Calculate LST values for F and E *i.e.* 9 and 12. $LST_F=13-4=9$, $LST_E=13-1=12$.

☆ Since event 3 is the burst event with respect to F and G activities, there will be two LST values, *i.e.*, 9 and 16 for F and G activities respectively and select MINIMUM *i.e.* 9. This forms the LFT for C and B activities leaving event 3. $LST_C=9-3=6$, $LST_B=9-4=5$.

☆ Since event 2 is the burst event with respect to E, D and C activities, there will be three LST values *i.e.* 12, 15 and 6 for E, D and C activities respectively and select MINIMUM *i.e.* 6. This forms the LFT value for A activity leaving event 2.

☆ Calculate LST values for A and B *i.e.* $LST_A=6-6=0$, $LST_B=9-4=5$.

Table 10.15: Computation of LST and LFT

Activity No.	Activity Duration	LST	LFT
A	6	0	6
B	4	5	9
C	3	6	9
D	5	15	20
E	1	12	13
F	4	9	13
G	2	16	18
H	6	14	20
I	5	13	18
J	3	20	23
K	5	18	23

Now, Table 10.16 and Figure 10.16 presents the overall picture about EST, EFT, LST and LFT of all the activities in the project.

c. Computation of Float/Slack/Cushion/Margin

Slack refers to the events and is used in PERT analysis. Float refers to activities and is used in CPM analysis. Slack/Float indicates the free/spare time associated with an event/activity. It is the time available for an activity in addition to its duration time. These are important for smoothening the resource utilization in a project. It is the length of time an activity can be delayed without delaying the entire project. When activities have no float time, it implies they cannot be delayed and if they are delayed, the project duration gets affected. On the critical path, there are critical

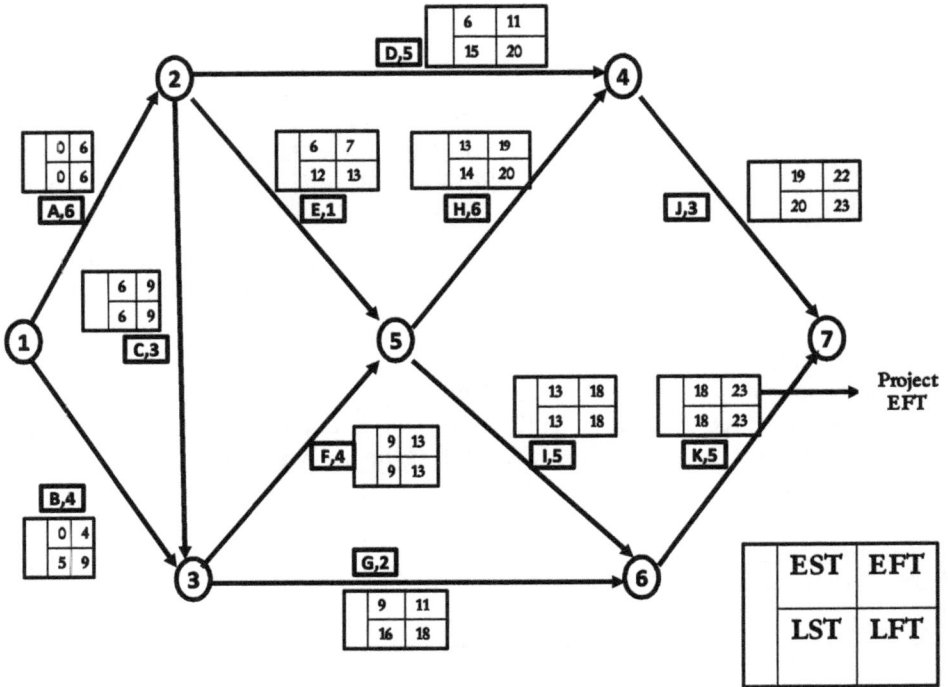

Figure 10.16: Network Diagram Showing Activities with their Respective TE , EST, EFT, LST and LFT.

Table 10.16: Computation of EST, EFT, LST and LFT

Activity No.	EST	EFT	LST	LFT
A	0	6	0	6
B	0	4	5	9
C	6	9	6	9
D	6	11	15	20
E	6	7	12	13
F	9	13	9	13
G	9	11	16	18
H	13	19	14	20
I	13	18	13	18
J	19	22	20	23
K	18	23	18	23

activities and for these, float is zero. Since, float is zero, they must be completed in time otherwise, total project duration will get affected. Since, every activity has different start and finishing times, there are 3 types of floats *viz.*, Total Float, Free Float and Independent Float.

☆ *Total float:* It is the amount of spare time available between completion of an activity and beginning of next activity or it is the amount of time that an event in a project network can be delayed without causing a delay to project or it is the difference between maximum time available to perform the activity and activity duration. Total Slack/Float = LST – EST = LFT – EFT

☆ *Free float:* It is the time by which an activity may be delayed or extended without delaying the start of any succeeding activity or it is the portion of total float within which an activity can be manipulated without affecting the floats of the subsequent activities.

Free Float = EST of succeeding activity – EFT of the activity for which free float is to be calculated

Free float = LFT – EFT for the activity

Free float = Total float – Head event float

Free float is found at merge events. If an activity has free float, the resources from such activity can be re-allocated to an activity on the critical path. In this way, total resources and project time may remain unaffected. For dummy activity, free float will be shown as zero, even if it works out as positive value.

☆ *Independent float (IF):* It is that portion of total float within which an activity can be delayed for start without affecting the floats of the preceding activities.

Independent Float = EST of succeeding activity – LFT of preceding activity – Duration of the activity for which independent float is to be calculated.

Independent Float = Free float – Tail event slack

If independent float is negative, it may be taken as zero

So, Total Float > Free float > Independent float

Considering the above formulae, Total Float, Free float and Independent float are calculated for all the activities and are shown through Table 10.17 and Figure 10.17.

d. Identification of Critical Activities

Critical activities are those activities, which determine the overall duration of the project. The critical activities of the project are identified by the total slack or total float *i.e.*, the difference between LST and EST or LFT – EFT. For critical activities, this total float is zero *i.e.*, the value of LST and EST or LFT and EFT are equal. For these critical activities, there should not be any delay in the execution and completion, as they form the critical path of the project *i.e.*, these activities must be completed in time as per their activity duration. If any critical activity is delayed, it will affect the entire project thereby, entire project gets delayed. In the earlier table for activities A, C, F, I and K, the Total slack or Float is zero implying these activities are critical activities. Sometimes, critical activities are also mentioned in terms of events *i.e.*, 1,2,3,5,6 and 7 events are critical events. In the Table 10.18, for activities A,C,F,I and K, the total float is zero and hence, A,C,F,I and K represent critical activities for the project. In terms of events, 1,2,3,5,6 and 7 are the critical events (Figure 10.18).

Table 10.17: Computation of different Types of Slacks/Floats

Activity (A)	Preceeding Activity (B)	Time (TE) (C)	EST (D)	EFT (E)	LST (F)	LFT (G)	Total Slack/ Float	Free Float	Independent Float
A	—	6	0	6	0	6	0*	6-6=0	6-0-6=0
B	—	4	0	4	5	9	5	9-4=5	9-0-4=5
C	A	3	6	9	6	9	0*	9-9=0	9-6-3=0
D	A	5	6	11	15	20	9	19-11=8	19-6-5=8
E	A	1	6	7	12	13	6	13-7=6	13-6-1=6
F	B,C	4	9	13	9	13	0*	13-13=0	13-9-4=0
G	B,C	2	9	11	16	18	7	18-11=7	18-9-2=0
H	E,F	6	13	19	14	20	1	19-19=0	19-13-6=0
I	E,F	5	13	18	13	18	0*	18-18=0	18-13-5=0
J	D,H	3	19	22	20	23	1	0	0-20-3=0
K	G,I	5	18	23	18	23	0*	0	0-18-5=0

Total float = LST – EST (or) LFT – EFT

Free Float = EST of succeeding activity – EFT of the activity for which free float is to be calculated

Independent float = EST of succeeding activity – LFT of preceeding activity – Activity duration for which IF is to be calculated

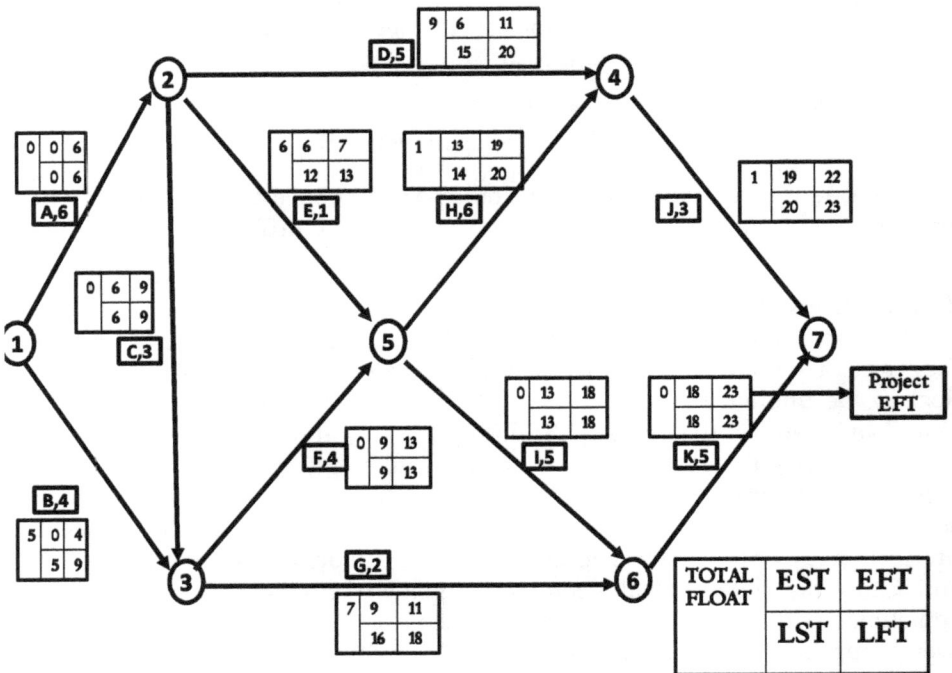

Figure 10.17: Network Diagram Showing Activities with their Respective TE , EST, EFT, LST, LFT and Total Float.

Table 10.18: Identification of Critical Activities

Activity	EST	EFT	LST	LFT	Total Slack/Total Float (LST-EST) = (LFT-EFT)	Critical Activity
A	0	**6**	0	6	**0***	**Critical**
B	0	**4**	5	9	5	
C	6	**9**	6	9	**0***	**Critical**
D	6	**11**	15	20	9	
E	6	**7**	12	13	6	
F	9	**13**	9	13	**0***	**Critical**
G	9	**11**	16	18	7	
H	13	**19**	14	20	1	
I	13	**18**	13	18	**0***	**Critical**
J	19	**22**	20	23	1	
K	18	**23**	18	23	**0***	**Critical**

A – C – F – I – K   are the critical activities.   (1,2,3,5,6,7 events).

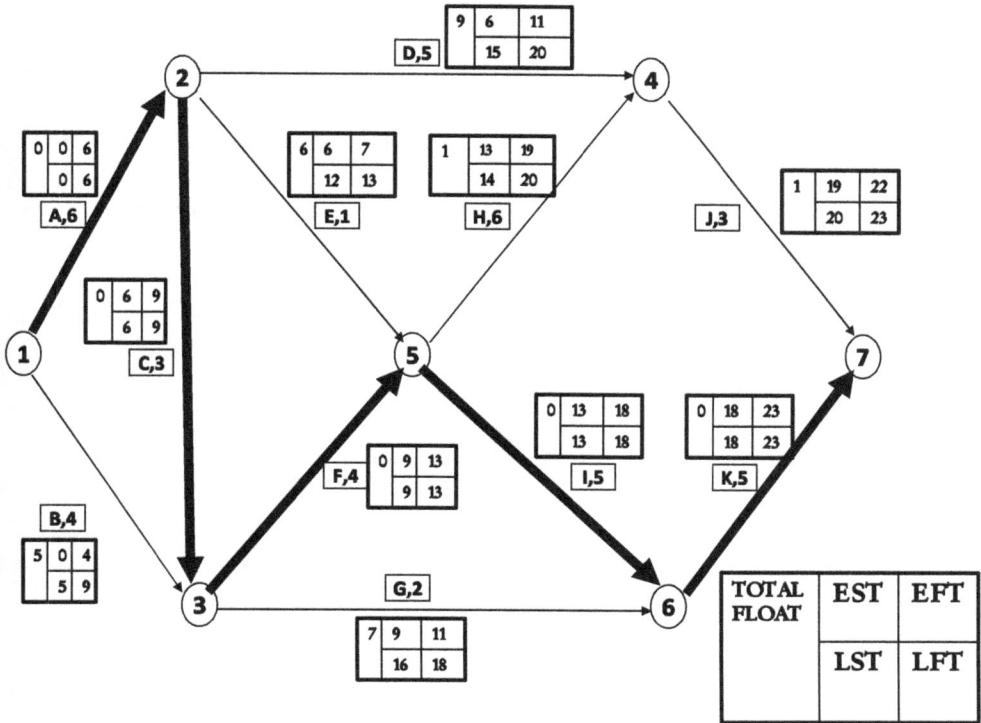

Figure 10.18: Network Diagram Showing Critical Activities (A,C,F,I and K) in the Project .

e. Identification of Critical Path and Duration

The critical path is the chain of critical activities in a network from start to end *i.e.* the path joining all the critical events. It is also the longest path from start to end of the project network. Comparing all the possible path lengths, we can identify the critical path (Flow diagram - Figure 10.8 with longest duration).

Thus, if we connect all the critical activities in a network from start to end of the project, it implies critical path. So, critical path indicates the longest duration of the project and it is the minimum time required for the project from start to end *i.e.*, for its completion.

☆ Instead of working out EST, LST, EFT, LFT and total float for different activities of the project, critical path can also be find out by comparing all possible path lengths from start to end taking the activity duration into consideration and this information is available from the flow diagram (Figure 10.8).

☆ Since, A-C-F-I-K path denotes highest duration of 23 weeks, so A-C-F-I-K represent critical path of the project (Table 10.19).

It is clear that,

☆ The critical path time is the longest duration of the project. It is the minimum time required for the project for its completion.

☆ The critical path is denoted by denoting the critical activities on the path (A – C – F – I – K).

☆ The critical path of the project is denoted in terms of the event numbers (1- 2 – 3 – 5 – 6 - 7).

☆ It is quite possible that, a project can have multiple critical paths. In such case, the duration of all the critical paths will be equal.

Table 10.19: Identification of Critical Path and Critical Activities from Flow Diagram (Figure 10.8)

Sl.No.	Path	Duration (Weeks)
1.	A – D - J	6+5+3 = 14
2.	B – G – K	4+2+5 = 11
3.	A – C – F – I – K	6+3+4+5+5 = 23
4.	A – C – G - K	6+3+2+5 = 16
5.	A – E – I - K	6+1+5+5 = 17
6.	A – E – H - J	6+1+6+3 = 16
7.	A – C – F – H - J	6+3+4+6+3 = 22

Importance of Critical Path

☆ Since there is no total slack or total float for any critical activity on the critical path, any delay in the execution of critical activity will delay the project. If any critical activity is delayed, it should be recovered during the downstream critical activities of the project and this is possible by increasing the resource usage on the downstream critical activities by resorting to project crashing.

☆ Since, the execution of critical activities on time is essential for the project, these activities must receive a hard look or a special attention from the project manager to complete them in right time.

☆ By identifying critical activities or critical path in advance, it will help the project manager to plan his resource procurement in advance for the execution of these critical activities.

☆ If the project manager wants to reduce total duration of the project, it is sufficient for him to concentrate only on critical activities towards going for project crashing and non critical activities need not be addressed for project crashing.

f. Estimation of Variance of Critical Activities

From the given time periods, employ the formula: Variance T_E $(\sigma^2) = [(P-O)/6]^2$ to compute variances of the project activities (Table 10.20).

Table 10.20: Estimation of Variance of Activities

Activity	Preceding Activity	Optimistic Time (O)	Most likely Time (M)	Pessimistic Time (P)	Expected Time (T_E) (O+4M+P)/6	Variance TE (σ^2) = $[(P-O)/6]^2$
A	—	4	6	8	6	0.444*
B	—	1	4.5	5	4	0.444
C	A	3	3	3	3	0.000*
D	A	4	5	6	5	0.111
E	A	0.5	1	1.5	1	0.028
F	B,C	3	4	5	4	0.111*
G	B,C	1	1.5	5	2	0.444
H	E,F	5	6	7	6	0.111
I	E,F	2	5	8	5	1.000*
J	D,H	2.5	2.75	4.5	3	0.111
K	G,I	3	5	7	5	0.444*

* - Variances of critical activities.

Duration of Critical path : **A – C – F – I – K (EVENTS: 1-2-3-5-6-7) = 23 weeks.**

g. Estimation of the Probability for Completion of the Project in Right Time

After computing the EST, EFT, LST, LFT, Float, identification of critical activities, critical path etc., then the question arises on the part of project manager, what is the probability of completing the project (*i.e.,* activities on critical path) in right time? This is because, completion of critical activities in right time is very important, as for these activities, float is zero and their duration influences the entire project duration. We

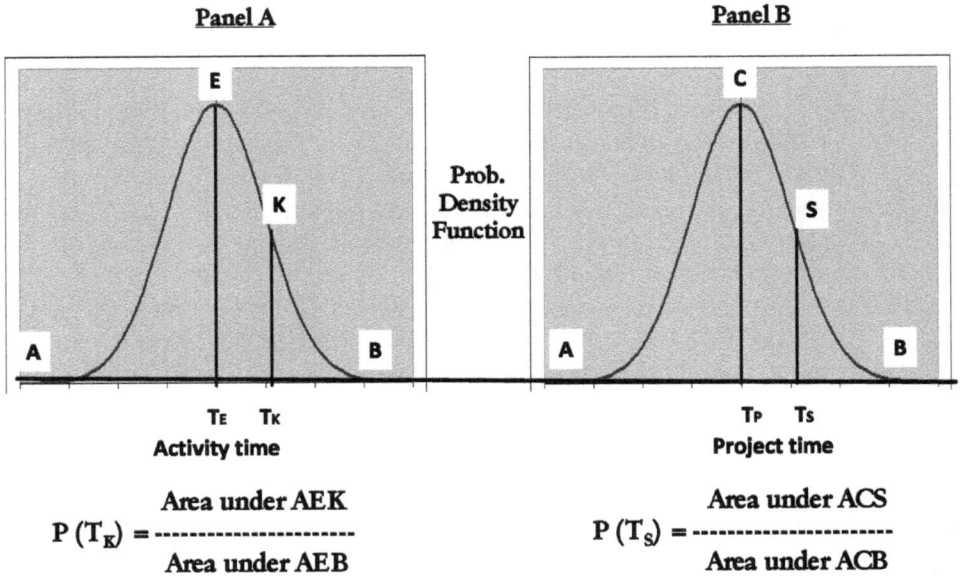

Figure 10.19: Probability for the Completion of Activities and Project.

already know that, in PERT, we generally assume 3 time periods *i.e.* optimistic, most likely and pessimistic and based on these, we compute expected time (T_E) for each activity by using the following formula: $TE = (O+4M+P)/6$.

For example, in the given Table 10.20 for activity A, which is a critical activity, the estimated activity duration is 6 weeks (T_E). But, the probability of completing this activity A in 6 weeks is only 50 per cent. This is so because, the estimated time for any activity *i.e.*, T_E will divide the area under normal distribution curve into two equal halves indicating that, probability of completing that activity in right time (T_E) is 50 per cent only. This is shown through the Panel A of Figure 10.19.

If the activity is completed in T_K period instead of T_E period, then the probability of completing the activity in T_K period is given by

$P(T_K) = $ (Area under AEK)/(Area under AEB)

In a project, there will be number of activities and each activity acts as an independent random variable. Hence, we have to work out probabilities for each and every critical activity. Since, all the critical activities influence project duration, the entire project duration can also be considered as an independent variable. So, we have to work out the probability for the entire project duration also.

Let us suppose, project takes T_P time period for its completion (23 weeks in this example). If the project is to be completed in T_S time period, the probability of completing the project in that time period T_S can be known in advance from the following graph (Panel B of Figure 10.19.) *i.e.* given by:

$P(T_S) = $ (Area under ACS)/(Area under ACB)

The P(Ts) value depends upon the location of Ts. Taking T_p as the reference point, the distance T_p and T_s can be expressed in terms of Standard Deviation (SD). To calculate the SD for the entire project's critical path, follow the given procedure here under.

Step 1

First, we have to work out the variance for each and every critical activity (Table 10.20) by employing the formula as given earlier *i.e.* Variance T_E $(\sigma^2) = [(P-O)/6]^2$

Step 2

Work out the variance for the entire critical path by summating the variances of all the critical activities in the critical path. That is, variance of critical path = $\Sigma \sigma i^2$, where i=1 to n representing only critical activities.

Variances of all critical activities on critical path = $V_A + V_C + V_F + V_I + V_K = 1.9999$

Step 3

Compute SD for the critical path.

SD of critical path $(\sigma) = \sqrt{\text{Sum of the variances of all the critical activities on the}}$ critical path

$= \sqrt{\Sigma \sigma_i^2}$

So, SD for the critical path $= \sqrt{(1.999 \approx 2)} = 1.414$

For the normal distribution curve, the SD is always equal to 1. So, the above calculated SD value for the entire critical path can be taken as scale factor to study the normal deviate (Z) based on which, we assess the probability of completing the project (Table 10.21).

Table 10.21: Probability for Completion of the Project

Specified Weeks (T_p)	Z Value [(E-S)/σ]	Probability (from area under normal curve)
20	Z =(20-23)/1.414 = -2.1216	=0.5-0.4830=0.017 = 1.7 per cent
22	Z =(22-23)/1.414 = -0.7072	=0.5-0.2612=0.2388=24 per cent
23	Z =(23-23)/1.414 = 0	=0.5=50 per cent
24	Z =(24-23)/1.414 = 0.7072	=0.5+0.2612=0.7612=76 per cent
25	Z =(25-23)/1.414= 1.4144	0.5+0.4207=0.9207=92 per cent

Normal deviate (Z) = [(E-S)/σ]

Where, E = Expected days of completion, S = Scheduled days of completion (*i.e.,* critical path duration in days), σ = SD.

☆ If the Z value is +ve, it implies, the probability of completion of project by scheduled date is more than 50 per cent.

☆ If the Z value is -ve, it implies, the probability of completion of project by scheduled date is less than 50 per cent.

☆ If the Z value is zero, it implies that, the expected date of completion of project and scheduled date of completion of project are same *i.e.*, the probability of completion of project by scheduled date is 50 per cent. That is, this will happen when expected and scheduled dates of completion are equal.

Let us study the possibility of completion of project in different weeks. From the Table 10.21, it is clear that, the project completion within 23 weeks is impossible. It will be completed in 23 weeks with probability of 50 percent. The project will however be completed in 25 weeks with certainty (P= 92 per cent) and in 24 weeks with certainty (P = 76 per cent). The same is shown through Figure 10.19.1.

$$Z = \left(\frac{25 \text{ weeks } - 23 \text{ weeks}}{1.414} \right) = 1.414$$

Area left of Y-axis = 0.50

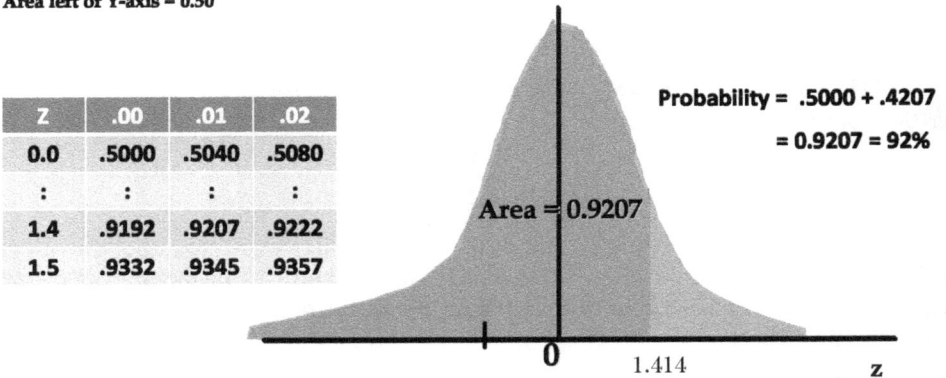

Z	.00	.01	.02
0.0	.5000	.5040	.5080
:	:	:	:
1.4	.9192	.9207	.9222
1.5	.9332	.9345	.9357

Probability = .5000 + .4207

= 0.9207 = 92%

Area = 0.9207

0   1.414   z

Figure 10.19.1: Probability of Completion of Project by 25 Weeks.

XII. Project Crashing and Fast Tracking

We know, there are two techniques in project management *viz.*, CPM and PERT. Among these two, CPM is a deterministic tool, where we generally assume only one time period for the completion of an activity. However, PERT is a probabilistic tool in which three different time periods are assumed and based on their weighted average, we compute T_E estimated time. Among these two techniques, CPM is a very useful tool because, it will take only one time period for the project activity and also helps to analyze the critical path of the project based on which, cost estimation can be done easily for the overall completion of the project. Generally, when the cost control outweighs the time control, CPM is the best tool. But, when time control outweighs the cost control of the project, PERT is the suitable tool. Sometimes when the selected project is running behind schedule, the project manager has to decide whether to go for 'project crashing' or 'fast tracking'. Before understanding these concepts, let's evaluate the factors, which force the management to speed-up project execution midway:

☆ While doing project planning, the project planners don't take into account various predictable/unpredictable risks thereby, initial time allotted to different activities in the project are too 'optimistic', but the ground realities are 'pessimistic'.

☆ Due to some unavoidable reasons say, non-availability of inputs, labour etc., in time, the project may run behind schedule and hence, the project manager needs to complete it on time.

☆ Market demands the product from the project at an earlier date than expected. This demand forces the project manager to speed-up the project in order to fulfill the requirements of the market.

i. Project Crashing

As mentioned earlier, project crashing refers to the process by which duration of project is reduced by increasing the amount of resources allocated. Thus, project crashing involves time-cost tradeoffs. It is important to note that, crashing is done only to critical activities. This can be achieved by any of the following ways:

☆ Increasing the resource use efficiency of the current resources.

☆ Bringing in new additional resources to speed up the processes.

☆ By evaluating alternatives available and analyzing them in order to find, which one will help in compressing the duration with lowest cost.

Note that, while allocating resources to critical activities, one needs to take into consideration the slack available in non-critical activities. This will help to make sure that, crashing will not affect other activities of the project nor the project's scope. Crash cost also needs to be taken into consideration and it shouldn't be more than the penalty cost.

ii. Fast-Tracking

This is another technique used in project management to compress the schedule. In fast tracking, activities that were planned to be performed in sequential order are rescheduled to be performed in parallel or partially in parallel. Examples include:

☆ Split long tasks into smaller chunks to squeeze more work into a shorter period of time.

☆ Reduce lag times between tasks.

☆ Reduce the scope to eliminate less important tasks.

This fast-tracking in project management, just like crashing, may lead to increase in costs and risks. Usually, the thumb rule followed by project managers while fast tracking is, to fast track the subsequent (2nd) activity after completion of 66 percent of scheduled (1st) activity.

Finally, sometimes, the best method is some combination of resource addition (project crashing) and re-schedule of activity alteration (fast-tracking). Let us now discuss in-detail about project crashing through considering an example, as it helps the students for easier understanding. Before going into the explanation note the following guidelines for crashing of the project:

☆ Crash only activities that are critical.

☆ Crash from the least expensive to most expensive.

☆ Crash an activity only until:

  ❖ It reaches its maximum time reduction.

  ❖ It causes another path to also become critical.

  ❖ It becomes more expensive to crash than not to crash.

The above discussion infers that, if the project manager wishes to complete the project at an earlier time than the critical path duration, he has to complete the activities at a faster pace. Generally, the project manager will concentrate only on critical activities lying on the critical path, if he wishes to reduce the duration of the project. This is because, the critical activities on the critical path represent the longest duration the project. To complete a critical activity at a faster pace, it is essential on the part of project manager to increase the level of resource usage regarding the execution of the critical activity. This process of reducing the time duration for completion of a critical activity by increasing resource usage is called Project crashing. So, in project crashing, non-critical activities are not considered. This is so because, these non critical activities do not represent the critical path duration. Even if their duration is crashed by using more of resources, critical path duration will not change and hence, it simply increases the cost of the project. Except for the fixed duration activities like crop duration, gestation period etc., which cannot be altered, the project manager generally lay emphasis on critical activities only, to reduce the duration of the project by increasing the resource usage. In project crashing, there are two types of costs involved:

☆ *Direct Cost:* For these costs, there exists inverse relationship between cost expenditure and time of completion of an activity (Figure 10.20). That means, for the activities to be completed in short period of time, the resource usage or cost expenditure should be increased. Examples include: material cost, labour cost etc.

☆ *Indirect Cost:* These are the costs associated with the project and not with the activities. Examples include, payment of salaries for employees, depreciation on machinery, general administrative over head cost etc. For these indirect costs, there exists a direct relationship between cost expenditure and time of activity (Figure 10.20).

iii. Procedure for Project Crashing

Step 1

A preliminary project schedule is generated showing all the activities of the project along with their preceding activities, normal duration of each activity, normal costs incurred if the activities are completed as per their normal duration. From this, draw a network diagram, identify critical path and critical activities (Table 10.22 and Figure 10.21) as discussed earlier.

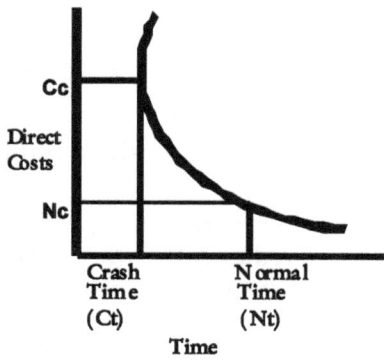

Direct costs

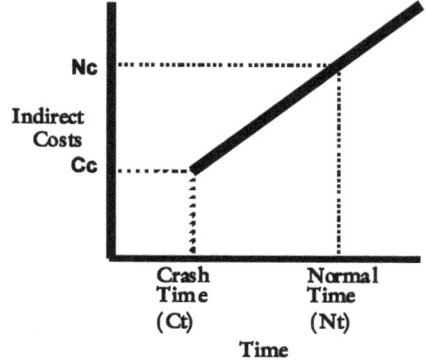

Indirect costs

Figure 10.20: Direct and Indirect Costs in a Project.

Table 10.22: Project's Precedence Table along with Activities Duration and Normal Costs

Activity	Symbol	Preceding Activity	Normal Duration (Weeks)	Normal Costs
Leveling the land	A	—	16	36000
Stone pitching	B	A	26	27000
Raising seedling	C	A	26	8000
Establishment of irrigation system	D	A	30	135000
Development of drainage system	E	C	28	20000
Making pits & transplantation	F	B	27	12000
Erection of fencing	G	D,E,F	18	35000

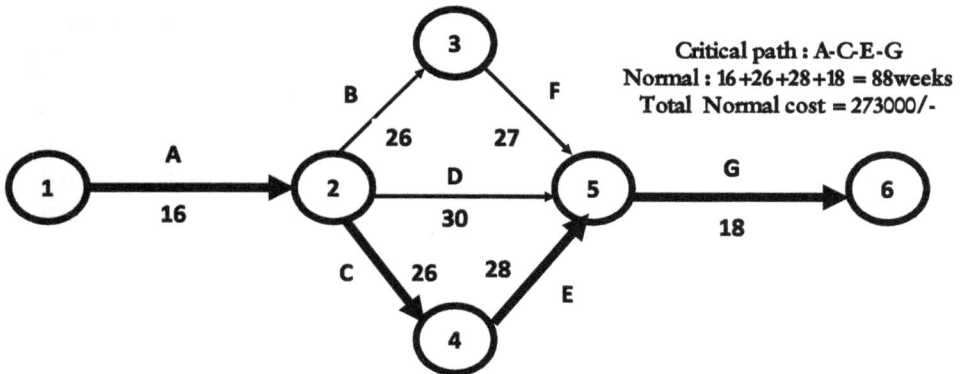

Critical path : A-C-E-G
Normal : 16+26+28+18 = 88weeks
Total Normal cost = 273000/-

Figure 10.21: Critical Activities in a Project.

Step 2

Computation of cost slope, for each activity.

Cost slope = Cost/Time = (Crash cost – Normal cost)/(Normal time- Crash time)

Step 3

Identify the activity on the critical path for which cost slope is lowest and crash that activity first and follow the same in ascending order.

In the process of crashing the critical activity, the duration of that activity will be reduced so that, the entire critical path duration will be reduced. So, other paths having duration more than the original path after crashing the activity on the original path will now become the critical path. So, due to the creation of new critical path, it implies that, the activities which are non-critical earlier will turn to critical activities. This new critical path will be crashed in the similar way by identifying an activity with low cost slope.

Step 4

If there are parallel critical paths in a project, then identify one activity each with low cost slope from each critical path and they have to be crashed at the same time.

This procedure is continued till no further crashing is possible in the project or depending upon the money resources available with the project manager.

In the above example (Figure 10.21), four critical activities are identified A-C-E-G on a critical path with duration of 88 weeks. The total normal cost of the project is Rs. 2,73,000/-. Since, A-C-E-G are the critical activities, we have to consider one of the activities with lowest cost slope for project crashing. Among these four activities A-C-E-G, activity C is having low cost slope (Table 10.23) and hence, it has to be considered first for crashing. Since cost slope is Rs. 180/week, this activity C is crashed for 5 weeks. So, total cost increased in the project is 5x180=Rs.900/-. So, the crash cost of activity C is increased from Rs.8000/- to Rs.8900/- and hence, the project is crashed from 26 weeks to 21 weeks. So, due to project crashing of C activity, the total cost of project is increased from 2,73,000 + 900 =2,73,900/-.

Table 10.23: Project Crashing – Estimation of Cost Slope Across Activities

Activity	Time (Weeks)		Cost (Rs/-)		Reduction in Time (Weeks)	Increase in Cost (Rs/-)	Cost Slope (Rs/week)
	Normal	Crash	Normal	Crash			
A	16	11	36000	38000	5	2000	400
B	26	18	27000	33000	8	6000	750
C	26	21	8000	8900	5	900	180
D	30	23	135000	138570	7	3570	510
E	28	20	20000	22400	8	2400	300
F	27	23	12000	13700	4	1700	425
G	18	12	35000	36500	6	1500	250
Total			273000	291070	43	18070	

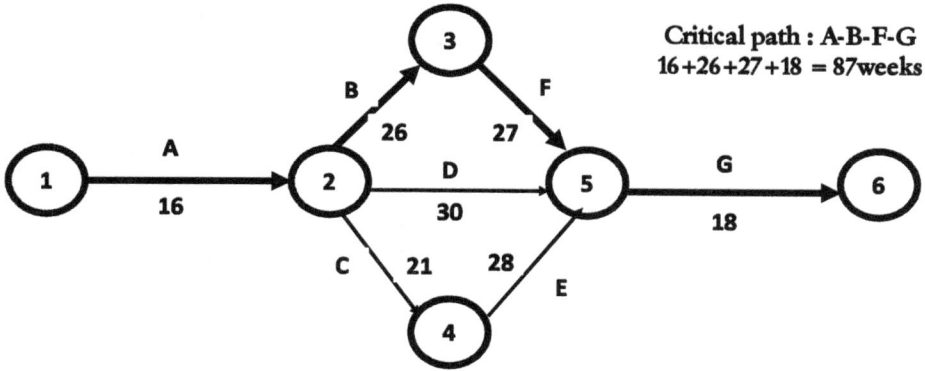

Figure 10.22: New Critical Path ABFG after Crashing 'C' Activity.

With the crashing of C activity, the total critical path duration has changed from 88 weeks - 5 weeks = 83 weeks. So, with the fall in critical path duration from 88 weeks to 83 weeks, A-B-F-G path with duration of 87 weeks now becomes the critical path (Figure 10.22). So, B and F activities, which are non-critical earlier, now turn to critical activities. This analysis further implies that, when C activity was crashed by 5 weeks in a critical path A-C-E-G, the total critical path duration was decreased by only one week *i.e.*, on new A-B -F-G critical path (87 weeks). That means, crashing of one activity by means of certain duration will not reduce the critical path duration by the same extent.

Thus, in the new critical path A-B-F-G, activity G is with low cost slope *i.e.*, Rs. 250/week and it is crashed for 6 weeks. So, total extra cost incurred in the project is 6x250 = Rs.1500/- and hence, the crash cost of activity G is Rs.36,500/- increased from a normal cost of Rs.35,000/-. So, activity duration is reduced to 12 weeks from 18 weeks. Now, by crashing G activity by 6 weeks in A-B-F-G path, the critical path duration is reduced to 81 weeks.

Again a network diagram has to be drawn, compare different path lengths, identify critical path, identify activity with low cost slope, crash the same, estimate the increase in cost and reduction in time period of activity. This procedure is continued till a stage is reached, where no further crashing is possible or depending upon the available funds with the project manager. If this crashing activity is still continued in the project, the findings are shown through the Table 10.24.

Generally, a case will arise in a project, where there may be two or more critical paths simultaneously. If one activity is crashed on one critical path, it will not change the project duration because, there is another critical path with the previous duration. For example, as shown in the Table 10.24, after crashing F activity, there are two critical paths A-B F-G and A-C-E-G. If we crash activity E by 8 weeks, there is no reduction in project duration because, A-B-F-G- still remains as the critical path duration. So, from the Table 10.24, it is clear that, the project can be finally crashed by 24 weeks by incurring an additional expenditure of Rs. 14,500/-.

Table 10.24: Project Crashing – Cumulative Reduction in Project Duration

Crashed Activity	Crashed Time (Weeks)	Project Duration (Weeks)			Project Cost (Rs.)		
		Before Crashing	After Crashing	Cumulative Reduction	Before Crashing	After Crashing	Cumulative Increase
Normal		88			273000		
C	5	88	87	1 (1)	273000	273900	900
G	6	87	81	7 (6)	273900	275400	2400
A	5	81	76	12 (5)	275400	277400	4400
F	4	76	72	16 (4)	277400	279100	6100
E	8	72	72	16 (0)	279100	281500	8500
B	8	72	64	24 (8)	281500	287500	14500

So, finally project crashing implies, time cost trade off. The decision up to which the project can be crashed mainly depends upon the resources available with the project manager.

Risks of Project Crashing in Project Management

Though project crashing ensures speedy completion of project than the given critical path duration, its execution also leads to the following risk factors that the project manager must be vigilant against them:

☆ Various external and internal factors may lead project manager to go for crashing, but it usually affects the quality of work as the time taken (besides cost) is the major issue on his mind.

☆ Using additional resources does not always guarantee better results.

Exercises

1. Assume the costs and benefits estimated in constructing a dam in a town. Appraise the economic viability of the investment (NPV, BCR, IRR, and NBIR). Assume discount factor:10 per cent.

Year	Construction Costs	Operating Costs	Recreation Benefits	Electricity Benefits	Total Benefits	Total Costs	Net Benefit
1	550,000	0	0	0	0	550,000	–550,000
2	550,000	0	0	0	0	550,000	–550,000
3	0	50,000	50,000	100,000	150,000	50,000	100,000
4	0	50,000	50,000	100,000	150,000	50,000	100,000
5	0	50,000	50,000	100,000	150,000	50,000	100,000
6	0	50,000	50,000	100,000	150,000	50,000	100,000
7	0	50,000	50,000	100,000	150,000	50,000	100,000
8	0	50,000	50,000	100,000	150,000	50,000	100,000
9	0	50,000	50,000	100,000	150,000	50,000	100,000

Year	Construction Costs	Operating Costs	Recreation Benefits	Electricity Benefits	Total Benefits	Total Costs	Net Benefit
10	0	50,000	50,000	100,000	150,000	50,000	100,000
11	0	50,000	50,000	100,000	150,000	50,000	100,000
12	0	50,000	50,000	100,000	150,000	50,000	100,000
13	0	50,000	50,000	100,000	150,000	50,000	100,000
14	0	50,000	50,000	100,000	150,000	50,000	100,000
15	0	50,000	50,000	100,000	150,000	50,000	100,000
16	0	50,000	50,000	100,000	150,000	50,000	100,000
17	0	50,000	50,000	100,000	150,000	50,000	100,000
18	0	50,000	50,000	100,000	150,000	50,000	100,000
19	0	50,000	50,000	100,000	150,000	50,000	100,000
20	0	50,000	50,000	100,000	150,000	50,000	100,000

2. Assume the costs and benefits estimated in constructing a project. Appraise the economic viability of the investment (NPV, BCR, IRR, and NBIR). Assume discount factor:10 per cent.

Year	0	1	2	3	4	5
Benefit (Rs.)	0	2500	2500	2500	3000	3000
Cost (Rs.)	10,000	500	500	500	500	500

3. For the given flow diagram below, write the Precedence Table and compute EST, EFT, LST and LFT.

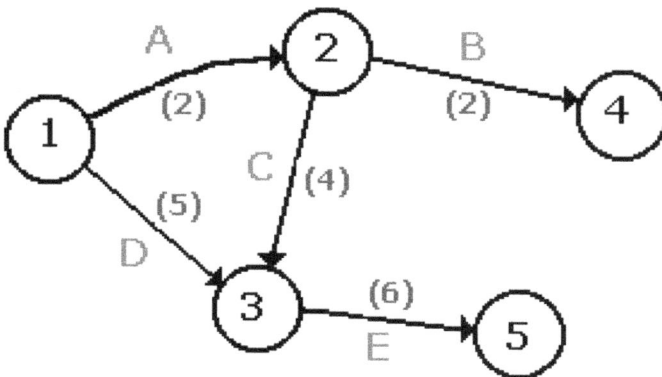

4. For the following data, draw the network diagram, and then crash the activities to find the time-cost trade-off points that the firm should want to consider. Start with the plan that has the longest duration.

Activity	Preceding Activity	Time (Weeks)		Cost (Rs.000s)	
		Normal Program	Crash Program	Normal Program	Crash Program
A	–	2	2	5	5
B	A	5	3	11	21
C	A	2	1	7	16
D	B, C	4	2	8	22
E	B	3	2	9	18
F	D, E	3	3	9	9

(*Key:* The plan with the longest duration takes 14 weeks at a cost of Rs.49,000. The one with the shortest duration takes 10 weeks at a cost of Rs.82,000.)

5. For the following data, draw the network diagram, and then crash the activities to find the time-cost trade-off points that the firm should want to consider. Start with the plan that has the longest duration.

Activity	Preceding Activity	Time (Weeks)		Cost (Rs.)	
		Normal Program	Crash Program	Normal Program	Crash Program
A	–	2	1	20,000	20,700
B	–	3	1	29,000	33,000
C	A	2	1	25,000	26,100
D	B	4	3	47,000	47,750
E	C	4	2	55,000	57,000
F	C	3	2	29,000	29,500
G	D, E	5	3	79,000	80,800
H	F, G	2	1	15,000	17,900

(*Key:* The plan with the longest duration takes 15 weeks and has a cost of Rs. 299,000. The one with the shortest duration takes 8 weeks and has a cost of Rs.312,250.)

References

Acharya S.S., Agribusiness in India: Some Facts and Emerging Issues, Agricultural Economics Research Review, Vol. 20 (Conference Issue) 2007 pp. 409-424.

Ahuja H.L., 'Modern Micro Economics- Theory and Applications', S. Chand and Company Limited, New Delhi, 2008.

Allen, R. G. D. (1934). "A Comparison Between Different Definitions of Complementary and Competitive Goods", Econometrica, Vol. 2, No. 2 (Apr. 1934), pp. 168-175.

Allen Ch., Hall St. (1997). Macroeconomic Modelling in a Changing World, John Willey and Sons, New York.

Anonymous (2004). Internal Rate of Return: A Cautionary Tale. Tempted by a project with high internal rates of return? Better check those interim cash flows again. The McKinsey Quarterly, McKinsey and Co., http://www.cfo.com/printable/article.cfm/3304945 (accessed on 14 Aug 2009).

Anonymous (2004). Project Appraisal and Impact Analysis, Course code: c207, c307, Centre for Financial and Management Studies, SOAS, University of London.

Antholt, C.H. (1994). Getting ready for the twenty-first century: technical change and institutional modernization in agriculture. World Bank Technical Paper #217. February.

Arrow, K.J., H.B. Chenery, B.S. Minhas and R.M. Solow (1961). "Capital-Labor Substitution and Economic Efficiency", Review of Economics and Statistic.

Ayoe Hoff, The Linear Approximation of the CES Function with 'n' Input Variables, Danish Research Institute of Food Economics, Marine Resource Economics, Volume 19, pp. 295–306.

Barnard, C.S. and J.S. Nix (1973). Farm Planning and Control, Cambridge University Press.

Baum WC (1982). The Project Cycle, Washington: World Bank.

Black S.E. and L.M. Lynch, 'How to Compete: The impact of Workplace Practices and Information Technology on productivity', Review of Economics and Statistics, 83(3), August, 2001, pp: 434-445.

Boulding E. and G. J. Stigler eds. (1952). Homewood, Ill.: Richard D. Irwin.

Butterfield, K.L. (1910). 'Analysis of the Rural Problem' in Report of the First Annual Meeting, American Farm Management Association, Ames.

Cary, David and Dunn, Michael (1997). Adjustment of modified internal rate of return for scale and time span differences, Proceedings of the Academy of Accounting and Financial Studies, 2(2).

Castle, E.N., M.H. Becker and A.G. Nelson (1987). Farm Business Management, 3rd edn, Macmillan, New York.

Chandy K. T., Farm Management, Booklet No.131, Farm Management: FMS - 6.

Chopra P.N. (2003). 'Principles of Economics', Kalyani Publications, Ludhiana.

Christiansen L.R., Jorgensen D.W, Lau L.J. (1971). "Conjugate duality and the transcendental. logarithmic production function", in Econometrica, vol. 39.

Christiansen L.R., Jorgensen D.W, Lau L.J. (1973). "Transcendental logarithmic production. frontier", in Review of Economics and Statistics, vol. 55.

Chukwuji Christopher O., Odjuvwuederhie E. Inoni, O'raye D. Ogisi, William J. Oyaide (2006): "A Quantitative Determination of Allocative Efficiency in Broiler Production in Delta State, Nigeria": Department of Agricultural Economics and Extension, Delta State University, Asaba Campus, Asaba. Delta State, Nigeria: Agriculturae Conspectus Scientifi cus, Vol. 71. No. 1 (21-26).

Cobb, C.W. and Douglas, P.H. (1928). "*A Theory of production" American economic review, supplement* 18 pp. 139 – 165.

Coelli, T.J., Rao, D.S. O'Donnell, C.J. and Battese, G.E. (2005). An Introduction to Efficiency and Productivity Analysis, Second Edition, Springer Science + Business Media, New York, USA.

Concepts, Definitions, Methodology and Scope of Census Data, Chapter: 2, All India Report on Agriculture Census 2005-06.

Courtney, Thomas B. The Law of Private Companies (2nd edition ed.). p. 26. ISBN 1-85475-265-0.

David Besanko and Ronald Braeutigam, 'Microeconomics'.

David L. Debertin, Agricultural Production Economics, Second Edition, University of Kentucky, Macmillan Publishing Company, ISBN 0-02-328060-3.

David Terfa Akighir and Terwase Shabu (2011). Efficiency of Resource use in Rice Farming Enterprise in Kwande Local Government Area of Benue State, Nigeria, *International Journal of Humanities and Social Science* Vol. 1 No. 4.

Declerck, R., Debourse, J. and Navarre, C. (1983). La Méthode de Direction générale : le management stratégique. Paris: Hommes et Techniques.

Declerck, R., Debourse, J., and Declerck, J. (1997). Le management stratégique: contrôle de l'irréversibilité. Lille: Les éditions ESC Lille.

Dexter, K. and D. Barber (1960). Farming for Profits, Penguin, Harmondsworth.

Dixit, A.K. and Pindyck, R.S. (1994). Investment under uncertainty. Princeton, USA, Princeton University Press.

Erhobor, P.O. (1982). *"Efficiency of Resources use under small Scale Irrigation Technology in Nigeria"* Purdue University; Water Resources Research Center West Lafayettse, Indiana, USA. Technical Report No 148 pp. 1 – 114.

Evenson, R.E. and McKinsey Jr., J.W. (1991). Research, extension, infrastructure and productivity change in Indian agriculture. In R.E. Evenson and C.E. Pray, eds. Research and productivity in Asian agriculture. Ithaca, USA, Cornell University Press.

FAO - *Farm Management* and Farm *Types* – *www.fao.org/docrep/w7365e/w7365e05.htm* ý.

FAO (1995). Guidelines for the Design of Agricultural Investment Projects.

FAO (2000). IFAD's Gender Strengthening Programme for East and Southern Africa – Uganda Field Diagnostic Study (Draft). Rome.

Farrell, M.J. (1957). "The Measurement of Productive Efficiency", *Journal of Royal Statistical Society*, Vol.120, No. 30, pp. 253-290.

Ferguson C.E. (1979). The Neo-Classical Theory of Production and Distribution, Cambridge. New York, Melbourne, Cambridge University Press.

Feder, G., Just, R.E. and Zilberman, D. (1985). Adoption of agricultural innovations in developing countries: a survey. Economic Development and Cultural Change, 33: 255-298.

Florin-Marius PAVELESCU, Some aspects of the translog production function estimation'.

Gerald Shively and Marta Galopin, An Overview of Benefit-Cost Analysis.

Gheorghe Zaman and Zizi Goschin, Technical change as exogenous or endogenous factor in the Production function models - Empirical evidence from Romania, Institute of Economic Forecasting, Romanian Journal of Economic Forecasting – 2/2010, pp: 29-45.

Giovanni L. Violante, Skill-Biased Technical Change, New York University, and CEPR, Prepared for The New Palgrave Dictionary of Economics, 2nd Edition (Steven Durlauf and Lawrence Blume, Editors).

Gittinger, J.P. (1982). Economic Analysis of Agricultural Projects, (World Bank). Baltimore and London: The Johns Hopkins University Press.

Gunnar Knapp, Economics of Resources, Lecture Notes for Economics 435.

Gupta P.K. and Hira D.S. (2003). 'Operations Research', S.Chand and Company Ltd., New Delhi.

Halter, A. N., H. O. Carter, and J. G. Hocking (1957). "A Note on the Transcendental Production Function." Journal of Farm Economics 39, pp. 966-974.

Heady, E.O. and H.R. Jensen (1954). Farm Management Economics, Prentice-Hall, Englewood Cliffs.

Herbert Kierulff (2008). 'MIRR: A better measure', Business Horizons. 51, 321—329.

http://home.ubalt.edu/ntsbarsh/opre640a/partviii.htm.

http://ricardo.ifas.ufl.edu/aeb6184.production/ProductionFunctions.html.

http://wps.prenhall.com/wps/media/objects/2234/2288589/ModB.pdf.

http://www.cob.sjsu.edu/yetimy_m/PERTCPM per cent 20Problems.htm.

http://www.stanford.edu/group/FRI/indonesia/documents/gittinger/Output/chap1.html.

http://www.beaconlearningcenter.com/documents/1509_01.pdf.

http://www.agecon.purdue.edu/staff/shively/COURSES/AGEC406/reviews/bca.htm.

http://www.business.com/sales-and-marketing/agriculture-advertising-and-marketing/.

http://www.uky.edu.

Huynh Viet Khai and Mitsuyasu Yabe (2011). Technical efficiency analysis of rice production in vietnam, J. ISSAAS Vol. 17, No. 1:135-146.

Inoni O.E. (2007): Allocative Efficiency in Pond Fish Production in Delta State, Nigeria: A Production Function Approach Agricultura Tropica Et Subtropica vol. 40 (4).

James G. Shanahan, Linear Programming Assumptions and Simplex (Algebraic, Tableau), TIM 206 (30155). Introduction to Optimization Theory and Applications, Winter 2013.

Jay Marshall Teets, Linear Programming: Graphical Solution Procedure and Spreadsheet Solution Procedure, QMB 4701, Managerial Operations Analysis, Decision and Information Sciences, University of Florida.

Jhingan M.L. 'Advanced Economic theory' (Micro and Macro Economics), Vrinda Publications (P). Limited. Delhi, 2006.

John E. Floyd, Microeconomics, University of Toronto, Toronto, Ontario, Canada.

Kalitzandonakes, N.G., W.U. Shunxiang and M.A. Jianchun (1992). The Relationship between Technical Efficiency and farm size retrieved *Canadian Journal of Agricultural Economics* Vol 40(3). pp. 427 – 440.

Kamal M. A. 'Development Project Appraisal for sustainable development', Lecture No. 6, National Academy for Planning and Development.

Kay, R.D. and W.M. Edwards (1994). Farm Management, 3rd edn, McGraw-Hill, New York.

Kim, H. Youn (1992). 'The Translog Production Function and Variable Returns to Scale, ' The Review of Economics and Statistics, Vol. 74, No 3, pp. 546-552.

Klacek J., Vosvrda M., Schlosser S. (2007). "KLE Production Function and Total Factor. Productivity", in Statistika, No. 4.

Kmenta, J. (1967). On Estimation of the CES Production Function. International Economic Review 8: 180–89.

Lydia Zepeda Agricultural Investment, Production Capacity and Productivity, Agricultural investment and productivity in developing countries<www.fao.org>.

Maheswari, S.N. (2005). Financial Management – Principles And Practice, S. Chand and Sons, New Delhi.

Mahi Pal (1992). Land productivity and Employment in Indian agriculture, Mittal Publications.

MANAGE, Project Management in Agricultural Extension, AEM 203, Post Graduate Diploma in Agricultural Extension Management (PGDAEM).

Manual on Project Cycle Management, Guidelines on Identification, Design and Implementation of Successful Local Authority Projects RPRLGSP, May 2009.

Mark Krause, Impacts of Product Differentiation on the Crop Input Supply Industry, 'Choices' – The Magazine of Food, Farm and Resource Issues.

Nelson, R. (1964). Aggregate production functions and medium-range growth projections. American Economic Review, 54(5): 575-606.

Nelson, R. (1981). Research on productivity growth and productivity differences: dead ends and new departures. Journal of Economic Literature, 19(3): 1029-1064.

Nelson, C. H., Braden, J.B. and Roh, J.S. (1989). Asset fixity and investment asymmetry in agriculture. American Journal of Agricultural Economics, 71 November: 970-979.

Nicodemus Ochani Agbulu, Lecture Note on The Farm as a Business - Introduction to Management, AED 703.

Olayide, S.O. and E.O. Heady (1982). *Introduction to Agricultural Production Economic: Principles and Application*. AGITAB Publishers Ltd. Zaria, Nigeria.

Pardey, P.G., Roseboom, J. and Craig, B.J. (1992). A yardstick for international comparisons: an application to national agricultural research expenditures. Economic Development and Cultural Change, 40: 333-349.

Pinto, J. K., and Slevin, D. P. (1988). Project Success: Definitions and Measurement Techniques. Project Management Journal, 19(1), 67–72.

PMI (2000). A Guide to the Project Management Body of Knowledge. Newtown Square, PA: Project Management Institute.

Prasanna Chandra (2004), Financial Management - Theory and Practice, Tata Mc Graw-Hill Publishing Company Limited, New Delhi.

Pray, C.E. and Evenson, R.E. (1991). Research effectiveness and the support base for national and international agricultural research and extension programs. In R.E. Evenson and C.E. Pray, eds. Research and productivity in Asian agriculture. Ithaca, USA, Cornell University Press.

Rahm, M.R. and Huffman, W.E. (1984). The adoption of reduced tillage: the role of human capital and other variables. American Journal of Agricultural Economics, 66: 405-413.

Randall S. Anderson, Jay A. Leitch and Cliff R. Fegert, 'Guidelines for Economic Evaluation of Public Sector Water Resource Projects', Agricultural Economics Report, No. 201, Department of Agricultural Economics, Agricultural Experiment Station, North Dakota State University, Fargo, North Dakota.

Rosenberg, N. (1976). Perspectives on technology, Cambridge University Press, Cambridge.

Rosenzweig, M.R. and Binswanger, H.P. (1993). Wealth, weather risk and the composition and profitability of agricultural investment. The Economic Journal, 103 January: 56-78.

Sami Fethi, Production Theory and Estimation, Department of Business Administration.

Sami Fethi (2007). Management Science, Department of Business Administration.

Sankhayan P.L., Introduction to the Economics of Agricultural Production, Prentice-Hall of India Private Limited, New Delhi-110001, India.

Scherer, F.M. (1971). "Industrial Market Structure and Economic Performance", Chicago: Rand McNally.

Shahi Kiran, A.S., Umesh, Kotrakerebasegowda, Crop Insurance- Strategy to minimize risk in Agriculture, http://ideas.repec.org/p/ags/iaae12/126734.html.

Syed M. Ahmed, 'Decision and Risk Analysis, BCN67755.

Tuman, G.J. (1983). Development and implementation of effective project management information and control systems, in Cleland, D.I. and King, W.R. (eds.) Project management handbook. New York: Van Nostrand Reinhold Co., 495-532.

Upton, M. (1979). *Farm Management in Africa: The Principles of Production and Planning*. Oxford University, Oxford pp. 1 – 260.

Vandana Shiva (2013). The Seeds of Suicide: How Monsanto Destroys Farming', Theme: Biotechnology and GMO, Global Research, April 05.

Verma S.R. Impact of Agricultural Mechanization on Production, Productivity, Cropping Intensity Income Generation and Employment of Labour, Status of Farm Mechanization in India, pp:133-153.

Viner, Jacob, "Cost Curves and Supply Curves, " Zeitschrift fur Nationalokonomie III. (1931). pp. 23-46. Also in American Economics Association, Readings in Price Theory, K.

Wozniak, G.D. (1989). The adoption of interrelated innovations: a human capital approach. Review of Economics and Statistics, 66: 70-79.

www.clt.astate.edu/crbrown/optimize.pptý.

www.eaton.math.rpi.edu/coursematerials/spring09/mk1620/LinProgIntro.pdf.

www.econ.ucsb.edu.

www.faculty.metrostate.edu.

www.homes.ieu.edu.tr/stunali/courses/ch02.pptý.

www.humanitarianforum.org/./resources/./Managing-the-Project-Cycle.

www.ianswer4u.com/2012/05/project-crashing-fast-tracking-in.htm.

www.ifad.org/ruralfinance/pub/weather.pdf.

www.iibf.org.in/documents/project-funding.do.

www.newagepublishers.com/samplechapter/002072.pdf.

www.oup.com/us/companion.websites/9780199811786/linear.

www.pages.intnet.mu/cueboy/education/notes/algebra/simplex.pdf.

www.site.airc.go.ke.

www.ingramcontent.com/pod-product-compliance
Lightning Source LLC
Chambersburg PA
CBHW020217290326
41948CB00001B/72